INTRODUCTION TO
QUANTUM CONCEPTS IN SPECTROSCOPY

McGraw-Hill Series in Undergraduate Chemistry

BARROW: *Physical Chemistry*
COMPANION: *Chemical Bonding*
CRAM AND HAMMOND: *Organic Chemistry*
KAUFMAN: *Advanced Concepts in Physical Chemistry*
LAIDLER: *Chemical Kinetics*
LAIDLAW: *Introduction to Quantum Concepts in Spectroscopy*
RICHARDS, CRAM, AND HAMMOND: *Elements of Organic Chemistry*
ROYER: *Bonding Theory*

Introduction to Quantum Concepts in Spectroscopy

W. G. LAIDLAW

Associate Professor of Chemistry
The University of Calgary
Calgary, Canada

McGraw-Hill Book Company

New York
St. Louis
San Francisco
London
Sydney
Toronto
Mexico
Panama

Introduction to
Quantum Concepts in Spectroscopy

Library of Congress Catalog Card Number
74-85164

35840

1234567890 MAMM 7654321069

This book was set in Modern by The
Maple Press Company, and printed on
permanent paper and bound by The
Maple Press Company. The designer
was Richard Paul Kluga; the drawings
were done by BMA Associates, Inc.
The editors were James L. Smith and
Joan A. DeMattia. Robert R. Laffler
supervised the production.

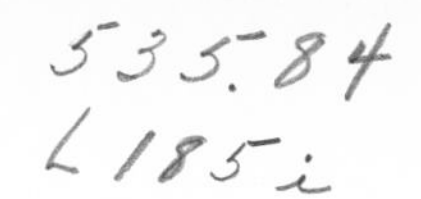

Preface

Material formerly reserved for senior university courses may now be found in the earlier years. Theories of orbitals and bonding, essentially quantum-mechanical in origin, are an integral part of freshman chemistry courses. Spectroscopic results, again quantum-mechanical in origin, are repeatedly encountered in the first- and second-year course work of organic, inorganic, and physical chemistry. As a result, the student may be exposed to bits and pieces of quantum mechanics until, in his senior university years, he encounters a unified, rigorous, but unfortunately often abstract, course in quantum mechanics.

An alternative procedure is to present quantum-mechanical concepts *as a unit* early in the student's career. Such a treatment should provide not only a sound understanding of the physical point of view but also familiarity with some simple mathematical applications to problems of chemical interest. Here spectroscopy plays a unique role, for not only did it provide the experimental evidence on which quantum mechanics was nurtured but also it provides many of the presently important applications of quantum concepts.

A course introducing and developing quantum concepts through their application to spectroscopic problems would seem appropriate. Ideally, such a course would provide the student with sufficient background for the many courses that draw upon basic quantum concepts. Even for the specialist such a course would provide the rationale for the more rigorous development of a senior course. The material presented herein is designed, hopefully, to do this. It has been used in the first semester (33 lecture hours and 66 laboratory hours) for *second*-year chemistry majors and *third*-year general science students. The only background expected is freshman mathematics, chemistry, and physics.

Problems appear throughout the text, and, it is hoped, these will allow the student to gain competence in the application of the more basic quantitative relations of quantum mechanics and spectroscopy. In addition there are a number of "Projects" at appropriate points in the text. These are essentially "dry labs" and are rather more full-blown applications of the textual material to chemical problems. With the "Projects" and with diligent attention to the aforementioned exercises. it is hoped that the text will be "self-teaching."

The text is divided into five chapters. The first chapter introduces basic concepts of quantum mechanics and presents their concise statement—the Schroedinger equation. In the second chapter this equation is solved for a number of separate systems and the results applied in the treatment of simple spectra. With the developments of the second chapter as background, the third chapter presents the overall energy and description of a molecule, emphasizing the interrelation of the separate "motions" of the molecule. The introduction of more complex spectra instigates the investigation which produces the "selection rules" at the end of chapter four. In the final chapter the selection rules and the quantum-mechanical descriptions given earlier are applied to the analysis of progressively more detailed molecular spectra.

A number of Appendixes are included for those topics whose proper treatment would have been out of place in the body of the text. In addition answers to selected problems are presented as Appendix VI.

In writing a book at this level, it goes without saying that the material owes much to more advanced presentation in the standard texts on the subject. The author acknowledges his debt to these sources, particularly Pauling and Wilson's "Introduction to Quantum Mechanics," Coulson's "Valence," and Herzberg's "Spectra of Diatomic Molecules." To those who were my teachers I owe much, both as to method and to understanding; to H. Madill, H. M. McConnell, F. W. Birss and C. A. Coulson I express my respectful thanks. To my former students, D. K. Jardine, H. Wieser, and R. B. Flewwelling, I am indebted for their earnest efforts toward clarifying and organizing my thoughts.

I am most grateful to V. Sorensen, who read and worked through the entire manuscript. My thanks also to P. Henderson, B. Kipling, H. Lekkerkerker, K. Vasudevan, and D. Smith for their help in preparing the text, and to my colleagues F. C. Adam, D. A. Armstrong, and R. Paul for their help and encouragement. To those who assisted in the typing, especially Marion Morton and Nancy Yurkowski, once again my thanks for your skill and patience. The shortcomings of the material presented are, however, entirely my own.

W. G. Laidlaw

Contents

List of Symbols

Ideally, the meaning of symbols should be clear from the immediate context. However, because many symbols are used so widely, this glossary should be of assistance to the student.

Symbol	*Meaning*	*Page where first used or defined*
au	atomic unit	90, 231
a_0	first Bohr radius	67, 231
A	absorbency	53
A	normalization constant for $\psi_n(x)$	31
A_i	in ESR, interaction of an electron with proton H_i	181
Å	angstroms	231
**	complex conjugate	27*n*
*	antibonding orbital	81

Symbol	*Meaning*			*Page where first used or defined*
B_n	nuclear magneton			121
c	velocity of light			12
C_f, C_2	coefficient in transition to a final state, e.g., $f = 2$			136, 142
CM	center of mass			48
$d\tau$	generalized element of "volume"			27n, 74
D_e	bond dissociation energy measured from minimum of potential well			187
D_0	bond dissociation energy measured from the zeroth vibrational level			191
e	elementary unit of charge			9
eV	electron volt			231
E	energy, can be subscripted to refer to: type of system, quantum number of energy state, coordinate associated with the energy, etc. Examples:			19
	E_{CM}	energy associated with motion of the center of mass		104
	E_l	energy associated with a rigid-rotor state designated by quantum number l		58
	E_M	molecular energy of electronic energy plus nuclear repulsion		106
	E_n	energy associated with a state designated by a quantum number n:		
		n	Bohr atomic number	10
		n	principal quantum number of an atomic orbital	67
		n	quantum number for a particle-in-a-box	25
		n	vibrational quantum number	50, 51
	E_n°	energy of the nth state for the hamiltonian H°		133
	$E_{n,\text{vib}}$	energy due to a vibrational state n		108
	E_{vib}	energy associated with vibrational motion		107
	E_{rot}	energy due to rotational motion		111
	E_x, E_y, etc.	energy associated with motion in the x, y, direction for a particle in a two-dimensional box		42, 48
ESR	Electron Spin Resonance			174

Symbol	*Meaning*	*Page where first used or defined*
f	as a subscript or label refers to the final state	10, 142
F	force	45, 199
g	nuclear-g-factor	121
g_1, g_2, etc.	sp^2 hybrid orbitals	92
h	Planck's constant	6, 231
H	hamiltonian operator, can be subscripted to refer to: type of system, the coordinates involved, etc.; or H can be followed by variables in parenthesis. Examples:	19
	H_p — spacial part of the hamiltonian H_{pt}	134
	H_{pt} — hamiltonian of a time dependent perturbation	134
	H_{vib}, H_{rot}, etc. — hamiltonian for vibrational, rotational, etc., motion	65
	$H(x)$, etc. — hamiltonian in terms of coordinate x	42
	$H(r,\theta,\phi)$, etc. — hamiltonian in terms of spherical polar coordinates r, θ, ϕ	65
	H^0 — unperturbed hamiltonian	133
H_0	magnetic field	120
i	as a subscript or label refers to the initial state	10, 142
i	square root of minus one, $\sqrt{-1}$	20*n*
I	moment of inertia	58
I, I_0	intensity	4
I_{if}	transition moment integral between initial and final states	138, 142
IR	Infrared	130, 160
J	Joule	7
J	molecular-rotational quantum number	161
$J_{NN'}$	NMR spin-spin interaction between nuclei N and N'	181
k	harmonic force constant	45
kT	Boltzmann's constant times temperature in degrees Kelvin	64, 231
KE	kinetic energy	6
l	orbital angular-momentum quantum number	65
l	rotational-(molecular) momentum quantum number	58
l_{C}	length of a carbon-carbon partial π-bond	33
l_{CN}	length of a carbon-nitrogen partial π-bond	33

Symbol	*Meaning*	*Page where first used or defined*
L	length of box in model	23, 33
L_x, L_y, etc.	length of box in x, y, etc. direction	40
m	angular-momentum projection quantum number	60
m	mass of particle	16
m_e	mass of an electron	9
m_s	spin quantum number	121, 166
m_1, m_2, etc.	mass of particle 1, 2, etc.	40
$m\mu$	millimicrons	168
M	symmetric top quantum number	165
M	total mass	47
n	nonbonding molecular orbital (lone pair)	85
n	quantum number for:	
	atomic orbital	65
	Bohr atom	10
	particle-in-a-box	24
	vibrational state	50
n_C	number of carbons in a delocalized π-electron system	33
N	Avogadro's number	52, 231
N	normalization constant	50
N	number of electrons in the particle in a box analogue of the π-electron system	32
NMR	Nuclear Magnetic Resonance	122
p	atomic orbital with $l = 2$	67, 70
p	linear momentum	15
p	para	174
p	penetration	33
P	refers to vibrational-rotational transitions in which $\Delta J = -1$	182
q_e	charge of an electron	14
q_n	charge of a nucleus	14
Q	refers to vibrational-rotational transitions in which $\Delta J = 0$	182
r	in an atom, distance of electron from the nucleus	9, 65
r	in harmonic oscillator, displacement of reduced mass from its equilibrium value R_e	47

Symbol	*Meaning*	*Page where first used or defined*
r_n	Bohr radius in hydrogen	10
r_{12}	distance between electrons one (1) and two (2)	68
R	distance between ends of rigid rotor, internuclear separation	56
R	refers to vibrational-rotational transitions in which $\Delta J = +1$	182
R_e	equilibrium value of internuclear separation	45
R_e	Rydberg constant	8
$R_{nl}(r)$	radial description of an electron for an atomic orbital having quantum numbers n and l	65, 67
s	atomic orbital with $l = 0$	67
sp, sp^2, sp^3	hybridized atomic orbitals formed from one s and one, two or three p atomic orbitals	87, 89
S	overlap integral of two orbitals	79, 220
SE	Schroedinger equation	21
$S_m(\phi)$	description of the ϕ dependence of angular motion for a state defined by the quantum number m	58, 210
t_1, t_2, etc.	tetrahedral hybrid atomic orbitals	87
T	transmittance	4
TMS	Tetramethylsilane	124
$T_{lm}(\theta)$	description of the θ dependence of angular motion for the state defined by the quantum numbers l and m	58, 212
UV	Ultraviolet	155
v	velocity	9
V	potential energy, can be subscripted, or the coordinates can be indicated, etc. Examples:	
	$V(1,2)$ potential energy depending on distance between electrons 1 and 2	67
	$V_2(1)$ potential due to attraction of electron 1 to nucleus of charge $2e$	67
V	electrostatic voltage	4
xyz	cartesian coordinates	57
XYZ	center-of-mass cartesian coordinates	56
Z	atomic number	67
Ze	nuclear charge	65
$Z_{eff}e$	effective nuclear charge	69

Symbol	*Meaning*		*Page where first used or defined*
α	alpha, spin state symbol		94
β	beta, spin state symbol		94
δ	delta, unit for measuring chemical shift in NMR		123
$\partial/\partial x$	partial derivative with respect to x		17
Δ	delta, except for Δp, Δx, the Δ indicates a change in value of the following symbol, etc. Examples:		
	ΔE_{system}	change in energy of a system	10
	ΔJ	change in molecular rotational quantum number J	161
	Δl	change in rotational quantum number l	62
	Δm_s	change in spin quantum number m_s	166
	Δn	change in vibrational quantum number n	152
Δp_x	uncertainty in momentum p_x		28
Δx	uncertainty in coordinate x		28
∇^2	Laplacian operator		218
ε	extinction coefficient		54
$\boldsymbol{\varepsilon}$	electric field vector		119
θ	theta, polar angle in spherical polar coordinates		51
λ	lambda, wavelength, can be subscripted to refer to transitions, etc. Example:		11
	λ_{max}	indicates a wavelength at which there is maximum absorption	36
μ	mu, reduced mass		47
$\boldsymbol{\mu}$, $\boldsymbol{\mu}_k$	electric dipole		121, 143
$\boldsymbol{\mu}_n$	magnetic moment (dipole) of a nucleus (proton)		121
ν	nu, frequency, can be subscripted to indicate: the transition, or to indicate the molecule for which the frequency was observed, etc. Examples:		6
	$\nu_{0\rightarrow 1}$	frequency corresponding to the energy change of transition from a state with quantum number 0 to a state with quantum number 1	52
	ν_{HCl}	frequency of maximum absorption for HCl	52
$\bar{\nu}$	"nu bar," reciprocal centimeters or wavenumber		11
ν_0	fundamental vibrational frequency		109
π	pi:		
	molecular orbitals formed from p atomic orbitals		81
π-electrons	electrons described by π-molecular orbitals		32
ρ	"point probability"		75

Symbol	*Meaning*	*Page where first used or defined*
$\rho_R(\mathrm{r})$, ρ_R	radial probability in an atom	75
σ	sigma:	
	screening constant in atomic orbitals	69
	shielding constant in NMR	122
	designation for axially symmetric molecular orbitals	81
	generalized spin coordinate	103
Σ	sigma, summation	157
τ	tau, unit for chemical shift (*See also* $d\tau$)	124
ϕ	phi, azimuthal angle in spherical polar coordinates	57
χ	chi	41
ψ	psi, function giving the spacial description of a system; in the SE it is the eigenfunction of the hamiltonian. It can be subscripted to refer to the quantum number of the state (ψ_n) or to refer to the motion described (ψ_{vib}) or the coordinates involved in the description can be indicated $\psi(r\theta\phi)$ etc. Examples:	19
	$\psi(R\theta\phi)$ or $\psi_R(\theta\phi)$ — description of angular motion of the reduced mass of a rigid rotor having a fixed distance R between the masses in the rotor	56, 208
	$\psi_n(r)$ — description of the displacement r of the reduced mass of the harmonic oscillator from its equilibrium position for a state with a quantum number n	50
	$\psi_n(x)$ — description of the motion of a particle-in-a-box for a state with quantum number n	25
	$\psi_{nlm}(r\theta\phi)$ — description of the motion of the reduced mass (the electron) about the nucleus in an atom for a system defined by the quantum numbers, n, l, m	65
	ψ_{vib} — description of the vibrational motion	104
Ψ	psi, as for ψ, but usually for a system of several degrees of freedom	41, 133
	$\Psi(x,t)$ — space and time dependent description	133
	$\Psi(x,y)$ — a description depending on two variables x, y	41
	$\Psi(1,2\cdots)$ — 1 and 2, etc. (e.g., electrons 1 and 2) are described by Ψ	83
$\omega_e\chi_e$	anharmonic energy term coefficient	191

I

The Basic Quantum-mechanical Description

I-1 INTRODUCTION

(i) Spectroscopy

Spectroscopy is the study of the characteristic electromagnetic radiation emitted or absorbed by matter. Although most species of atoms are not found free in nature, a plentiful supply can usually be generated. For example, an arc electrode produces highly energetic atomic species that *emit* electromagnetic radiation as they lose energy. On the other hand, molecules can be obtained readily in either the gas phase or in dilute solution. In this case low-energy species, capable of *absorbing* electromagnetic radiation, are in plentiful supply.

The basic emission spectroscopy experiment consists in supplying thermal energy to a system of interest, for example, the iron atoms in an arc electrode, and examining the atoms by studying the *emitted* radiation. In the apparatus illustrated in Fig. I-1, a prism is used to spacially separate the radiation of different frequencies, and the separated frequencies

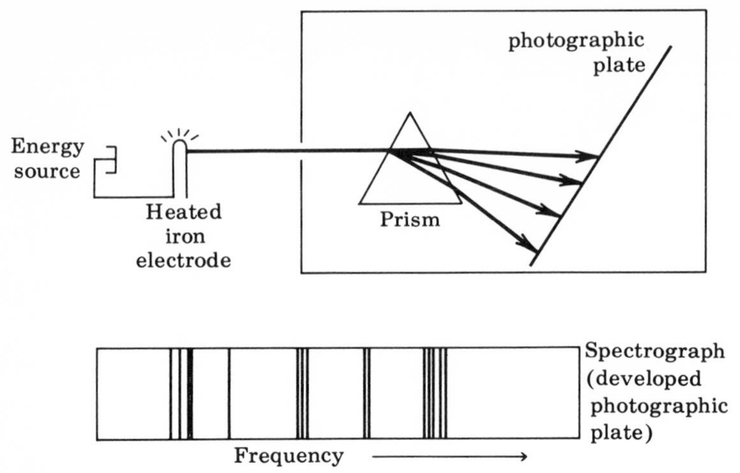

Fig. I-1 Emission spectroscopy.

produce bands, or lines, on a calibrated photographic plate. (The photographic plate is usually calibrated by allowing light of a known frequency to pass through the system and fall on the plate.) The frequency of the radiation can be determined from the position of the line on the plate, and the relative intensity of the different frequencies can be assessed by comparing the darkness of the lines. The result is information regarding the frequency and intensity of the light emitted by the system in question.

In absorption spectroscopy (Fig. I-2), electromagnetic energy of a certain frequency and intensity is allowed to interact with a molecule of interest, and the intensity of this radiation as it leaves the system is measured. When the experiment is repeated with various frequencies, the result is information regarding the degree to which light of a given

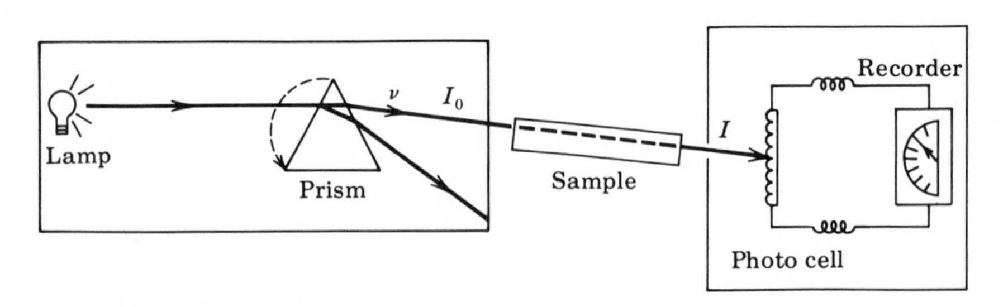

Fig. I-2 Absorption spectroscopy.

frequency is absorbed or transmitted by the system; for example:

Frequency A	No change in intensity (completely transmitted).
Frequency B	Intensity decreased by one-half (partially transmitted, partially absorbed).
Frequency C	Intensity reduced to zero (no transmission, completely absorbed).
Frequency D	No change in intensity (completely transmitted).

As illustrated in Fig. I-3, this information can also be plotted in the form of a spectrum.

Although it is the intensity and frequency that constitute the data in both emission and absorption spectroscopy, it is the electromagnetic radiation that is the carrier of this information. Some understanding of the nature of this radiation would seem to be in order!

(ii) Electromagnetic radiation

(a) *Classical*[1] *description*

To the scientists of the early nineteenth century, electromagnetic radiation, particularly the then more familiar visible light, appeared to be adequately described in terms of wave motion. (Wave motion will be discussed in more detail in Sec. I-3 and in Appendix I.) Certainly diffraction, interference, and energy transmission could all be explained by assuming that space was filled with an "incompressible elastic medium," the ether, capable of transmitting wave motion with the speed of light. In these terms light was characterized by a *wavelength* or frequency,

[1] "Classical" refers to a description obtained using Newton's laws of motion.

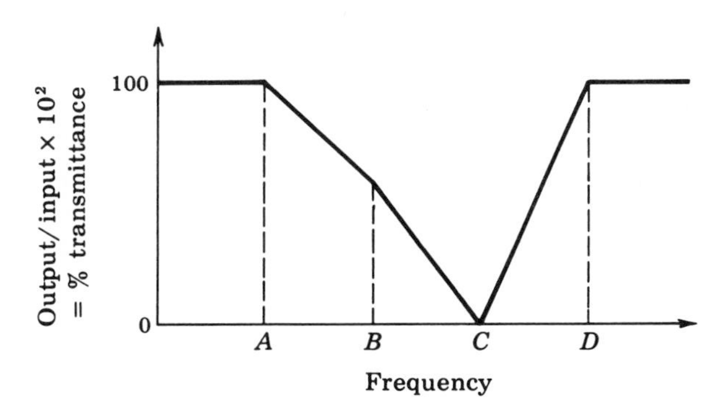

Fig. I-3 An absorption spectrum.

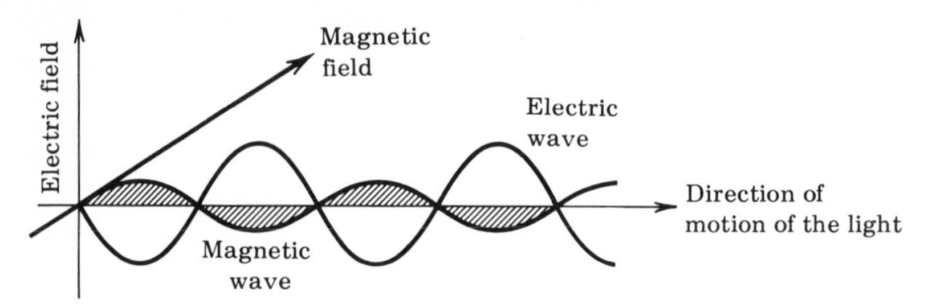

Fig. I-4 An electromagnetic wave.

whereas the energy of the radiation was proportional to the square of the *wave amplitude.*

Indeed, attention became focused on the nature of the *wave motion,* and, by mid-century, the work of Maxwell and others had apparently established that light consisted of an electric wave at right angles to a magnetic wave, as illustrated in Fig. I-4. The experiments of Michelson and Morley[1] indicated that the concept of ether as a medium for the wave motion was incorrect. Although it could be argued that ether was not essential to Maxwell's work, the results[2] of the "photoelectric experiment," directly contradicting the classical *wave aspect,* could not so easily be set aside.

(*b*) *Nonclassical*[3] *description*

In the "photoelectric-effect" experiment depicted in Fig. I-5, light strikes the metal surface A, and electrons ejected from the metal surface by the impinging light are collected at B. The resulting electric current is proportional to the number of ejected electrons, as

$$\text{Current} = (\text{charge/electron})(\text{number of electrons/unit time})$$

The potential V required to stop the flow of ejected electrons can be used to calculate their kinetic energy as they leave A, that is,

$$(V)(\text{charge/electron}) = \text{kinetic energy}$$

According to classical wave theory the amplitude of a wave, and thus its intensity I, could be increased continuously. Consequently a *sufficiently intense* wave should provide the energy necessary to eject an

[1] See, for example, the discussion in I. Kaplan, "Nuclear Physics," p. 89, Addison-Wesley, 1955.

[2] P. von Lenard, *Ann. Physik,* **9** (1902).

[3] "Nonclassical" generally refers to the approach required to explain phenomena that are not amenable to treatment by newtonian mechanics.

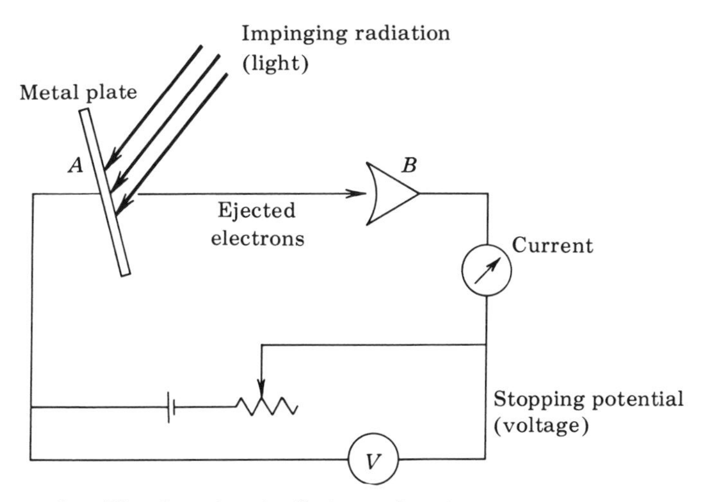

Fig. I-5 The photoelectric-effect experiment.

electron from the metal surface. But, as shown in Fig. I-6, this was not observed! Rather, there was a threshold frequency, below which the amount of energy required to knock the electron free of the metal was not available to the electron, *no matter how intense the light.* It appeared that the energy necessary to eject the electron was related to the *frequency,* not the intensity, of the light.

Above the threshold frequency the energy that the electron received in excess of that required to free it from the metal would appear as its kinetic energy, as measured by voltage. Classical wave theory suggested that this kinetic energy should increase as the intensity of the light increased. But experiment showed that, for a given frequency of light,

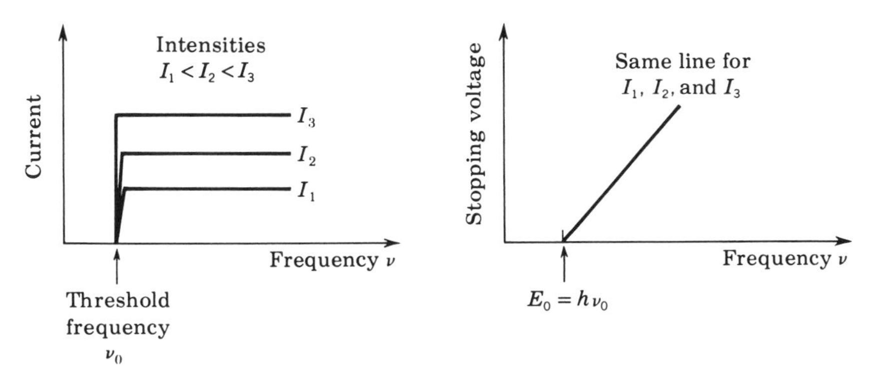

Fig. I-6 The effect of intensity and frequency.

the kinetic *energy* was always the *same;* only the *number* of ejected electrons *increased* with intensity. It appeared that not only the energy required to free the electron but also its excess energy was related to the frequency of the light. In fact it seemed that the energy of light could not be absorbed continuously by the system but could be taken up only in little packets! The amount of energy in such packets was proportional to their frequency, and the number of such packets was proportional to the intensity of the radiation. But this description implies that radiation is rather like a stream of particles (note that no ether is required as a medium for particles). The photon "particle" might be represented as in Fig. I-7 by a "wave packet," i.e., a "wave" whose amplitude is large at one point in space but decreases rapidly away from that point. Indeed, Einstein,[1] who provided this explanation in 1905, proposed that the *energy of radiation* was quantized in photons—"particles" with a packet of energy $E_{\text{photon}} = h\nu$, where h is the proportionality constant.

Since the energy of the absorbed photon equaled the sum of energy required to eject the electron E_0 plus the kinetic energy KE, one can write

$$E_{\text{photon}} = h\nu = E_0 + \text{KE}$$

For a given metal E_0 will be a constant. By measuring KE and plotting it against frequency, Millikan[2] found the proportionality constant h had almost the same value as had been given several years earlier by Planck,[3] when he suggested that the energy change of a material oscillator was proportional to the frequency—h was Planck's constant, and indeed, $E = h\nu$ is often referred to as *Planck's relation.* (It might be pointed out that Planck studied the radiation emitted and absorbed by a glowing *solid,* and, although he was the first to invoke quantization of

[1] A. Einstein, *Ann. Physik,* **17**:132 (1905); **20**:199 (1906).

[2] R. A. Millikan., *Phys. Rev,* **7**:355 (1916).

[3] M. Planck, *Ann. Physik,* **4**:553 (1901).

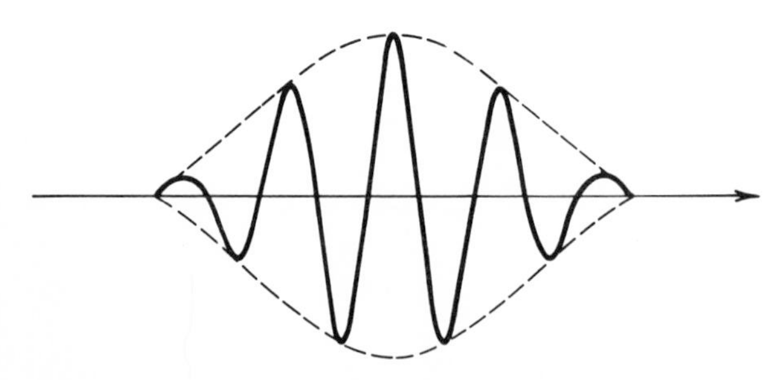

Fig. I-7 The photon "wave packet."

energy, he quantized the energy of "idealized oscillators" in the surface of the solid—to Planck, radiation was still essentially a classical wave in equilibrium with these oscillators.)

PROBLEM I-1

In one set of "photoelectric-effect" experiments, Millikan obtained the following data:

Frequency, $sec^{-1} \times 10^{14}$	5.50	6.90	7.42	8.22	9.58
Retarding potential V, V	−2.06	−1.49	−1.30	−0.92	−0.38

By an appropriate graph, show that these results confirm Einstein's theory. Use the graph to calculate a value for h (1 V = 1.6×10^{-19} J/elementary charge).

We might now examine the implications this concept of radiation has for the atomic or molecular systems in which radiation is absorbed or from which it is emitted.

(iii) Energy states

If radiation consisted of packets of energy $E = h\nu$, then the absorption of light of frequency ν by a molecule meant that the molecule accepted a *discrete quantity of energy* $h\nu$. Conversely, emission of radiation of frequency ν meant that the atom or molecule lost a discrete quantity of energy. But the spectra for atoms and molecules given at the outset indicated that only certain characteristic frequencies were emitted or absorbed, i.e., *only certain energy changes could take place!* Since energy changes were the result of the system having assumed different initial and final energy values, the characteristic energy changes observed could be a consequence of a restricted set of initial and final energies. Thus energy values of an atom or molecule might well be discontinuous, i.e., with a particular *set* of values, the energy values could be discrete! Thus it seemed that an atom or molecule could accept or emit only those amounts of energy that enabled it to change from one of its allowed energy values (states) to another of its allowed energy states.

Certainly this situation is rather different from the classical case, where a system could have any energy! And one might ask: Is there any cohesive theory that indicates only certain allowed energy states for a system? Can one start with the constituents of an atom or molecule and the forces operating on these parts and arrive at a description of the allowed energy states? How does the radiation bring about the change from one state to another? Which changes are allowed? The answers to these questions are to be found in the study of the relatively unfamiliar, but increasingly important, field of quantum mechanics.

Table I-1 Emission frequencies‡ for the hydrogen atom

3,198	165.0	314.3	755.6
3,158	154.5	298.5	731.3
3,083	139.0	274.2	691.2
2,923	114.0	234.0	617.1
2,467		160.0	477.1

‡ Entries must be multiplied by 10^{12} to give frequencies in sec^{-1}.

I-2 THE DEVELOPMENT OF QUANTUM THEORY

(i) Introduction

The emission spectrum of hydrogen is known to consist of a certain set of frequencies, some of which are presented in Table I-1. By a process of trial and error it was eventually possible for Balmer, Lyman, and others to show that associated with each of the frequencies of the set were two simple integers n and m related to the frequency by

$$\nu_{nm} = R_e\left(\frac{1}{n^2} - \frac{1}{m^2}\right)$$

where R_e is the Rydberg constant, having a value $R_e = 3.291 \times 10^{15}\ sec^{-1}$. (Although Rydberg's principal contributions were concerned with alkali metal spectra, his name has been given to the constant noted in Balmer's work.)

Such a formula certainly related many different frequencies and was tremendously useful in this sense. It did not, however, give any explanation of the origin of the integers n and m nor to what they referred, and it certainly provided no answer to the question of why only certain frequencies were emitted. In 1913, Bohr was able to give a theoretical description of hydrogen in which not only were the energy levels discrete but the allowed energy changes were, indeed, those that corresponded to the emission frequencies observed experimentally.

(ii) The Bohr theory

On the basis of experimental evidence (see Probs. I-2 and I-3), Rutherford suggested that the hydrogen atom consisted of a central positive charge surrounded by the negative electronic charge.

PROBLEM I-2

Assume that, in gold, the atoms are hard spheres in contact with one another in such a way that lines joining their centers form cubes; i.e., the lattice structure is simple cubic,[1] and the unit cell will be a cube containing eight atoms. Given the atomic weight and the density to be 197 and 19.3 g/cm^3, respectively, calculate the "radius" R of the gold atoms. [*Hint:* The density of gold equals (mass of a gold atom)/(volume of unit cell), and the unit cell has a length $2R$.]

PROBLEM I-3

In a scatter experiment, Geiger and Marsden[2] noted that a few (about 1 in 8,000) of the α particles incident on the gold foil were scattered through 90° or more. Taking the thickness of the foil in this experiment to be 10^{-3} cm, calculate an upper limit for the radius of the nucleus in the gold atom. (*Hint:* Such large deflections must be assigned to single collisions of an α particle with a nucleus. Since these deflections must be the result of "head-on" collisions, the fraction of the foil that appears solid must be equal to the fraction of particles deflected through 90° or more.)

Taking the Rutherford model as his starting point, Bohr[3] considered the electron as a *particle* of mass m_e and charge e moving with velocity v in an orbit of radius r about the nucleus. The attractive coulombic force $-e^2/r^2$ opposed the centrifugal force m_ev^2/r and maintained the circular orbit

$$\frac{-e^2}{r^2} + \frac{m_ev^2}{r} = 0 \qquad \text{(I-1)}$$

As such, his model followed almost all the well-established classical laws of newtonian mechanics. Almost but not all, for it was known from electromagnetic theory that an accelerated electric charge (an electron moving in a circular orbit is continually changing direction, i.e., changing velocity) should lose energy. Furthermore, and more to the point as far as spectroscopy was concerned, the energy (see Prob. I-4) was given by

$$E = -\frac{e^2}{2r} \qquad \text{(I-2)}$$

and, since r was variable, the energy could have any value! But the emission of a restricted set of frequencies, as given in Table I-1, implied that there were only certain energy values for hydrogen!

[1] See chap. 8 and questions 8.9, 8.10, 8.11, M. Sienko and R. Plane, "Chemistry," 3d ed., McGraw-Hill, 1966.
[2] H. Geiger and E. Marsden, *Proc. Roy. Soc.*, **A82**:492 (1909); *Phil. Mag.*, **25**:604 (1913).
[3] N. Bohr, *Phil. Mag.*, **26**:2 (1913); **30**:396 (1915).

Faced with this dilemma, Bohr arbitrarily, but judiciously, imposed the constraint that the orbital *angular momentum of the electron was quantized* in units of $nh/2\pi$ (n was a quantum number 1, 2, . . .). With this restriction the allowed energies (see Prob. I-5) were found to be

$$E_n = \left(\frac{-2\pi^2 m_e e^4}{h^2 n^2}\right) \tag{I-3}$$

and the allowed descriptions, i.e., orbits, to be

$$r_n = \left(\frac{h^2}{4\pi^2 m_e e^2}\right) n^2 \tag{I-4}$$

PROBLEM I-4

The total energy of any system is a sum of the kinetic energy plus the potential energy. In the H atom the potential energy is due to the coulombic force $-e^2/r^2$. The force represents an ability to do work, i.e., a potential energy. Since at infinite separation there is no force, this position is taken as the zero of potential energy. As the charges approach one another, work is done (i.e., the potential energy decreases), and, since it was initially zero, the potential energy becomes negative. Indeed, the potential energy at a distance r apart is the initial potential energy minus the work done in moving from infinity to position r. Thus,

$$\text{Potential energy} = V(r) = V(\infty) - \text{work}$$
$$= 0 - \int_\infty^r \left(\frac{-e^2}{r^2}\right) dr = \frac{-e^2}{r}$$

Using

$$E = \text{kinetic energy} + \text{potential energy}$$
$$= \tfrac{1}{2} mv^2 - \frac{e^2}{r}$$

and Eq. (I-1), derive Eq. (I-2).

PROBLEM I-5

Using angular momentum $= (m_e v)r = nh/2\pi$ and Eqs. (I-2) and (I-1), derive Eq. (I-3) for the energy.

The difference between the energy of the initial state E_{n_i} (with quantum number n_i) and the energy of the final state E_{n_f} (with quantum number n_f) would be given by

$$\Delta E_{\text{system}} = E_{n_f} - E_{n_i} = -\frac{2\pi^2 m_e e^4}{h^2}\left(\frac{1}{n_f^2} - \frac{1}{n_i^2}\right) \tag{I-5}$$

But this is the energy emitted in the spectroscopic experiment, corresponding, by the relation $\Delta E_{\text{system}} = E_{\text{photon}} = h\nu$, to a frequency

$$\nu_{if} = \frac{-\Delta E}{h} = \frac{2\pi^2 m_e e^4}{h^3}\left(\frac{1}{n_f^2} - \frac{1}{n_i^2}\right) \tag{I-6}$$

[It should be noted that the energy given by Eq. (I-5) for *emission* must be multiplied by -1 before it is equated to the energy of the photon. This ensures that the frequencies will always be positive.] Expression (I-6) is of the same form as Rydberg's. Indeed, on evaluation of $2\pi^2 m_e e^4/h^3$, Rydberg's value (to four significant figures) is obtained.

PROBLEM I-6

Use Eq. (I-6) to predict the frequency of the photon emitted in the transition of the hydrogen atom to the ground state ($n = 1$) from the first excited state ($n = 2$). The experimental value is 2.467×10^{15} (sec^{-1}).

PROBLEM I-7

Use Eq. (I-5) to predict the ionization energy of the ground-state hydrogen atom. The experimental value is 2.18×10^{-11} erg.

(iii) Project 1. Elementary atomic spectroscopy

This is the first of 11 "Projects"—essentially paper and pencil laboratories. They encompass more material than do the individual problems found throughout the text, but like those problems they are designed to illustrate the material just covered.

(a) Introduction

It has already been pointed out that since the Rydberg relation

$$\nu_{nm} = R_e\left(\frac{1}{n^2} - \frac{1}{m^2}\right) \tag{I-7}$$

and that given by Bohr are identical in form, both formulas correctly give the frequencies of the emission spectrum shown in Table I-1. The significance of Bohr's relation

$$\nu_{if} = \frac{2\pi^2 m_e e^4}{h^3}\left(\frac{1}{n_f^2} - \frac{1}{n_i^2}\right) \tag{I-8}$$

is, of course, that n and m are replaced by integers that are characteristic of the initial and final states of the system. Consequently an analysis of the emission spectrum of hydrogen in terms of the Bohr equation could generate some familiarity with quantum numbers, energy level diagrams, and transitions as well as with the line spectrum itself.

(b) Units

Up to this point electromagnetic radiation has been characterized by either frequency ν(sec^{-1}) or wavelength λ(cm). The relation between λ

and ν, namely, $\nu\lambda = c$, where c is the velocity of light, means that when ν increases, then λ decreases. In addition spectroscopists frequently characterize radiation in terms of "wave numbers" $\bar{\nu}(\text{cm}^{-1})$, where $\bar{\nu} = 1/\lambda = \nu/c$.

PROBLEM 1-1

Select the frequency in Table I-1 that corresponds to the highest-energy radiation ($E = h\nu$) and convert it to λ and to $\bar{\nu}$. Do the same for the lowest-energy radiation. The result should give an indication of the range of radiation for the electronic transitions in the H atom in terms of λ, ν, and $\bar{\nu}$.

(c) *Assignment of spectral lines*

To assign a frequency to its parent transition, it is necessary to know the quantum number of the initial state as well as that of the final state; i.e., each frequency is characterized by *two* (unknown) parameters. Consequently some additional characteristic besides the frequency is required to make the assignment.

Fortunately the grouping of frequencies among themselves provides the necessary hint. For example, the frequencies of the first column of Table I-1 are well separated from the remaining frequencies. In addition, the frequencies in this set are progressively more closely spaced as one moves up the column. This can be explained in the following manner. The quantum numbers n_f and n_i in Eq. (I-8) are independent, so it is possible that one of them, say, n_f, could be held fixed while the other, n_i, varies. This is equivalent to considering a set of transitions in which the final state is always the same, but the initial state differs for every member of the set. If, for example, n_f were fixed in Eq. (I-8), then, as n_i becomes larger, $1/n_i^2$ becomes smaller and the frequencies ν_{if} become similar, finally approaching a *limiting frequency* characteristic of n_f only.

PROBLEM 1-2

Show that the limiting frequency of Eq. (I-8) is characteristic of n_f only.

PROBLEM 1-3

Find the value of the limiting frequencies in each column of Table I-1. [*Hint:* The difference between succeeding frequencies in a given column decreases from bottom to top, e.g., the difference (3158 − 3083) = 75 is approximately *one-half* the preceding difference (3083 − 2923) = 160.]

PROBLEM 1-4

Find the value of n_f (an integer) common to the transitions producing the frequencies given in the first column of Table I-1. Do the same for each of the other columns. (*Hint:* Use the limiting frequency obtained in Prob. 1-3 and the result of Prob. 1-2.)

Thus if the value of n_f common to a set of frequencies is known, the appropriate value of n_i for each frequency can be obtained and the assignment completed.

PROBLEM 1-5

Find the initial and final quantum numbers for seven or eight of the frequencies given in Table I-1. [*Hint:* If n_f is known for a transition, then n_i can be found by solving Eq. (I-8) for the n_i.]

(*d*) *Transitions and energy level diagrams*

The observed frequencies are the result of the transition of the electron from one energy level of the hydrogen atom to another level. These transitions can be represented diagrammatically. The usual procedure is to draw horizontal lines labeled for energy and quantum number and then draw an arrow between the lines to represent a transition, labeling the arrow with the appropriate frequency. Figure I-8 illustrates the procedure and includes a schematic representation of the line spectrum.

PROBLEM 1-6

Draw, to scale, an energy level diagram for the hydrogen atom. Indicate seven or eight transitions, and label the arrows with the appropriate frequency. In the schematic representation of the line spectrum, mark four lines as well as the limiting frequency.

PROBLEM 1-7

Compare the emission spectrum obtained in Prob. 1-6 to the absorption spectrum that would be obtained for hydrogen at room temperature.

(*e*) *The Rydberg constant*

In addition to providing the significance of the integers n and m, the development of the Bohr relation also indicates why the fundamental constants e, m_e, etc., should occur in the Rydberg constant. In particular the term e^4 arises through considering the potential energy of an electronic charge $-e$ in the presence of a nucleus of charge $+e$, that is,

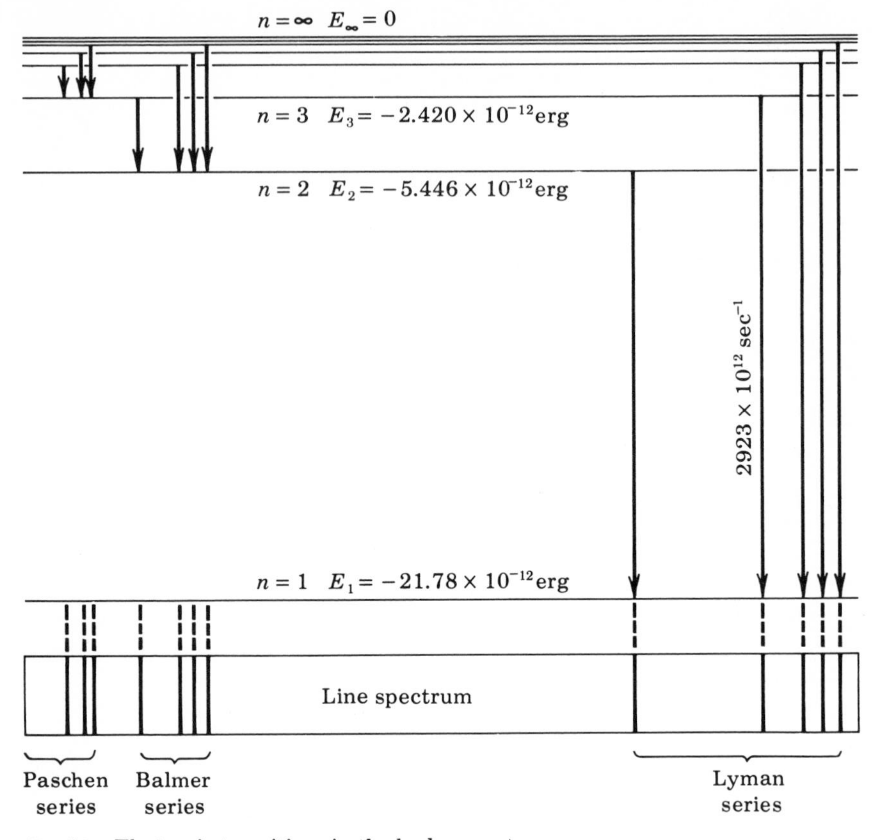

Fig. I-8 Electronic transitions in the hydrogen atom.

$V = (q_e)(q_n)/r = -e^2/r$. Since Bohr's approach gives the basis for the parameters in the energy formula, one can extend the method to similar one-electron–one-nucleus systems such as He^{+1}.

PROBLEM 1-8

Derive the potential energy formula for the He^{+1} ion.

PROBLEM 1-9

Derive the energy level formula similar to Eq. (I-3) for the He^{+1} ion.

PROBLEM 1-10

Give the wavelength of the photons emitted in the transitions $n_i = 3 \rightarrow n_f = 2$, $n_i = 2 \rightarrow n_f = 1$, etc., for He^{+1}.

PROBLEM 1-11

Draw an energy level-transition diagram similar to Fig. I-8 for the He^{+1} emission spectrum.

(iv) Wave-particle dualism

As indicated earlier, Eq. (I-8) from Bohr's theory explained much of the spectral data then available on the hydrogen atom and on hydrogenic systems. However, it failed when applied to more complex systems or, for that matter, to the finer details of the hydrogen spectrum. Although modifications,[1] which became increasingly complex and arbitrary, were put forward and applied with varying degrees of success, it became clear that Bohr's theory was somehow fundamentally inadequate for the task.

Einstein's explanation of the photoelectric effect had suggested a corpuscular, or particle, character for light. This point of view had been substantiated in 1923 by the billiard-ball-like behavior of photons in the experiments of Compton.[2] Yet, there were experiments involving light, for example diffraction, that were still best explained in terms of the wave nature of light. It appeared that light, at least, had both wave and particle character. In 1923, Louis de Broglie[3] proposed that *all* matter had both wave (wavelength λ) and particle (momentum p) character related by

$$\lambda = \frac{h}{p} \qquad \text{de Broglie's relation} \qquad \text{(I-9)}$$

This meant that the electron, to which Bohr had ascribed only particle character, would have to be treated as having *both* wave and particle character. The approach proposed in 1927 by Schroedinger combined both wave and particle characteristics! An appropriate point from which to approach the new "quantum mechanics" would be to start with both a wave description and a particle description and bring them together through the de Broglie relation.

PROBLEM I-8

Compare the wavelength associated with a 50-eV electron, an α particle of velocity 1.5×10^9 cm/sec, and a 1-g mass of velocity 1 cm/sec.

[1] The Bohr-Sommerfeld and similar theories introduced elliptic orbits and half-integral quantum numbers. See D. Bohm, "Quantum Theory," pp. 45–47, Prentice-Hall, 1951.

[2] A. H. Compton, *Am. J. Phys.*, p. 817 (1961), gives a historical account.

[3] See L. de Broglie, "Matter and Light," Dover Publications, 1939.

I-3 THE NEW QUANTUM THEORY

(i) Wave and particle motion

Since the description that apparently must be used to explain atomic and molecular systems is to be some combination of wave and particle characteristics, it would seem wise to stop first and consider the nature of wave and particle motions.

Particle motion is, of course, very simple. The particle moves from point x_1 in space at time t_1 to point x_2 at time t_2, etc., which, taken together, means that its position is some function of time, written symbolically as $x = f(t)$. Furthermore, it is implicit that as the mass moves in space, it possesses kinetic energy $mv^2/2$ by virtue of this motion and potential energy V by virtue of its position. The total energy is then given by

$$E = \frac{mv^2}{2} + V \tag{I-10}$$

Wave motion, however, is somewhat more difficult to characterize. There is no transference of mass in the direction of motion; nevertheless, energy is transmitted by the wave. Further, the wave motion extends over a region of space and, in fact, may extend over an extremely large region. Perhaps the simplest way to approach this is to consider the motion of a wave in a material medium, such as water. The movement of the wave is then characterized by a description of the relative motion of the points in the medium, as shown in Fig. I-9.

Consider the motion of the unit mass m (in Fig. I-9) located at x_1 and having, at the moment of observation, a value y_1 for the displacement coordinate y. Certainly the y value of this point will change with time.

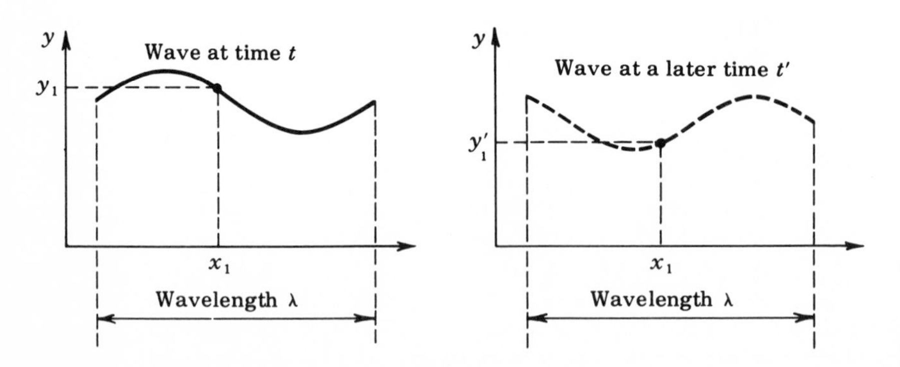

Fig. I-9 Displacement of a point in wave motion.

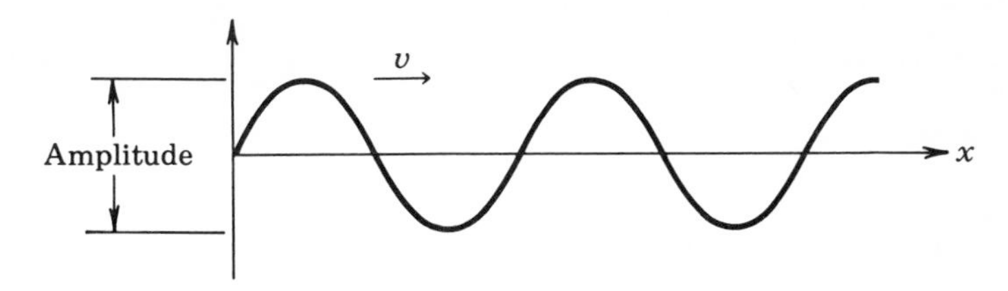

Fig. I-10 A traveling wave.

Thus y_1 is a function of time, a relation that can be written symbolically as $y_1 = f_1(t)$. Since the wave extends over space, there are many points x_i that, as the point at x_1, are executing a time-dependent motion. For a description of the wave, i.e., the motion of *all* the points x_i, all the $y_1 = f_1(t)$, $y_2 = f_2(t)$, . . . , etc., must be combined into one description that can be written as $y = f(x,t)$—in words, the displacement, or y value, depends on both the position x and the time t.

The displacement described in the previous paragraph is, of course, brought about by a disturbance, and the displaced point is returned to its original position by a restoring force characteristic of the medium. The simplest wave description is obtained when the restoring force is proportional to the displacement (Hooke's law force). This situation is examined in detail in Appendix I, with the result that the wave motion must satisfy the classical wave equation[1]

$$\frac{\partial^2 y(x,t)}{\partial x^2} = \left(\frac{1}{\nu\lambda}\right)^2 \frac{\partial^2 y(x,t)}{\partial t^2}$$

A solution to this equation is $y(x,t) = a_0 \sin 2\pi(x/\lambda - \nu t)$. Here ν is the frequency of oscillation, and λ is the wavelength. The velocity of the wave is $v = \nu\lambda$. This wave corresponds to the motion of the profile $a_0 \sin (2\pi x/\lambda)$ along the x axis with velocity v, illustrated in Fig. I-10. The wave "transmits" energy to the right.

PROBLEM I-9

Show that $y(x,t) = a_0 \sin 2\pi(x/\lambda - \nu t)$ is a solution to the classical wave equation and that this is a wave moving to the right with velocity v [note that $dx/dt = (-\partial y/\partial t)/(\partial y/\partial x)$].

Consider a region for which energy remains constant. The only way to satisfy this requirement and to have wave motion is to have *two*

[1] The symbol $\partial/\partial x$ is a partial derivative with respect to x, for example, $\partial/\partial x(x^2y) = 2xy$; similarly $\partial/\partial y(x^2y) = x^2$, that is, the operator treats all variables, save that in the "denominator" of the operator, as constants.

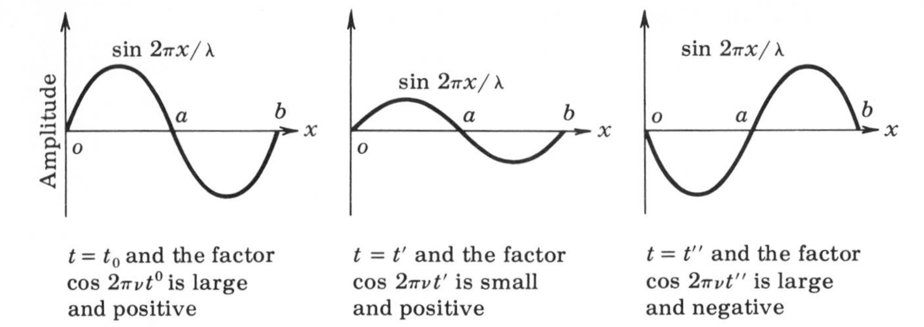

Fig. I-11 Modification of the wave profile.

waves that transmit equal amounts of energy but are of "opposite sign." In this situation the wave is described by a sum of waves one traveling in the positive direction and one in the negative direction. This can be represented algebraically by

$$y(x,t) = a_0 \sin 2\pi \left(\frac{x}{\lambda} - \nu t\right) + a_0 \sin 2\pi \left(\frac{x}{\lambda} + \nu t\right)$$

Applying the trigonometric formulas for multiple angles, one obtains

$$y(x,t) = 2a_0 \sin \frac{2\pi x}{\lambda} \cos 2\pi\nu t$$

This solution is a product of two functions: one of position,

$$\psi(x) = \sin \frac{2\pi x}{\lambda}$$

and one of time, $g(t) = \cos 2\pi\nu t$. The *profile of* $\psi(x)$ *does not travel* but is merely modified in amplitude with passage of time, as illustrated in Fig. I-11. The profile is larger or smaller only as the value of the time-dependent function changes.

The majority of systems that one is concerned with are systems for which the energy is constant and for which the time dependence is of no concern. Hence it is the spacial description $\psi(x)$ and the equation governing this function that are of interest. In other words, from classical wave motion the aspect of most interest for the development of descriptions of the atomic and molecular systems is $\psi(x)$ and the equation governing $\psi(x)$. The equation governing $\psi(x)$, obtained in Appendix I, is

$$\frac{d^2\psi(x)}{dx^2} = -\left(\frac{2\pi}{\lambda}\right)^2 \psi(x) \tag{I-11}$$

(ii) The Schroedinger equation

The classical statement of particle kinetic energy and the equation governing wave motion have been developed in the previous section. The equation that describes matter in terms of the wave-particle duality may now be found with the aid of de Broglie's suggestion relating the particle to the wave nature of matter:

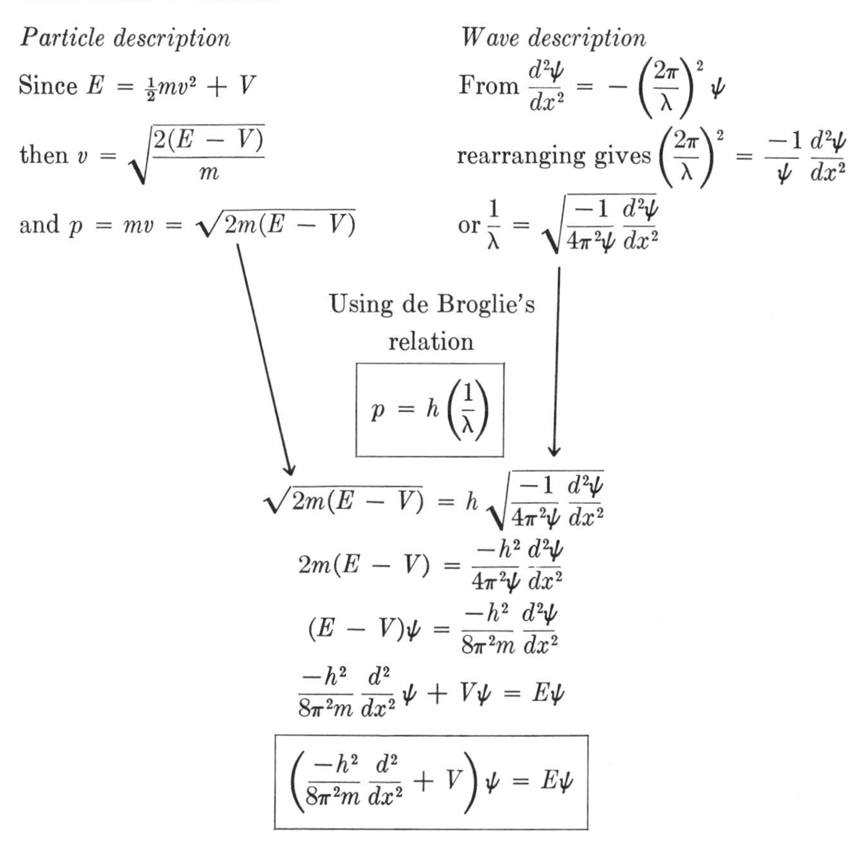

Since d^2/dx^2 is an operator (It says: "Operate on ψ by taking the second derivative."), and V can be thought of as an operator (It says: "Operate on ψ by multiplying by V."), the two operators might well be combined into one, $H = [(-h^2/8\pi^2 m)(d^2/dx^2) + V]$. *The result is* $H\psi = E\psi$, *the Schroedinger equation.* This is not a derivation of the Schroedinger equation—among other things a postulated relation $p = h/\lambda$ was used. Indeed, there is no strict derivation available; nevertheless, this should indicate the origin of the Schroedinger equation. Furthermore, since the results predicted by this equation are observed, we can use this equation with some confidence.

Table I-2 The classical and quantum-mechanical equivalents

	Classical statement	*Quantum operator*
Kinetic energy	$\frac{1}{2}m\left(\frac{dx}{dt}\right)^2$	$\Rightarrow \frac{-h^2}{8\pi^2 m}\frac{d^2}{dx^2}$
Momentum	$p = m\left(\frac{dx}{dt}\right)$	$\Rightarrow \left(\frac{-ih}{2\pi}\right)\frac{d}{dx}$
Potential	$V = f(x)$	$\Rightarrow f(x)$ (no change)

The classical expression for the energy is Hamilton's function, and, since the operator H gives rise to the total energy, it is given the name *hamiltonian operator*. Further, since the classical energy is made up of a kinetic energy term and a potential given as $(\frac{1}{2}mv^2) + V$, the first term of the quantum-mechanical hamiltonian is taken to correspond to the operator for kinetic energy. Thus $(-h^2/8\pi^2 m)(d^2/dx^2)$ is the operator replacing $\frac{1}{2}mv^2$ in going from the classical to the quantum treatment. Also, since $\frac{1}{2}mv^2 \equiv (mv)^2/2m = p^2/2m$ and since $(-h^2/8\pi^2 m)(d^2/dx^2)$ can be written[1] as $\frac{1}{2}m[(ih/2\pi)(d/dx)]^2$, one can say that $(-ih/2\pi)(d/dx)$ replaces p, the momentum, in going to the quantum description. The results are summarized in Table I-2.

Not only has the Schroedinger equation $H\psi = E\psi$ been "derived" but the "recipe" for getting the quantum-mechanical operators from the classical statements has also been obtained!

PROBLEM I-10

What is the quantum-mechanical operator for "kinetic energy in the y direction"?

PROBLEM I-11

What is the quantum-mechanical operator for the potential energy of the hydrogen atom?

I-4 THE SOLUTION OF THE SCHROEDINGER EQUATION

(i) The solution of differential equations

(a) *Introduction*

Having obtained the Schroedinger equation, we must now solve for ψ and E. At first glance many features of the procedure of solution and

[1] $i = \sqrt{-1}$, that is, i^2 generates the $-$ sign required here.

the features of the solution itself would appear to be novel and might be attributed to the quantum origin of the equation. They are not quantum in origin but are simply features of the particular type of equation to which the SE[1] belongs. It would be wise to consider first the nature of such equations and the method of their solution.

Since the Schroedinger equation involves differential operators, for example d^2/dx^2, it is referred to as a *differential equation*, and, although the general procedure for obtaining the solutions of such equations may appear to be much more difficult than for ordinary algebraic equations, one is, nevertheless, concerned with the same problems. For example, when presented with the equation $y^2 = 4 - 3y$, we are immediately aware of the problem—find those *values* of y that make the left-hand side equal to the right-hand side. One can apply the same principle to the differential equation $(-d^2/dx^2)g(x) = Kg(x)$ and look for a function that makes the two sides equal; i.e., one seeks a *function* $g(x)$ that when operated on gives back itself times a constant K. Trying $g(x) = x^2$ gives -2 for the left-hand side and Kx^2 for the right-hand side, which are equal *only* if x^2 takes the value $-(2/K)$. If the solution is to be valid for *all* values of x, then $g(x) = x^2$ is not a proper solution.

(b) *Form*

This attempt, however, does emphasize that the solution $g(x)$ must have a *form* such that, after double differentiation, the variable x must occur in the same way on both sides of the equation. A suitable *form* for this equation is $g(x) = D \sin kx$, for which the left-hand side, after differentiation, is $k^2 D \sin kx$, and the right-hand side is simply $KD \sin kx$, giving

$$k^2 D \sin kx = KD \sin kx$$

Canceling the $D \sin kx$ on both sides leaves $k^2 = K$. Since the argument x has been removed, and as long as $k = \sqrt{K}$, the function $D \sin kx$ is a solution to the equation (D can, of course, have any value). A solution of a differential equation has been obtained by rather simple steps!

Perhaps the most significant feature is that the form of the solution depends on the operator. If the operator is different, then the solution may have a different form. Looking ahead, then, the form of the solutions for the Schroedinger equation will depend on the H operator; but since the H operator is simply a quantum-mechanical statement of the energy interactions (i.e., kinetic energy and potential energy) of the system, one may expect the form of ψ that describes two vibrating nuclei, for example, to be different from the form that describes the bound electron in the hydrogen atom.

[1] The symbol SE will frequently be used in place of the words "Schroedinger equation."

(c) *Boundary conditions*

Although the procedure outlined above has provided the general form of a solution to the differential equation, it has given no assurance that there are not other solutions as well. Indeed, for the example treated, $\cos kx$ is also an acceptable solution. One must then write the general solution as $g(x) = A \sin kx + B \cos kx$, where A and B are constants.

PROBLEM I-12

Show that $g(x) = \cos kx$ is also an acceptable solution to the differential equation $(-d^2/dx^2)g(x) = Kg(x)$.

Since the differential equation provides no indication as to the value of A and B, additional equations are required to determine them. If, for example, it is known that $g(x)$ must have certain values C_1 when $x = x_1$ and C_2 when $x = x_2$, then one has the additional equations

$$g(x = x_1) = C_1 \qquad g(x = x_2) = C_2$$

and the two unknowns A and B can be determined. These equations depend on the problem being studied and are usually determined by the physical requirements, or boundaries, of the system for which $g(x)$ is a description—they are the *boundary conditions*.

(ii) Allowed solutions and energy values for the Schroedinger equation

The hydrogen atom would appear to be a rather obvious choice to illustrate the features of the Schroedinger equation, for not only is it the simplest atomic system but its energy levels and descriptions have already been introduced in connection with the Bohr theory. However, the description of the hydrogen atom would involve six coordinates—three (x_e,y_e,z_e) for the electron and three (x_n,y_n,z_n) for the nucleus; hence the Schroedinger equation would be rather complicated. Even the boundary conditions, requiring that the description must go to zero at an infinite distance from the nucleus and that the system be spherically symmetrical, would appear cumbersome to introduce. Thus the description of the hydrogen atom could involve more complicated mathematics than is wise to introduce at the moment. Instead a simpler system should be used and the properties of the SE investigated. Then, having obtained a thorough understanding of the properties of the Schroedinger equation for the simple system, the more complicated and important cases will be argued by analogy.

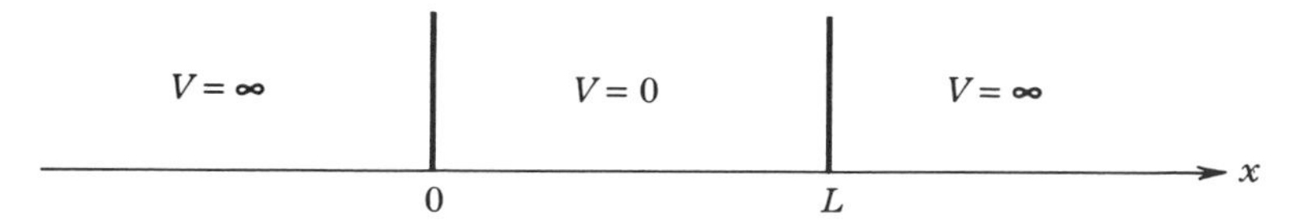

Fig. I-12 Potential of the particle-in-a-box.

The particle-in-a-box system

The simplest system that can be found to illustrate the properties of the SE is that of a "one-dimensional particle" allowed to move freely in a "box." In other words, the system can move in the x direction between only certain limits, say between $x = 0$ and $x = L$.

The "walls" of the box at $x = 0$ and $x = L$ are an insurmountable barrier; i.e., the potential energy is infinity at the walls of the box. One has, then, that V is infinity when x is equal to or less than zero, and V is infinity when x is equal to or greater than L. Inside the box the particle moves freely and V is zero; this is illustrated in Fig. I-12.

The classical hamiltonian for the region outside the box is

$$H = KE + V$$

and, from the recipe obtained previously, the quantum-mechanical statement of the kinetic energy is $(-h^2/8\pi^2m)(d^2/dx^2)$, where m is the mass of the particle, and $V = \infty$, so the hamiltonian is $[(-h^2/8\pi^2m)(d^2/dx^2) + \infty]$. The Schroedinger equation is then

$$\left(\frac{-h^2}{8\pi^2m}\frac{d^2}{dx^2} + \infty\right)\psi(x) = E\psi(x)$$

In this equation $\psi(x)$ is multiplied by infinity in one term $\infty\psi(x)$ and everywhere else by terms that are finite, for example $E\psi$ and $(-h^2/8\pi^2m)(d^2/dx^2)\psi$. The only possibility for the equation to be true is if $\psi = 0$ in all these terms—then $\infty\psi \rightarrow (\infty)0 = 0$. Similarly the other terms are zero. Hence for the region with $V = \infty$, ψ is zero—just another way of saying that the particle is not found outside the box. Thus the *physical* requirement on the system can be expressed either by stating V as above or by saying that $\psi(x)$ must be zero whenever x is less than or equal to zero and when x is greater than or equal to L. The latter alternative is given diagrammatically in Fig. I-13.

Inside the "box" the quantum-mechanical expression H required for the Schroedinger equation is simply the operator for kinetic energy, and so

$$H = \frac{-h^2}{8\pi^2m}\frac{d^2}{dx^2} \qquad (V = 0 \text{ here})$$

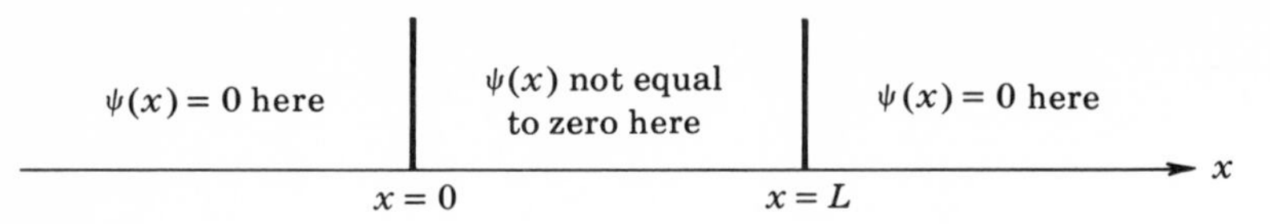

Fig. I-13 Restrictions on the description of the particle-in-a-box.

The SE is thus

$$\frac{-h^2}{8\pi^2 m}\frac{d^2}{dx^2}\psi(x) = E\psi(x)$$

Rearranging gives

$$\frac{-d^2}{dx^2}\psi(x) = \left(\frac{8\pi^2 mE}{h^2}\right)\psi(x) \qquad \text{or} \qquad \frac{-d^2}{dx^2}\psi(x) = K\psi(x)$$

where

$$K = \frac{8\pi^2 mE}{h^2} \tag{I-12}$$

But this equation is formally the same as $(-d^2/dx^2)g(x) = Kg(x)$, already encountered in Sec. I-4(i). Thus the correct *form* of the solution is found to be

$$\psi(x) = A \sin kx + B \cos kx \qquad \text{where } k^2 = K \tag{I-13}$$

This form is, of course, dependent on the operator H and thus on the "interactions" of the system (that is, $V = 0$).

The solution is not complete, for one must now ensure that the physical constraints, or boundary conditions, $\psi(x = 0) = 0, \psi(x = L) = 0$ are satisfied.[1] Inserting $x = 0$ into the solution [Eq. (I-13)] gives

$$\psi(x = 0) = A \sin k0 + B \cos k0 = A.0 + B.1 = 0 + B$$

But since $\psi(x = 0)$ is zero, $B = 0$. The solution becomes simply

$$\psi(x) = A \sin kx \tag{I-14}$$

Turning to the second restriction imposed by the physical model and inserting $x = L$ in the solution (I-14), one obtains $\psi(L) = A \sin kL$. But $\sin kL$ will not, in general, be zero unless some restriction is imposed upon k. From trigonometry, $\sin\theta = 0$ whenever $\theta = 180$, 360, etc., or, in terms of π, whenever $\theta = 1\pi, 2\pi$, etc., i.e., when $\theta = n\pi$, where $n = +1, +2$, etc. Hence the physical constraint could be satisfied by requiring

[1] The boundary condition $\psi(x = 0) = \psi(x = L) = 0$ ensures the continuity of $\psi(x)$ at the ends of the box. Although the first derivative is not continuous at the boundaries, the second derivative is continuous!

Table I-3 The particle-in-a-box descriptions

Eigenfunction form				
Analytical	*Diagrammatic*	*Eigenvalue*	*n*	*SE*
$\psi_1(x) = A \sin \dfrac{\pi x}{L}$	$\psi_1(x)$ $x = 0$ $x = L$	$E_1 = \dfrac{h^2}{8mL^2}$	1	$H\psi_1 = E_1\psi_1$
$\psi_2(x) = A \sin \dfrac{2\pi x}{L}$	$\psi_2(x)$ $x = 0$ $x = L$	$E_2 = 4\dfrac{h^2}{8mL^2}$	2	$H\psi_2 = E_2\psi_2$
$\psi_3(x) = A \sin \dfrac{3\pi x}{L}$	$\psi_3(x)$ $x = 0$ $x = L$	$E_3 = 9\dfrac{h^2}{8mL^2}$	3	$H\psi_3 = E_3\psi_3$

that $\theta = kL = n\pi$ or that $k = n\pi/L$. But $k^2 = K$, and, hence, from Eq. (I-12), $k^2 = 8\pi^2 mE/h^2$. Inserting the allowed values of k gives $n^2\pi^2/L^2 = 8\pi^2 mE/h^2$. Rearranging and solving for E gives the energy as $E_n = n^2h^2/8mL^2$, with the description

$$\psi_n(x) = A \sin \frac{n\pi x}{L}$$

Since n can be 1, 2, etc., there are a number of *different solutions* to the SE, each solution having its *particular value of the energy*. The solutions ψ_n are frequently called the *eigenfunctions*, and the value of the energy E_n associated with each eigenfunction is called the *eigenvalue*. It might be emphasized that the quantum-mechanical energy is associated with a function describing the system, not with a particular coordinate value. No matter what the coordinate value, the energy is always the same. The particle-in-a-box energy description is summarized in Table I-3.

PROBLEM I-13

By operating on $\psi_2(x)$ of Table I-3 with the hamiltonian, show that one, indeed, obtains the eigenvalue; i.e., one gets back a number $h^2/2mL^2$ times the original function.

In trying to understand modern concepts, the questions: Why only certain functions? Why only certain allowed energies? have already been posed. If the Schroedinger equation is accepted, and a fairly convincing "derivation" has been presented, then this simple example gives an answer; for, as shown, the SE does impose a certain form on the wave function—a form that depends largely on the hamiltonian and thus on the interactions (kinetic energy and potential energy) of the system. This form is further limited by the physical restrictions placed on the system, and, in imposing these restrictions, one automatically introduces only certain allowed functions and allowed energy levels.

(iii) The use of the ψ function

(a) Commutation

The preceding section has indicated that only certain eigenfunctions ψ_n with certain energies (energy eigenvalues) E_n are allowed for bounded quantum-mechanical systems. This means that if one makes a measurement for the energy of a particular energy state, one *always* obtains a particular value of the energy. Can one also make a measurement of the momentum and always expect to obtain a particular value of the momentum; i.e., are these energy states also eigenfunctions of the momentum operator? More generally we might ask whether it is possible for us to obtain states with well-defined values of more than one property. For example, can one obtain well-defined values of both momentum and position?

From the recipe given in Table I-2, the operator for coordinate x, say, is just x itself, whereas the operator for momentum in the x direction is $(-ih/2\pi)(d/dx)$. Operation on a state $\psi(x)$ to determine the position (i.e., the coordinate x) is indicated by $x\psi(x)$, and if this operation were to be followed by a "measurement" of the momentum, one might write $[(-ih/2\pi)(d/dx)][x\psi(x)]$, where the first operation is always with the furthest-right operator. For convenience this result is given the symbol R_1. If, however, a measurement of momentum were carried out first and this followed by a "measurement" of position, one might write $x[(-ih/2\pi)(d/dx)\psi(x)] = R_2$.

In R_1, the derivative of a product of functions of x is required, and the use of the rule from calculus for the derivatives of a product gives

$$R_1 = \frac{-ih}{2\pi}\frac{d}{dx}[x\psi(x)] = x\left[\frac{-ih}{2\pi}\frac{d}{dx}\psi(x)\right] + \psi(x)\frac{-ih}{2\pi}\frac{d}{dx}x$$

But the first term on the right is simply R_2. Hence

$$R_1 = R_2 + \frac{-ih}{2\pi}\psi(x)$$

Clearly the result R_1 is not the same as the result R_2—they differ by $(h/2\pi)i\psi(x)$. It appears that, for the representation given above, the act of first "measuring" the momentum (in R_2) is such that the position "measured" subsequently is different from the case where the position had been "measured" first (as in R_1). But if a *state* were always to have a particular value for momentum and for position, we would expect the same answer no matter how the measurement were carried out. Thus it would appear that well-defined values of both position and momentum of a state $\psi(x)$ cannot be obtained,[1] since the order in which they are measured *does* matter. Indeed, this can be condensed by saying: If the operators for two observables do not commute (i.e., if their order *is* important), then one cannot obtain a state that has well-defined values of both observables.

PROBLEM I-14

Does the operator for energy for a particle-in-a-box commute with the operator for momentum? Could one measure energy and momentum for this system? [*Hint:* Remember that the potential here is a function of x; that is, $V(x) = 0$ when $0 < x < L$, but $V(x) = \infty$ otherwise.]

PROBLEM I-15

By operating on the energy states $\psi_n(x)$ of Table I-3 with the momentum operator $(-ih/2\pi)\, d/dx$, show that one does *not* get back a momentum eigenvalue (i.e., a number) times the *original* function.

(b) *Expectation values*

The function ψ is a description of the whole system such that, if it is operated on with H, the quantum-mechanical-operator statement of the energy, the result is the energy multiplied by ψ. If $H\psi$ is multiplied by ψ^* from the left,[2] integrated,[3] and divided by $\int \psi^*\psi\, d\tau$, the explicit statement of the energy is obtained as an "expectation" value $\bar{E}$ as

$$\bar{E} = \frac{\int \psi^* H \psi\, d\tau}{\int \psi^* \psi\, d\tau} \qquad \text{(I-15)}$$

In this statement for the expectation value, if ψ is an eigenfunction of the operator (that is, E is a contant), H the expectation value $\bar{E}$ is identical to E;

$$\bar{E} = \frac{\int \psi^* E \psi\, d\tau}{\int \psi^* \psi\, d\tau} \qquad \text{[replacing } H\psi \text{ in Eq. (I-15) by } E\psi]$$

$$= \frac{E \int \psi^* \psi\, d\tau}{\int \psi^* \psi\, d\tau} = E$$

[1] In fact the "operator products" $x\, d/dx$ or $(d/dx)x$ do *not* correspond to any observable property of the system. See L. D. Landau and E. M. Lifshitz, "Quantum Mechanics," Addison-Wesley, 2d ed., 1965, pp. 14 and 15, for a simple discussion.

[2] Here ψ^* is the complex conjugate of ψ. The complex conjugate of a function $z = a + ib$ is $z^* = a - ib$, where i is $\sqrt{-1}$.

[3] The integration is over the argument of ψ and the symbol $d\tau$ is the volume element (discussed in detail in Project 5). If ψ is a function of x, then $d\tau$ is simply dx.

But this is rather what one would expect if the *expectation*-value formula was equivalent to taking the *average* value—certainly the "average" value of a constant is just the constant. Although such average values are of little advantage for cases where the function is an eigenfunction of the operator, the same type of formula may be used for any function ψ or operator A. Consequently the average value $\bar{a}$ of a quantity "a," whose corresponding quantum-mechanical operator is A, is taken to be

$$\bar{a} = \frac{\int \psi^* A \psi \, d\tau}{\int \psi^* \psi \, d\tau}$$

For example, the average value of momentum p_x would be

$$\bar{p}_x = \frac{\int \psi^* [(-ih/2\pi)(d/dx)] \psi \, d\tau}{\int \psi^* \psi \, d\tau}$$

PROBLEM I-16

Calculate the expectation (average) value of the momentum for the particle-in-a-box energy eigenstates ψ_1 and ψ_2.

Certainly the average value is a statistical result and implies that if many measurements on similar systems were carried out, then there would be some average value, although the result of a particular measurement would not necessarily be the average value. Consider the measurement of momentum of the electrons in a beam produced by a hot filament. An apparatus to measure the momentum of an electron could be set up and the value $p_x(1)$ obtained for the first electron, $p_x(2)$ for the second, and so on, obtaining after many measurements an expectation (or average) value $\bar{p}_x = [p_x(1) + p_x(2) + \cdots + p_x(n)]/n$. Clearly if some of the measured p_x differed from the mean value, we would say that some uncertainty exists for the value we would get for p_x on performing a particular measurement. This we call the *uncertainty* in the momentum of an electron in the beam, defined quantitatively as

$$\Delta p_x = \left\{ \frac{[p_x(1) - \bar{p}_x]^2 + [p_x(2) - \bar{p}_x]^2 + \cdots + [p_x(n) - \bar{p}_x]^2}{n} \right\}^{\frac{1}{2}}$$

As such, Δp_x is a statistical or probabilistic quantity. A similar relation holds for Δx.

(c) The Heisenberg uncertainty relation

If a description that always has a particular value for momentum and a particular value for position *cannot* be obtained, then the best one can hope for are expectation values with consequent uncertainties Δp and Δx.

Indeed, one can show[1] that the product of the uncertainties is the Heisenberg uncertainty relation $\Delta p \, \Delta x \geq \frac{1}{2}(h/2\pi)$. Such a result is not unexpected, for the previous section clearly indicates that measurement of position and momentum are not independent. Consequently it is not surprising that the more accurate one attempted to make a measurement p_x, the less accurate would be the other measurement x.

PROBLEM I-17

Calculate the minimum uncertainty in the velocity of an electron confined to a box of length 1 Å.

It is interesting to consider this uncertainty relation in terms of the measuring process. To measure the position of an electron, one could use light and, for such a small particle, a microscope or lens arrangement. Unfortunately the use of light of *wavelength* λ immediately introduces an uncertainty in position that is proportional to the *length* of the wave:

$$\Delta x \sim \lambda \tag{I-16}$$

In addition, the light flash used in defining the position of the electron is the result of light colliding with an electron and being scattered back into the lens of the microscope. But for small entities such as an electron, such a collision will certainly change the future career of the electron—i.e., the momentum of the electron will no longer have its previous value. The probable value of this change in momentum will depend on the energy of the colliding photon, and, hence, is inversely proportional to the wavelength:

$$\Delta p_x \sim \frac{h}{\lambda} \tag{I-17}$$

Obviously the larger the wavelength, the smaller Δp_x in Eq. (I-17) but the larger Δx in Eq. (I-16), so that what is gained in one measurement is lost in the other. If one multiplies Eqs. (I-16) and (I-17), one finds the product to be proportional to h: $\Delta p \cdot \Delta x \sim h$—the same form as the Heisenberg uncertainty principle.

(d) Probability density

The previous sections have been concerned with obtaining various properties of the system. Perhaps the most fundamental property is that of "existence," in particular, existence at a point in space—i.e., can the sys-

[1] One can show, for any two observables a and b whose operators A and B are, respectively, $A = a$ and $B = (h/2\pi)(d/da)$, that $\Delta a \, \Delta b \sim \frac{1}{2}(h/2\pi)$. The proof is beyond the scope of the present development but can be found in standard quantum-mechanics texts, e.g., H. Merzbachen, "Quantum Mechanics," p. 154, Wiley, 1961.

tem be found at a certain point in space? Contrary to the classical situation this is not a trivial question, for now the system has both the properties of a particle (i.e., localization in space) and the properties of a wave (extension over space). For example, the wave description gives the intensity of the light as proportional to the square of the amplitude of the wave function. In terms of the particle description, the intensity of a light beam must be proportional to the number of photons striking in unit time a unit area at position x. Since both descriptions must be equivalent, this *number* of photons must be proportional to the *square of amplitude* of the light wave. Although the unit area could be divided into an infinite number of smaller "unit areas," the beam of light cannot—the number of photons in the beam is finite. Consequently there could be more such small unit areas than there are photons, and one should not refer to the number of photons striking a unit area but, rather, to the *probability* of a photon striking a unit area. Hence, the probability of having a photon strike a unit area at x is proportional to the square of the amplitude of the wave.

In the case of an electron, the square[1] of the "wave" description $\psi(x)\psi^*(x)$ may be regarded as a measure of the intensity of the electron "wave," or, for the particlelike point of view, $\psi^*(x)\psi(x)$ may be regarded as proportional to the *probability that the electron will be found with coordinate* x. Thus $\psi^*(x)\psi(x)$ can be taken as the probability of the electron having coordinate x. The probability of finding the electron in all of space is simply the sum of the probability for each value of x. The total probability is $\psi^*(x_1)\psi(x_1) + \psi^*(x_2)\psi(x_2) + \cdots = \int dx\psi^*(x)\psi(x)$. But since the electron *must* be found somewhere in all of space, the total probability is unity. Hence one must have $\int_{-\infty}^{\infty} dx\, \psi^*(x)\psi(x) = 1$, or, as this is more frequently stated, ψ must be normalized.

The solution of the particle-in-a-box problem might be reconsidered in view of this requirement. Although the imposition of the boundary conditions has removed one of the arbitrary coefficients, one coefficient A is still available for adjustment to ensure that ψ is normalized. Since $\psi(x)$ is zero, except between $x = 0$ and $x = L$, one has[2]

$$\int_{-\infty}^{\infty} A \sin \frac{n\pi x}{L} A \sin \frac{n\pi x}{L}\, dx = A^2 \int_0^L \sin^2 \frac{n\pi x}{L}\, dx = 1$$

The value of A^2 is then

$$A^2 = \frac{1}{\displaystyle\int_0^L \sin^2 \frac{n\pi x}{L}\, dx}$$

[1] If ψ is real $\psi^* = \psi$, then $\psi^*\psi \equiv \psi^2$.

[2] Since $A \sin (n\pi x/L)$ is real, then $\psi_n^*(x) = \psi_n(x)$.

The integral of $\int_0^L \sin^2 (n\pi x/L)\, dx$ is most easily found by changing the variable of integration by defining $y = n\pi x/L$, giving $dy = (n\pi/L)\, dx$ and, when $x = L$, $y = n\pi$. The integral becomes $(L/n\pi) \int_0^{n\pi} \sin^2 y\, dy$, where the integrand is a standard form found in any table of integrals[1] and has a value $n\pi/2$. Then $(L/n\pi) \int_0^{n\pi} \sin^2 y\, dy = (L/n\pi)(n\pi/2) = L/2$ giving $A = (2/L)^{\frac{1}{2}}$ and thus the normalized $\psi_n(x) = (2/L)^{\frac{1}{2}} \sin (n\pi x/L)$.

PROBLEM I-18

What is the probability of finding the particle between $0.45L$ and $0.55L$ for the lowest-energy description of the particle-in-a-box? Compare this answer to the result obtained for the second-lowest-energy description.

It is worthwhile commenting here on the fundamental difference between the classical and the quantum viewpoints. In classical science if the value of position and momentum were known, then both past and future values of those quantities could be given. In the previous sections we have seen that the measurement of the position or momentum of some small particles produces a change in the momentum of statistical magnitude Δp_x (or, for position, Δx), so that the future behavior cannot be predicted in the same sense as for the classical viewpoint. Only a *probabilistic* statement concerning the value of these quantities can be provided. But in the present section the function $\psi(x)$ has been considered as providing a *probability* description of the system through $\psi^*(x)\psi(x)$. Thus the $\psi(x)$-function picture is consistent with the limitations to our knowledge as expressed earlier in the Heisenberg relation.

(iv) Project 2. The particle-in-a-box analog for the electronic transitions of a molecule

(a) *Introduction*

The one-dimensional particle-in-a-box dealt with in the previous section has provided a simple method of investigating the major features of a quantum-mechanical description. It would be worthwhile seeing if there is, in fact, any real system that approximates this very simple model. Although real systems are three dimensional, it appears that there are real systems that may be treated as one-dimensional problems for certain purposes. For example, the molecule-ion

```
A                                               A
 \       |       |       |       |             /
  N—C=C—C=C—C=C—C=C—C=⁺N
 /    |       |       |       |       |        \
B                                               B
```

[1] See Appendix VII.

can, as is indicated in introductory chemistry courses, be written in the equivalent form

```
A                                                 A
 \    |       |       |       |       |          /
  N+=C—C=C—C=C—C=C—C=C—N
 /        |       |       |       |              \
B                                                 B
```

Since the double bonds can be in either of the positions given in these structures, it would appear that the electrons represented by the double bond are not localized in one bond area but, rather, appear to be spread out over the entire length of the double-bond chain. Thus these electrons, the so-called π electrons (this term will be discussed in Chap. II), "move" along the chain between the terminal nitrogen atoms. If it is assumed that the potential encountered by the electrons due to the carbon centers is constant over the length of the chain, the potential may, for convenience, be taken as zero. But this is just like the one-dimensional particle that is free ($V = 0$) to move along the x direction between the limits $x = 0$ and $x = L$. In the real analog the electrons are free to move along the chain (x) between the limits $x = 0$ and $x = L$, where L is the length of the chain. The energy values and eigenfunctions are thus

$$E_n = \frac{n^2h^2}{8mL^2} \quad \text{and} \quad \psi_n(x) = \left(\frac{2}{L}\right)^{\frac{1}{2}} \sin \frac{n\pi x}{L}$$

In this system there are several one-dimensional particles (electrons) all confined to the one box. Each such particle must be described by a particular eigenfunction, and, although the concept of spin has not been formally introduced, let it be said that, because of spin, a maximum of two electrons can have the same spacial description. In the molecule-ion indicated above, there are a total of 12 delocalized electrons, one from each of the nine carbons and three from the two nitrogens. This means that, in the ground state, the 12 π electrons would be described by means of the first six functions ψ_n ($n = 1, 2, \ldots 6$). There would be two electrons "in" each of the first six levels. For the general case of N electrons the first $N/2$ levels would be filled.

In absorption spectroscopy, energy is absorbed by an electron "in" one level (in a given energy state), and the electron achieves the energy of a higher state. For example, in the real system under consideration, one of the electrons in the sixth energy level could be excited to, say, the seventh level. The energy absorbed would be

$$\Delta E_{\text{system}} = E_7 - E_6 = \frac{h^2}{8mL^2}(7^2 - 6^2)$$

But $\Delta E_{\text{system}} = E_{\text{photon}} = h\nu$, and the frequency ν of the absorbed radiation would be

$$\nu = \frac{E_{\text{photon}}}{h} = \frac{\Delta E_{\text{system}}}{h}$$
$$= \frac{h}{8mL^2}(7^2 - 6^2)$$
$$= \frac{(h)(13)}{8mL^2}$$

The transition is illustrated in the energy level diagram (Fig. I-14).

In general, for a transition from n_i (the initial n value of the electron, i.e., the highest filled level) to n_f (the lowest empty level), the energy change would be

$$\Delta E = \frac{h^2}{8mL^2}(n_f^2 - n_i^2)$$

But $n_i = N/2$ and $n_f = (N/2) + 1$, so that $\Delta E = h^2/8mL^2(N + 1)$. Since $\Delta E = h\nu = hc/\lambda$,

$$\frac{hc}{\lambda} = \frac{h^2}{8mL^2}(N + 1) \tag{I-18}$$

For molecule-ions such as the above:

N = No. of electrons
= [No. of carbon atoms (since each carbon contributes one electron to the π system)] + [three electrons from the two nitrogens (each nitrogen would contribute two electrons but an electron has been lost to form the ion, so $2 \times 2 - 1 = 3$)]
= $n_C + 3$ where n_C is the number of carbons that contribute an electron to the π-electron system under investigation

L = length of the box
= (No. of carbon C—C bonds)l_C + (No. of carbon-nitrogen bonds)l_{CN} + penetration
= $(n_C - 1)l_C + 2(l_{CN}) + 2p$ where l_C is the carbon-carbon bond distance, l_{CN} is the carbon-nitrogen bond distance, and p is some unknown penetration beyond each end

The formula (I-18) for the wavelength of the absorbed photon can then be written

$$\lambda = \frac{8mc}{h}\frac{[(n_C - 1)l_C + 2(l_{CN}) + 2p]^2}{n_C + 4} \tag{I-19}$$

Ground state π-electron system		Excited state π-electron system		
$n = 8$ ———		$n = 8$ ———		
$n = 7$ ———		$n = 7$ —×—	Net effect	$n = 7$ ———
$n = 6$ —××—	Incident	$n = 6$ —×—		$n = 6$ —×—
$n = 5$ —××—	$\longrightarrow$	$n = 5$ —××—		
$n = 4$ —××—	light (correct frequency)	$n = 4$ —××—		
$n = 3$ —××—		$n = 3$ —××—		
$n = 2$ —××—		$n = 2$ —××—		
$n = 1$ —××—		$n = 1$ —××—		

Fig. I-14 Energy level diagram.

Dye I 1-1′-Diethyl-2-2′-Cyanine Iodide

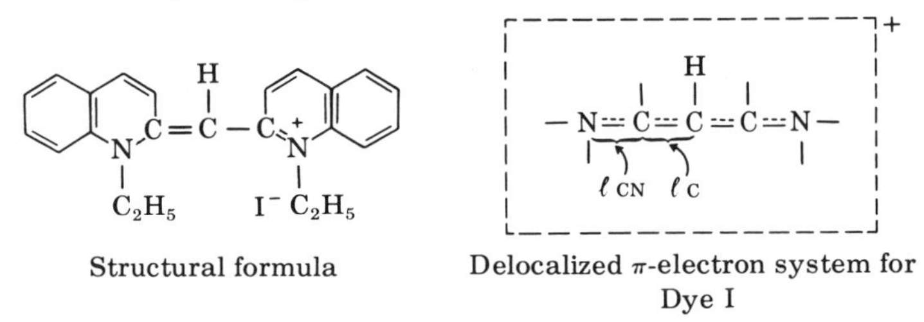

Structural formula

Delocalized π-electron system for Dye I

Dye II Pinacyanol Chloride

$C=CH-CH=CH-C$ (N–C_2H_5; N^+–C_2H_5, Cl^-)

Dye III 1-1′-Diethyl 2-2′-Dicarbocyanine Iodide

$C=CH-CH=CH-CH=CH-C$ (N–C_2H_5; N^+–C_2H_5, I^-)

Fig. I-15 Dyes.

In Eq. (II-19) there are four quantities that must be known before the wavelength can be calculated. The first, the number of carbons n_C, is assumed known and, of course, depends on the molecule concerned. The values of the quantities l_{CN}, l_C, and p are difficult to determine exactly for these molecules; however, as will be shown, appropriate values can be found. This model will now be tested by comparing experimental and predicted absorption wavelengths for several dyes. Then the results will be used to predict the λ of absorption of a new molecule. The dyes are indicated in Fig. I-15.

The absorption spectra of these species can be obtained[1] readily and are given for reference in Fig. I-16.

(b) Calculations with the model

PROBLEM 2-1

What value of n_C should be used in Eq. (I-19) for each of the dyes?

PROBLEM 2-2

Sketch the delocalized π-electron system for dyes II and III in the same way as done for the first dye in Fig. I-15.

PROBLEM 2-3

Draw an energy level diagram for each dye in the same way as in Fig. I-14.

Assume that the bond length l_C is the same as in benzene, a somewhat similar delocalized system, where $l_C = 1.40$ Å, and that the bond length l_{CN} is the same as in pyridine, where $l_{CN} = 1.34$ Å. Since the contribution of the penetration p to L is hard to assess, as an initial attempt assume that there is no penetration, that is, $p = 0$. Hence $L = [(n_C - 1)1.40 + 2(1.34)]$ Å. The equation for λ for these three dyes is then

$$\lambda = \frac{8mc}{h} \frac{\{[(n_C - 1)(1.40) + 2(1.34)]10^{-8}\}^2}{n_C + 4} \tag{I-20}$$

[1] An approximately 10^{-5} molar solution in ethanol is satisfactory for its determination on the Spectronic 20. For the operation of the Spectronic 20, see C. N. Reilly and D. T. Sawyer, "Experiments for Instrumental Methods," McGraw-Hill, 1961.

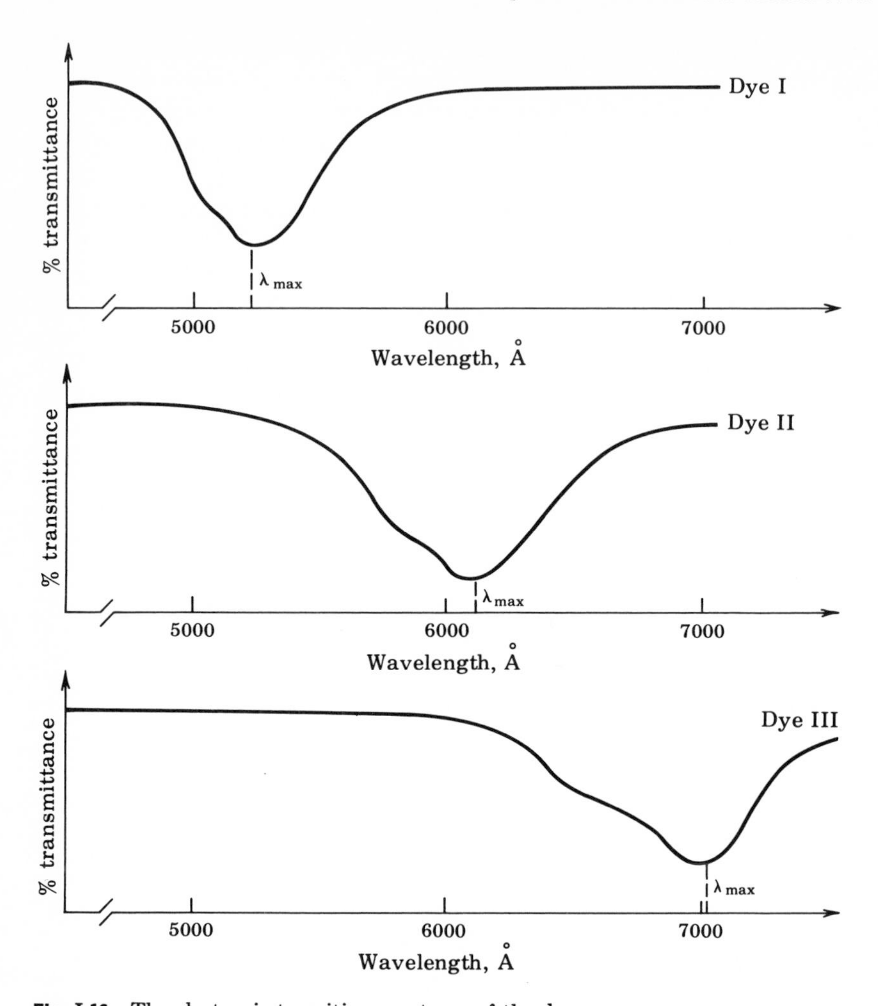

Fig. I-16 The electronic transition spectrum of the dyes.

PROBLEM 2-4

Using formula I-20, calculate the λ for the three dyes and compare to the experimental value, λ_{max}, obtained from the spectra of Fig. I-16.

(c) *Modifications to the model*

The comparison in Prob. 2-4 is not satisfactory, and so there must be some recognition of the penetration p. An arbitrary value of p might be taken in an attempt to improve the calculated values; but one might just as well recognize that p is *not* known, and only an experiment will indicate its proper value. A "semiempirical value" for this unknown can be found by using the experimental value of λ for the dye I(n_C = 3) and solving the equation for p.

PROBLEM 2-5

Using the value of λ_{max} for dye I (from Fig. I-16) and Eq. (I-19), solve for the value of p.

PROBLEM 2-6

With the value for p obtained in Prob. 2-5, calculate the value of λ for the remaining two dyes.

Thus one piece of experimental evidence, λ for the dye with $n_C = 3$, has been used to give what is hoped to be a better value for a parameter describing the system. This technique improves the model, so that satisfactory predictions for other molecules can be made; i.e., the predicted values for $\lambda(n_C = 5)$ and $\lambda(n_C = 7)$ are quite similar to the λ_{max} obtained experimentally (Fig. I-16).

(d) Implications

PROBLEM 2-7

What is the physical and mathematical meaning of the penetration p? Explain the large value for p obtained for these dyes. (*Hint:* Recall that, in the particle-in-a-box, the walls are infinite, corresponding to an infinite potential outside the box.)

PROBLEM 2-8

Would the compound given in the formula below be colored?

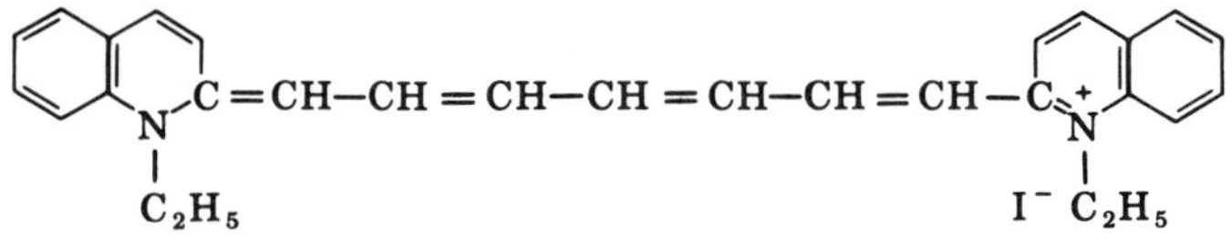

C=CH—CH=CH—CH=CH—CH=CH—C$^+$

N (C_2H_5) N (I^- C_2H_5)

PROBLEM 2-9

Calculate the λ_{max} for hexatriene. (*Hint:* One would expect very much different end effects here than in the case of the dyes.)

II
The Quantum-Mechanical Description of Some Simple Systems

II-1 THE GENERAL METHOD

(i) Introduction

By the treatment of the very simple system, the one-dimensional particle-in-a-box, it has been possible to illustrate many significant features of quantum mechanics. It has even been possible to treat the spectroscopy of a molecule. However, most atomic and molecular systems are not capable of such a simple description—more than one coordinate, or degree of freedom,[1] is required for their description, and the potential is unlikely to be constant in the region of interest. If the spectroscopy of such systems is to be discussed, it would seem necessary first to find their quantum-mechanical description and energy.

Fortunately there are methods available that enable these systems to be treated. The basis of all these methods consists in separating, even

[1] A degree of freedom is an independent variable, and for the purposes of this development it is equivalent to a coordinate required to describe the system.

if only approximately, a Schroedinger equation involving many degrees of freedom into separate equations, each dealing with only one degree of freedom. Each of the separated equations is then capable of being solved in the manner already indicated, and the resulting energy levels and descriptions can be used in simple spectroscopic problems.

(ii) The particle in a two-dimensional box

The particle in a two-dimensional box is the simplest system illustrating the method. Here there are two degrees of freedom, for example, x and y, and the potential $V = 0$ inside the box is the simplest possible.

Figure II-1 illustrates the potential and its equivalent statement in terms of the restrictions on the description Ψ. The description clearly requires two variables x and y, and so the hamiltonian inside the box must account for the total kinetic energy, i.e., the kinetic energy by virtue of the motion in both the x direction and the y direction. Using the recipe of Table I-2 for quantum-mechanical operators gives

$$\text{KE} = \tfrac{1}{2}mv^2 = \tfrac{1}{2}mv_x{}^2 + \tfrac{1}{2}mv_y{}^2 = \tfrac{1}{2}m\left(\frac{dx}{dt}\right)^2 + \tfrac{1}{2}m\left(\frac{dy}{dt}\right)^2$$
$$\Rightarrow \frac{-h^2}{8\pi^2 m}\frac{d^2}{dx^2} - \frac{h^2}{8\pi^2 m}\frac{d^2}{dy^2}$$

and the Schroedinger equation becomes,[1] for $V = 0$,

$$\left(\frac{-h^2}{8\pi^2 m}\frac{\partial^2}{\partial x^2} - \frac{h^2}{8\pi^2 m}\frac{\partial^2}{\partial y^2}\right)\Psi(x,y) = E\Psi(x,y)$$

[1] Where confusion could arise, the kinetic energy operator in, for example, the x direction, is written as $(-h^2/8\pi^2 m)(\partial^2/\partial x^2)$; the partial derivative $\partial/\partial x$ treats all variables other than x as constants.

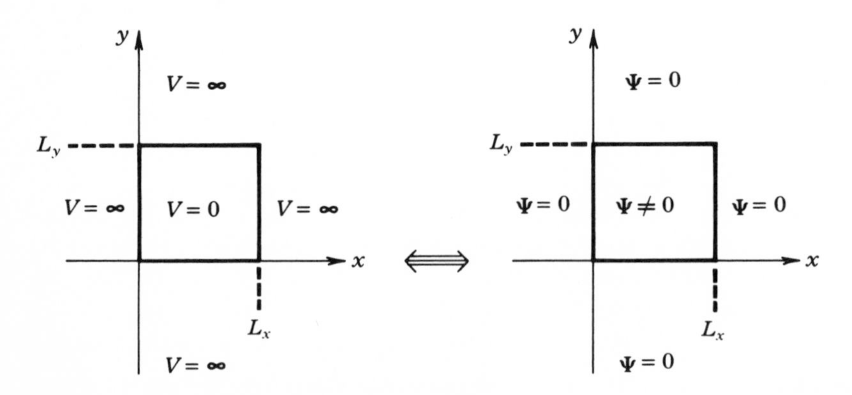

Fig. II-1 The particle in a two-dimensional box.

Since the operator H is clearly split into two parts, one a function of x and the other a function of y, it would seem reasonable to take $\Psi(x,y)$ as a *product* of two separate functions, $\Psi(x,y) = \chi(x)\phi(y)$. [The advantages of using a product of functions has already been demonstrated in solving the classical wave equation; see, for example, Sec. I-3(i) and Appendix I.] The SE then becomes

$$\left(\frac{-h^2}{8\pi^2 m}\frac{\partial^2}{\partial x^2} - \frac{h^2}{8\pi^2 m}\frac{\partial^2}{\partial y^2}\right)\chi(x)\phi(y) = E\chi(x)\phi(y)$$

Since $\partial^2/\partial x^2$ operates only on x, $(\partial^2/\partial x^2)\chi(x)\phi(y) = \phi(y)(d^2/dx^2)\chi(x)$, where $\phi(y)$ has been brought to the left of the operator, and, similarly, $(\partial^2/\partial y^2)\chi(x)\phi(y) = \chi(x)(d^2/dy^2)\phi(y)$. This yields

$$\frac{-h^2}{8\pi^2 m}\phi(y)\frac{d^2}{dx^2}\chi(x) - \frac{h^2}{8\pi^2 m}\chi(x)\frac{d^2}{dy^2}\phi(y) = E\chi(x)\phi(y)$$

If this equation is multiplied by $1/\chi(x)\phi(y)$, the Schroedinger equation is completely separated as

$$\left[\frac{-h^2}{8\pi^2 m}\frac{1}{\chi(x)}\frac{d^2\chi(x)}{dx^2}\right] - \left[\frac{h^2}{8\pi^2 m}\frac{1}{\phi(y)}\frac{d^2\phi(y)}{dy^2}\right] = E$$

Transposing the second term to the right-hand side of the equality, one obtains

$$\underbrace{\frac{-h^2}{8\pi^2 m}\frac{1}{\chi(x)}\frac{d^2\chi(x)}{dx^2}}_{\text{Dependent only on } x} = \underbrace{\frac{h^2}{8\pi^2 m}\frac{1}{\phi(y)}\frac{d^2\phi(y)}{dy^2}}_{\text{Dependent only on } y} + E \qquad \text{or} \qquad F(x) = G(y)$$

The variables x and y are *independent* of one another; yet, this equation claims that a function $F(x)$, depending on x, is always equal to a function $G(y)$, depending on y. The only way that this could be possible is if each side were independently equal to the same constant C, as

$$\frac{-h^2}{8\pi^2 m}\frac{1}{\chi(x)}\frac{d^2\chi(x)}{dx^2} = C \qquad \text{and} \qquad \frac{h^2}{8\pi^2 m}\frac{1}{\phi(y)}\frac{d^2\phi(y)}{dy^2} + E = C$$

Multiplying the first equation by $\chi(x)$, the second by $\phi(y)$, and rearranging the resulting equations gives

$$\frac{-h^2}{8\pi^2 m}\frac{d^2}{dx^2}\chi(x) = C\chi(x) \tag{II-1}$$

$$\frac{-h^2}{8\pi^2 m}\frac{d^2}{dy^2}\phi(y) = (E - C)\phi(y) \tag{II-2}$$

The operator in Eq. (II-1) is simply the quantum-mechanical hamiltonian operator $H(x)$ for the energy in the x coordinate, so the constant C must be "the energy in the x direction" E_x. Similarly the operator in Eq.

Table II-1 Separation of variables

Coordinate transformation	$(x, y) \Rightarrow (x, y)$	*(No change)*
Hamiltonian separability	$H(x,y) \Rightarrow H_x(x) + H_y(y)$	(A sum of operators)
Solution form	$\Psi(x,y) \Rightarrow \chi(x)\phi(y)$	(A product of functions)
SE separability	$H(x,y)\Psi(x,y) = E\Psi(x,y) \Rightarrow \left.\begin{array}{l} H_x(x)\chi(x) = E_x\chi(x) \\ H_y(y)\phi(y) = E_y\phi(y) \end{array}\right\}$	(Two simpler equations)

(II-2) is the quantum-mechanical hamiltonian operator for the y coordinate $H(y)$, so $E - C$ must be "the energy in the y direction" E_y. The two equations may then be written

$$H_x(x)\chi(x) = E_x\chi(x) \tag{II-3}$$

$$H_y(y)\phi(y) = E_y\phi(y) \tag{II-4}$$

and, since $C = E_x$ and $E - C = E_y$, one has $E = E_x + E_y$ and, of course, $\Psi(x,y) = \chi(x)\phi(y)$.

Because the *hamiltonian could be separated* into a sum of coordinate distinct parts $H = H_x(x) + H_y(y)$, it was *possible to separate the original Schroedinger equation into two separate and simpler Schroedinger equations.* These equations were then solved to give energies E_x and E_y and descriptions $\chi(x)$ and $\phi(y)$ in terms of which $\Psi(x,y)$ and E of the original equation can be expressed. The procedure might be summarized schematically as in Table II-1, where the left-hand side is the original situation, and the right-hand side is the transformed result.

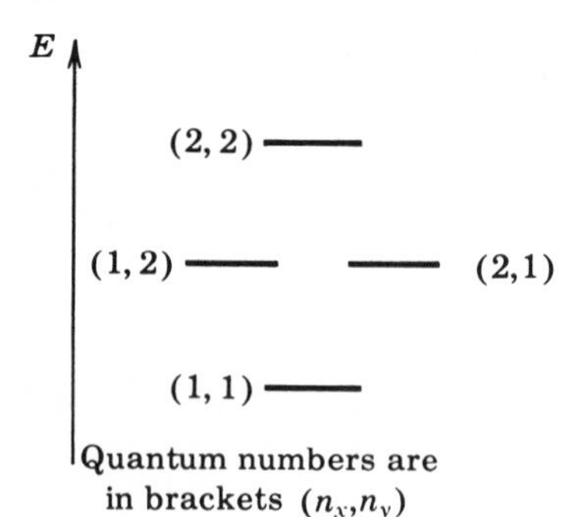

Fig. II-2 Degeneracy.

Table II-2 Description of the two-dimensional particle-in-a-box

n_x	n_y	$E = E_x + E_y$	$\Psi(x,y) = \chi(x)\phi(y)$
1	1	$\frac{h^2}{8mL^2}(1+1) = \frac{h^2}{8mL^2}2$	$\frac{2}{L}\sin\frac{\pi x}{L}\sin\frac{\pi y}{L}$
1	2	$\frac{h^2}{8mL^2}(1+4) = \frac{h^2}{8mL^2}5$	$\frac{2}{L}\sin\frac{\pi x}{L}\sin\frac{2\pi y}{L}$
2	1	$\frac{h^2}{8mL^2}(4+1) = \frac{h^2}{8mL^2}5$	$\frac{2}{L}\sin\frac{2\pi x}{L}\sin\frac{\pi y}{L}$
2	2	$\frac{h^2}{8mL^2}(4+4) = \frac{h^2}{8mL^2}8$	$\frac{2}{L}\sin\frac{2\pi x}{L}\sin\frac{2\pi y}{L}$

For the particular problem investigated, the solutions of

$$H_x\chi(x) = E_x\chi(x) \qquad \text{and} \qquad H_y\phi(y) = E_y\phi(y)$$

are those already obtained in Sec. I-4(ii), so that one can immediately write

$$\Psi(x,y) = \chi(x)\phi(y) = \left(\frac{2}{L_x}\right)^{\frac{1}{2}} \sin n_x \frac{\pi x}{L_x} \left(\frac{2}{L_y}\right)^{\frac{1}{2}} \sin n_y \frac{\pi y}{L_y}$$

$$E = E_x + E_y = \frac{h^2 n_x^2}{8mL_x^2} + \frac{h^2 n_y^2}{8mL_y^2} = \frac{h^2}{8m}\left(\frac{n_x^2}{L_x^2} + \frac{n_y^2}{L_y^2}\right)$$

$$n_x = 1, 2, \ldots ; n_y = 1, 2, \ldots \qquad \text{(II-5)}$$

For a square box $L_x = L_y = L$, the energies and descriptions of the first few levels are indicated in Table II-2. The graphical representation of the energy levels in Fig. II-2 serves to emphasize the fact that there are two different sets of quantum numbers, n_x and n_y, that is, 1, 2 and 2, 1 having the same energy—or, as it is usually stated: the second energy level is twofold degenerate, for the same energy can be associated with either of two distinct descriptions.

PROBLEM II-1

What is the degeneracy of the fourth energy level of the two-dimensional particle in a square box?

PROBLEM II-2

Find the energy levels and solutions for a particle in a three-dimensional box of sides L_x, L_y, and L_z. Do not give all the details but proceed by drawing the appropriate analogy to the important steps (e.g., *separability* of the hamiltonian, Ψ a *product* of functions, etc.) in the two-dimensional case given in Sec. II-1(ii).

II-2 DESCRIPTION OF THE MOTION OF NUCLEI

(i) The harmonic oscillator

(a) *Introduction*

The previous system, although not a very realistic one, has nevertheless illustrated the means by which systems with more than one degree of freedom may be tackled. For more complex systems, e.g., more degrees of freedom or $V \neq 0$ in the region of interest, the usual description of the system may produce a statement of the interactions in such a way that the quantum-mechanical hamiltonian is not so obviously separated into parts, as was the case with the two-dimensional box. Instead some new choice of coordinates may be required to allow the separation of the hamiltonian.

The simplest illustration is the harmonic oscillator. In this system the force between two masses is proportional to their displacement from the equilibrium separation (a Hooke's law force) and, as such, leads to the so-called harmonic potential—a close approximation, it might be noted, to the potential for vibrations of nuclei in a molecule. When the harmonic oscillator is described in terms of the position coordinates of the two masses, the hamiltonian is not separable. Since a new pair of coordinates must be introduced to separate the hamiltonian, a detailed discussion of the problem will be given. Not only will the procedure of selecting coordinates be illustrated, but the important concepts of the internal coordinate (with its equivalent mass, the "reduced" mass) and the external coordinate (describing the total mass of the system) will be introduced.

Consider two masses m_1 and m_2 held together by a force due, for example, to a spring or, in the molecular case, the nuclei held together by a

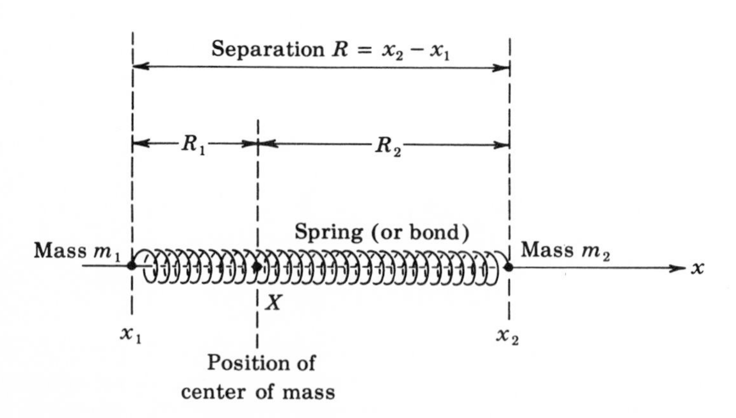

Fig. II-3 The harmonic oscillator.

bond. When two masses move along the x axis, the system is completely described by positions x_1 and x_2, shown in Fig. II-3. (It is interesting to note that, here, there are *two* variables, or degrees of freedom, x_1 and x_2 but only one dimension x in the usual sense). The two masses will have some equilibrium separation $\bar{x}_2 - \bar{x}_1$, and, if the separation is changed to some other distance, there is a force that tends to return the system to the equilibrium position. For the harmonic oscillator this force F is proportional to the *difference* between two quantities: the separation $x_2 - x_1$ and the equilibrium separation $\bar{x}_2 - \bar{x}_1$. Thus $F = -k$ (separation − equilibrium separation) $= -k[(x_2 - x_1) - (\bar{x}_2 - \bar{x}_1)]$, where k is the proportionality constant characteristic of the spring (or, in the molecular case, characteristic of the bond). The potential energy of such a force is simply $V = (k/2)[(x_2 - x_1) - (\bar{x}_2 - \bar{x}_1)]^2 = (k/2)[(x_2 - x_1) - R_e]^2$, where the constant $\bar{x}_2 - \bar{x}_1$ has been replaced by R_e, the equilibrium separation.

PROBLEM II-3

Show that the potential energy of the force $F = -k[(x_2 - x_1) - R_e]$ is $V = (k/2)[(x_2 - x_1) - R_e]^2$. Sketch the potential as a function of $x_2 - x_1$ (let $x_2 - x_1 = R$, and plot $V = (k/2)[R - R_e]^2$ vs. R).

As indicated earlier, separation of the SE can be accomplished if the hamiltonian is separated. In the following paragraphs the *classical* energy statement will be separated into two parts. Once we have accomplished the separation of the classical energy statement, the recipe (Table I-2) for going from the classical to the quantum-mechanical situation will be used to generate a separated quantum-mechanical hamiltonian. First consider the classical separation.

(b) Classical development

The total energy of the system in *classical* terms is

$$\begin{aligned} E &= \mathrm{KE}(m_1) + \mathrm{KE}(m_2) + V \\ &= \frac{m_1}{2}\left(\frac{dx_1}{dt}\right)^2 + \frac{m_2}{2}\left(\frac{dx_2}{dt}\right)^2 + \frac{k}{2}[(x_2 - x_1) - R_e]^2 \\ &= \frac{m_1}{2}\left(\frac{dx_1}{dt}\right)^2 + \frac{m_2}{2}\left(\frac{dx_2}{dt}\right)^2 + \frac{k}{2}[(x_2 - x_1)^2 + R_e^2 - 2R_e(x_2 - x_1)] \end{aligned} \tag{II-6}$$

On squaring $x_2 - x_1$ in this formula, a term $2x_1x_2$ will be obtained; and, because of this term, it will be impossible to separate the energy statement into *only* two parts, one in terms of x_1 and the other in terms of x_2. It would appear that some other pair of coordinates must be chosen to effect this separation. Since it is the term $(x_2 - x_1)^2$ that is causing the trouble, one might well use $R = x_2 - x_1$ as one of the new set of coordinates. This is a *relative* coordinate, for it tells only how far apart the masses are—it does not state where the system as a whole is on the x axis. An additional coordinate is required that speaks of the system as a whole, and a natural choice would be one giving the position of the center of gravity X—that point about which the moments of the two masses of the system are equal. Thus

$$m_1R_1 = m_2R_2 \tag{II-7}$$

where R_1 and R_2 are the distances indicated in Fig. II-3, defines X. With this choice of coordinates, the energy statement of Eq. (II-6) can be transformed into the separated form as follows. From Fig. II-3, $R_1 = X - x_1$, giving $x_1 = X - R_1$, and $R_2 = x_2 - X$, giving $x_2 = X + R_2$. The statement of the energy in terms of x_1 and x_2, Eq. (II-6), can then be rewritten in terms of R, X, R_1, and R_2. (Although R_1 and R_2 will appear at the outset, this is not a further complication, since $R_1 + R_2 = R$.) The rewritten version of Eq. (II-6) is

$$E = \frac{m_1}{2}\left[\frac{d}{dt}(X - R_1)\right]^2 + \frac{m_2}{2}\left[\frac{d}{dt}(X + R_2)\right]^2 + \frac{k}{2}(R - R_e)^2$$

which, after squaring terms and rearranging, becomes

$$E = \left(\frac{m_1 + m_2}{2}\right)\left(\frac{dX}{dt}\right)^2 + \frac{1}{2}m_1\left(\frac{dR_1}{dt}\right)^2 + \frac{1}{2}m_2\left(\frac{dR_2}{dt}\right)^2 + \frac{dX}{dt}\left(-m_1\frac{dR_1}{dt} + m_2\frac{dR_2}{dt}\right) + \frac{k}{2}(R - R_e)^2 \tag{II-8}$$

Since $-m_1R_1 + m_2R_2 = 0$ by definition, the term

$$\left[-m_1\left(\frac{dR_1}{dt}\right) + m_2\left(\frac{dR_2}{dt}\right)\right] = \left(\frac{d}{dt}\right)(-m_1R_1 + m_2R_2) = \left(\frac{d}{dt}\right)(0)$$

is in fact zero, and Eq. (II-8) reduces to

$$E = \left(\frac{m_1 + m_2}{2}\right)\left(\frac{dX}{dt}\right)^2 + \frac{1}{2}\left[m_1\left(\frac{dR_1}{dt}\right)^2 + m_2\left(\frac{dR_2}{dt}\right)^2\right] + \frac{k}{2}(R - R_e)^2 \tag{II-9}$$

Multiplying the second term in Eq. (II-9), $\frac{1}{2}[m_1(dR_1/dt)^2 + m_2(dR_2/dt)^2]$, by $[1/(m_1 + m_2)](m_1 + m_2)$ gives

$$\frac{1}{2}\frac{1}{m_1 + m_2}\left\{m_1{}^2\left(\frac{dR_1}{dt}\right)^2 + m_2{}^2\left(\frac{dR_2}{dt}\right)^2 + m_1m_2\left[\left(\frac{dR_1}{dt}\right)^2 + \left(\frac{dR_2}{dt}\right)^2\right]\right\}$$

Now adding and subtracting $2m_1m_2[(dR_1/dt)(dR_2/dt)]$ inside the braces gives

$$\frac{1}{2}\frac{1}{m_1+m_2}\left\{m_1^2\left(\frac{dR_1}{dt}\right)^2 + m_2^2\left(\frac{dR_2}{dt}\right)^2 - 2m_1m_2\frac{dR_1}{dt}\frac{dR_2}{dt} + 2m_1m_2\frac{dR_1}{dt}\frac{dR_2}{dt} + m_1m_2\left[\left(\frac{dR_1}{dt}\right)^2 + \left(\frac{dR_2}{dt}\right)^2\right]\right\}$$

Collecting the first three terms and the last two terms as

$$\frac{1}{2}\frac{1}{m_1+m_2}\left[\left(m_1\frac{dR_1}{dt} - m_2\frac{dR_2}{dt}\right)^2 + m_1m_2\left(\frac{dR_1}{dt} + \frac{dR_2}{dt}\right)^2\right]$$

gives

$$\frac{1}{2}\frac{1}{m_1+m_2}\left\{\left[\frac{d}{dt}(m_1R_1 - m_2R_2)\right]^2 + m_1m_2\left[\frac{d}{dt}(R_1+R_2)\right]^2\right\}$$

which, since the first term is again zero and since $R = R_1 + R_2$ can be substituted in the second term, finally reduces the second term in Eq. (II-9) to $\frac{1}{2}[m_1m_2/(m_1+m_2)][(dR/dt)^2]$. The total energy is then given as

$$E = \frac{m_1+m_2}{2}\left(\frac{dX}{dt}\right)^2 + \frac{1}{2}\frac{m_1m_2}{m_1+m_2}\left(\frac{dR}{dt}\right)^2 + \frac{k}{2}(R-R_e)^2$$

The first term, $[(m_1+m_2)/2](dX/dt)^2$, involves only the total mass $m_1 + m_2 = M$ and the center-of-mass coordinate X. Hence this term is the kinetic energy of the center-of-mass system. The last two terms involve only the relative coordinate R and a quantity $m_1m_2/(m_1+m_2)$ that has the dimensions of mass and plays the role of mass in the statement of the kinetic energy of the relative coordinate. This quantity is given the symbol μ and the name *reduced mass*. The energy then takes the form

$$E = \frac{M}{2}\left(\frac{dX}{dt}\right)^2 + \frac{\mu}{2}\left(\frac{dR}{dt}\right)^2 + \frac{k}{2}(R-R_e)^2$$

To facilitate further solution, the displacement variable $r = R - R_e$ is introduced. Since R_e is a constant, $(dR/dt) = (dr/dt)$, and the classical energy may be rewritten as

$$E = \underbrace{\frac{M}{2}\left(\frac{dX}{dt}\right)^2}_{\text{Center-of-mass coordinate}} + \underbrace{\frac{\mu}{2}\left(\frac{dr}{dt}\right)^2 + \frac{k}{2}r^2}_{\text{Relative, or internal, coordinate}} \qquad \text{(II-10)}$$

A separation of the classical energy statement into two parts, one for the center-of-mass coordinate X and the other for a relative coordinate r, has been effected!

(c) Quantum-mechanical treatment

Use of the recipe for going from the classical energy statement of Eq. (II-10) to the quantum statement of energy (see the following table)

Energy contribution	*Classical statement*		*Quantum statement*
Center-of-mass kinetic energy	$\frac{M}{2}\left(\frac{dX}{dt}\right)^2$	$\Rightarrow$	$-\frac{h^2}{8\pi^2 M}\frac{d^2}{dX^2}$
Reduced-mass kinetic energy	$\frac{\mu}{2}\left(\frac{dr}{dt}\right)^2$	$\Rightarrow$	$-\frac{h^2}{8\pi^2 \mu}\frac{d^2}{dr^2}$
Potential energy	$\frac{k}{2}r^2$	$\Rightarrow$	$\frac{k}{2}r^2$

allows the Schroedinger equation for the harmonic oscillator to be written as

$$\left(\underbrace{-\frac{h^2}{8\pi^2 M}\frac{d^2}{dX^2}}_{\substack{\text{Center-of-mass}\\ \text{coordinate}\\ \text{system}}}\underbrace{-\frac{h^2}{8\pi^2 \mu}\frac{d^2}{dr^2}+\frac{k}{2}r^2}_{\substack{\text{Relative}\\ \text{coordinate}\\ \text{system}}}\right)\Psi(X,r) = E\Psi(X,r) \tag{II-11}$$

Equation (II-11) may be separated, just as for the particle in a two-dimensional box, by putting $\Psi(X,r) = \chi(X)\psi(r)$ to yield the two Schroedinger equations

$$\left(-\frac{h^2}{8\pi^2 M}\frac{d^2}{dX^2}\right)\chi(X) = E_X\chi(X) \tag{II-12}$$

$$\left(-\frac{h^2}{8\pi^2 \mu}\frac{d^2}{dr^2}+\frac{k}{2}r^2\right)\psi(r) = E_r\psi(r) \tag{II-13}$$

Again the procedure can be summarized schematically, as in Table II-3.

Table II-3 Separation of the SE for the harmonic oscillator

Coordinate transformation	x_1, x_2 $\Rightarrow$ M, X, X_{CM}; X_{CM}, R, r, μ, R_e	
Hamiltonian separability	$H(x_1x_2) \Rightarrow H(X) + H(r)$	(A sum of operators)
Solution form	$\Psi(x_1x_2) \Rightarrow \chi(X)\psi(r)$	(A product of functions)
SE separability	$H(x_1x_2)\Psi(x_1x_2) = E\Psi(x_1x_2) \Rightarrow \begin{cases} H(X)\chi(X) = E_X\chi(X) \\ H(r)\psi(r) = E_r\psi(r) \end{cases}$	(Two simpler equations)

The solution to Eq. (II-12) has already been studied and is of no importance for applications to molecular systems, since it describes only the system as a whole, not the relation between the parts of the system. Equation (II-13) is the description of the relative motion, or vibration, of the masses (or atoms in the molecular case) and is, of course, of importance.

It is rather tedious to obtain *all* the solutions of Eq. (II-13), and consequently only the lowest-energy solution will be attempted. To facilitate solution, Eq. (II-13) is first rewritten as

$$-\frac{h^2}{8\pi^2\mu}\frac{d^2\psi(r)}{dr^2} + \left(\frac{k}{2}r^2 - E_r\right)\psi(r) = 0 \qquad \text{(II-14)}$$

The solution $\psi(r)$ must satisfy Eq. (II-14) for *all* values of r. To obtain a hint as to the correct form, consider this equation when r is large. If r is large and E_r is finite, then the term $kr^2/2$ is much greater than E, so that $(kr^2/2) - E_r$ is approximately $kr^2/2$. This reduces Eq. (II-14) to approximately $-(h^2/8\pi^2\mu)(d^2/dr^2)\psi(r) + (kr^2/2)\psi(r) = 0$ or, upon rearranging, to $[d^2\psi(r)/dr^2] = (k4\pi^2\mu/h^2)r^2\psi(r)$, where the left-hand side is the second derivative of the function, and the right-hand side is a constant $k4\pi^2\mu/h^2$ times the argument r squared times the function. Following the principles discussed in Sec. I-4, it is clear that the solution must be of a *form* that, when differentiated twice, gives back itself times the argument r squared. Such a form is e^{-ar^2}, and so, as a start, this function can be inserted into Eq. (II-14), the derivative operations carried out, and the equation rearranged to give

$$-\frac{h^2}{8\pi^2\mu}(4a^2r^2 - 2a)e^{-ar^2} + \frac{k}{2}r^2e^{-ar^2} = E_re^{-ar^2}$$

Canceling e^{-ar^2} on both sides and collecting terms in r^2 gives

$$\left(-\frac{h^2}{8\pi^2\mu}4a^2 + \frac{k}{2}\right)r^2 + \frac{h^2 2a}{8\pi^2\mu} = E_r \qquad \text{(II-15)}$$

Since this statement must be true for *all* values of r, the coefficient of r^2 *must* be zero, as discussed in Sec. I-4. Thus $[-(h^2/8\pi^2\mu)4a^2 + (k/2)] = 0$, which gives $a = \pm(\pi/h)(k\mu)^{\frac{1}{2}}$. The negative root must be rejected, since $\psi(r)$ must go to zero as r goes to infinity; otherwise, it would not be possible to normalize $\psi(r)$ as $\int\psi^2(r)\,dr = N^2\int_{-\infty}^{\infty} e^{-2ar^2}\,dr = 1$. [Unless the exponent is negative, the integral becomes infinite at $r = \pm\infty$, and only $N = 0$ would allow normalization. But $N = 0$ means the solution Ne^{-ar^2} is zero. Thus $a < 0$ must be rejected, and only $a > 0$ (making the exponent $-ar^2$ negative) is allowed.] This requirement is a "boundary condition" (that is, $\psi(r)$ must go to zero as $r \to \infty$). Hence this step plays the same role as imposing the boundary condition in the particle-in-a-box.

Table II-4 The harmonic-oscillator solutions

Quantum number	*Energy*‡	*Function*‡	*Graphical representation*	*Probability*
0	$\frac{1}{2}\frac{h}{2\pi}\sqrt{\frac{k}{\mu}}$	$\psi_{0,\text{vib}}(r) = e^{-ar^2}$	ψ_1	ψ_1^2
1	$\left(1+\frac{1}{2}\right)\frac{h}{2\pi}\sqrt{\frac{k}{\mu}}$	$\psi_{1,\text{vib}}(r) = e^{-ar^2}r$	ψ_2	ψ_2^2
2	$\left(2+\frac{1}{2}\right)\frac{h}{2\pi}\sqrt{\frac{k}{\mu}}$	$\psi_{2,\text{vib}}(r) = e^{-ar^2}(4ar^2 - 2)$	ψ_3	ψ_3^2
n	$\left(n+\frac{1}{2}\right)\frac{h}{2\pi}\sqrt{\frac{k}{\mu}}$	$\psi_{n,\text{vib}}(r) = e^{-ar^2}\cdot$ (power series in r)		

‡ Here k and $a = (\pi/h)(k\mu)^{\frac{1}{2}}$ are characteristic of the oscillator or, in the molecular case, characteristic of the bond.

The solution is then $\psi(r) = e^{-(\pi/h)(k\mu)^{\frac{1}{2}}r^2}$. Since the first term in the left-hand side of Eq. (II-15) is now zero, the equation is just $(h^2a/4\pi^2\mu) = E_r$, and, on substituting the value obtained above for a, E_r becomes $E_n = (h^2/4\pi^2\mu)[+(\pi/h)\sqrt{k\mu}] = \frac{1}{2}(h/2\pi)\sqrt{k/\mu}$. (Since E_r can take only certain values, we replace the subscript r by the quantum number n; for this solution, $n = 0$.) Some of the other solutions[1] and their associated energies are listed in Table II-4.

PROBLEM II-4

The functions given in Table II-4 are not normalized. Find the normalized function $\psi(r) = Ne^{-ar^2}$. (*Hint:* the argument r is the displacement from equilibrium, the limits of which are $\pm\infty$; that is, $N^2\int_{-\infty}^{\infty} e^{-2ar^2}\,dr = 1$.)

PROBLEM II-5

Show that $\psi(r) = re^{-ar^2}$ is a solution to Eq. (II-14), with the eigenvalue $E = (1 + \frac{1}{2})(h/2\pi)\sqrt{k/\mu}$.

Just as there were certain allowed energies and allowed solutions for the SE in the particle-in-the-box case, here, for the harmonic oscillator, there are certain *allowed energies* $\frac{1}{2}(h/2\pi)\sqrt{k/\mu}$, $(1+\frac{1}{2})(h/2\pi)\sqrt{k/\mu}$,

[1] The general solution of the harmonic oscillator problem in quantum mechanics can be found in L. Pauling and E. B. Wilson, "Introduction to Quantum Mechanics," McGraw-Hill, 1935.

Table II-5 Comparison of the particle-in-a-box and the harmonic-oscillator solution

	Particle-in-a-box	*Harmonic oscillator*
Quantum number	$n = 1,2, \ldots$	$n = 0, 1, 2, \ldots$
Energy (eigenvalue)	$E_n = n^2 \dfrac{h^2}{8mL^2}$	$E_n = \left(n + \dfrac{1}{2}\right)\left(\dfrac{h}{2\pi}\right)\sqrt{\dfrac{k}{\mu}}$
Solution (eigenfunction)	$\psi_n(x) = \sin \dfrac{n\pi x}{L}$	$\psi_{n,\text{vib}}(r) = e^{-ar^2} \cdot$ (power series in r)
Potential	$V = 0$	$V = \dfrac{k}{2} r^2$

$(2 + \frac{1}{2})(h/2\pi)\sqrt{k/\mu}$, etc., and certain *allowed solutions*, e^{-ar^2}, re^{-ar^2}, etc., to the SE. Again, as in the particle-in-a-box, one says that the energy is quantized with allowed eigenvalues for the allowed eigenfunctions. The two cases are compared in Table II-5.

As indicated, the *form* of the solution and the allowed eigenvalues of the harmonic oscillator are different from those of the particle-in-a-box system. But this is really what one should expect, for the form is dictated by the interactions expressed in the operator H, and certainly the interactions in the harmonic oscillator are different from the interactions of the particle-in-a-box. Further, as one would expect, the energy levels are different. Each *type* of system will have *its own descriptions* and *its own energy levels.*

(ii) Project 3. The elementary spectroscopy of vibrational transitions

(a) *Introduction*

Just as the particle-in-a-box system was found to be appropriate for the description of electrons in certain molecules, so the harmonic oscillator is found to be the appropriate description of the vibrational motion of nuclei in a molecule. Although a more detailed discussion will be given [Sec. III-2(ii), Fig. III-6], for the present it is sufficient to say that the bond force between the nuclei in a molecule can be approximated by the Hooke's law force of the harmonic oscillator. The *relative motion* (or *vibration*) of the *nuclei* may then be described in terms of the harmonic oscillator.

The vibrational levels of the CO molecule, for example, would be

$$E_n = \left(n + \frac{1}{2}\right)\frac{h}{2\pi}\sqrt{\frac{k}{\mu}}$$

where k is the force constant characteristic of the bond in CO, and μ is the reduced mass $\mu = m_C m_O/(m_C + m_O)$. If m_C and m_O are given in *molar* units as $M_C = 12.0\text{g}$ and $M_O = 16.0\text{g}$, then the reduced mass μ for the *molecule* is

$$\mu = \frac{(M_C/N)(M_O/N)}{(M_C/N) + (M_O/N)} = \frac{M_C M_O}{M_C + M_O} \frac{1}{N}$$

where N is Avogadro's number. The energy difference between the vibrational states $n = 0$ and $n = 1$ is simply

$$\Delta E_{\text{system}} = \Delta E(0 \rightarrow 1) = E_1 - E_0 = \frac{h}{2\pi}\sqrt{\frac{k}{\mu}} \tag{II-16}$$

This change in energy involves an absorption of energy $\Delta E(0 \rightarrow 1)$. If this energy is provided by radiation, then the frequency of the absorbed energy is, by Planck's relation, $\Delta E_{\text{system}} = E_{\text{photon}} = h\nu$:

$$\nu_{0\rightarrow 1} = \frac{\Delta E(0 \rightarrow 1)}{h} = \frac{1}{h}\left[\left(1 + \frac{1}{2}\right)\frac{h}{2\pi}\sqrt{\frac{k}{\mu}} - \left(0 + \frac{1}{2}\right)\frac{h}{2\pi}\sqrt{\frac{k}{\mu}}\right]$$
$$= \frac{1}{2\pi}\sqrt{\frac{k}{\mu}}$$

Thus the knowledge of the absorbed frequency provides k, a characteristic of the bond.

(*b*) *Calculation based on the model*

The spectrum for CO is given in Fig. II-4. The frequency corresponding to the energy absorbed in the vibrational transition $n = 0 \rightarrow n = 1$ is indicated by ν_{CO} and can be read from the figure.

PROBLEM 3-1

Find the force constant for CO. (*Hint:* Fig. II-4 provides $\nu_{0\rightarrow 1}$ for CO.)

As indicated in Project 1, spectra may be presented in terms of $\bar{\nu}(\text{cm}^{-1})$ instead of frequency ν. Figure II-5 provides such a spectrum

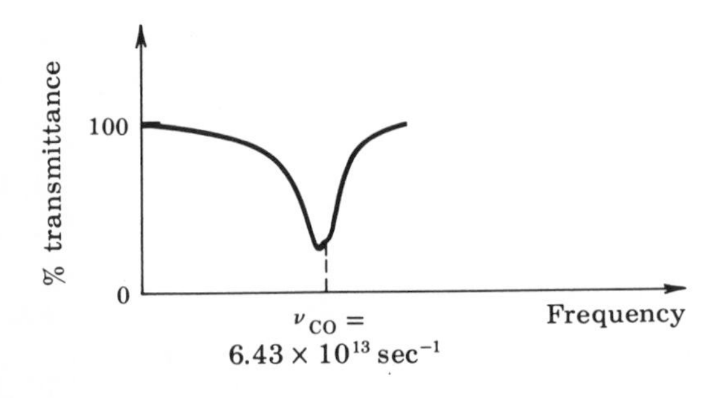

Fig. II-4 A vibrational spectrum of carbon monoxide.

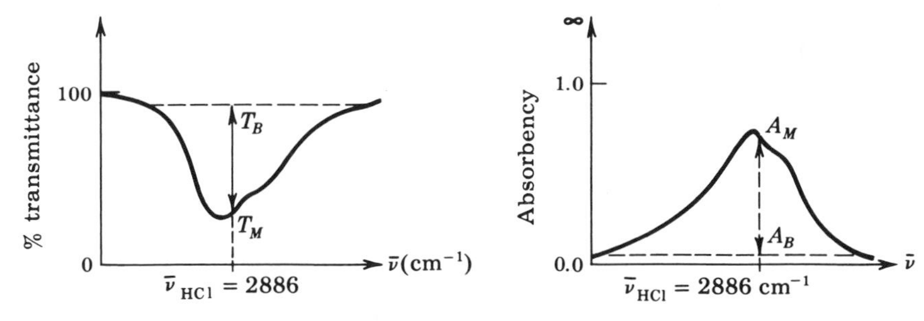

Fig. II-5 Spectra for the vibrational transition in HCl.

for HCl. Further, the absorption of energy can be indicated by the so-called *absorbency* $A = -\log$ transmittance $= \log (I_0/I)$. The limits of this quantity are zero to infinity, but they are usually obtained under conditions where $I \neq 0$. The absorbency spectrum of HCl is indicated in Fig. II-5, with a maximum absorbence at the value of $\bar{\nu}$ corresponding to the vibrational energy change.

PROBLEM 3-2

Find the force constant for HCl. (*Hint:* Fig. II-5 provides $\bar{\nu}_{0\to 1}$ for HCl.)

PROBLEM 3-3

If the force constant for HF is 9.7×10^5 dyn cm^{-1}, calculate $\bar{\nu}$ for the vibrational transition $n_{\text{vib}} = 0 \to n_{\text{vib}} = 1$.

(c) *Isotopic shifts*

Equation (II-16) indicates that the energy change in, for example, a transition $n = 0 \to n = 1$ depends on only the force constant k and the reduced mass μ. The force constant is characteristic of the bond in the molecule, and this, in turn, should depend principally on the electrostatic interactions in the molecule. Since an isotope of an element differs from the element only in mass, it is reasonable to expect the bond to be the same. For example, the bond in HCl and DCl (D = deuterium) would be unchanged, and, consequently, the force constant would be the same in HCl and DCl.

PROBLEM 3-4

Calculate the value of $\nu_{0\to 1}$ for DCl and DF. Sketch the spectrum of a mixture of HCl, DCl, HF, and DF.

(d) *The Beer-Lambert law*

So far the discussion of spectra has emphasized the value of the frequency at which the % transmittance has been a minimum. In other words the absorbed energy, or at least the frequency corresponding to the absorbed energy, has been the prime concern; however, the % transmittance $[= (I_{\text{output}}/I_{\text{input}}) \times 10^2 = (I/I_0)10^2]$, with the emphasis on the "%" aspect, should also be considered. If the molecules in a sample *can* absorb energy of a certain frequency, then surely the number of photons of this frequency that are absorbed will depend on the *number* of molecules available for the transition. Indeed, the relative change in intensity $\Delta I/I$ due to absorption should be proportional to the length of the path Δl over which ΔI is measured times the concentration C as $\Delta I/I = -KC\Delta l$. Considering infinitesimal changes, that is, $\Delta I \rightarrow dI$ and $\Delta l \rightarrow dl$, and integrating over the sample cell yields

$$\int_{I_0}^{I} \frac{dI}{I} = -KC \int_0^L dl$$

where I is the intensity of the beam coming out of the sample, I_0 is the intensity of the beam going into the cell, L is the length of the path of the beam in the cell, and C is the molar concentration. Performing the integration gives $\log I - \log I_0 = -KCL$, which can be rewritten in the conventional *Beer-Lambert* form as absorbency $A = \log (I_0/I) = \varepsilon CL$. Here ε, the so-called molar extinction coefficient, replaces the proportionality constant K and indicates the efficiency of the absorption process by the absorbing species at the frequency of absorption. The utility of absorbency (sometimes called *optical-density*) spectra should now be clear, for not only do they indicate the energy change of the transition but they are also directly related to the concentration of the species. This is especially important when there are base-line problems, i.e., a background of "absorption" that is not due to the absorbing species. For example, in Fig. II-5 subtraction of $A_M - A_B$ is directly related to the concentration of absorbing species—such would not be the result on subtracting $T_M - T_B$, since the transmittance is not directly related to concentration.

PROBLEM 3-5

A sample of HCl gas at room temperature is contained in a cell 10 cm long and 5 cm in diameter. For the absorption maximum at $\bar{\nu} = 3.0 \times 10^3$ cm^{-1} in Fig. II-6, demonstrate that the Beer-Lambert law holds by plotting $A = \log (I_0/I)$ vs. concentration. [*Hint*: Consider HCl as a perfect gas at these pressures. Since the figure gives only the transmittance, it will be necessary to read the $\%T$ at $\bar{\nu} = 3.0 \times 10^3$ cm^{-1} and convert it to absorbence A. Further, since there is considerable "background % transmittance" in the figure, it will be necessary to read the percent of the noise from the figure (e.g., approximately 90 percent for pressure 2), convert it to absorbence,

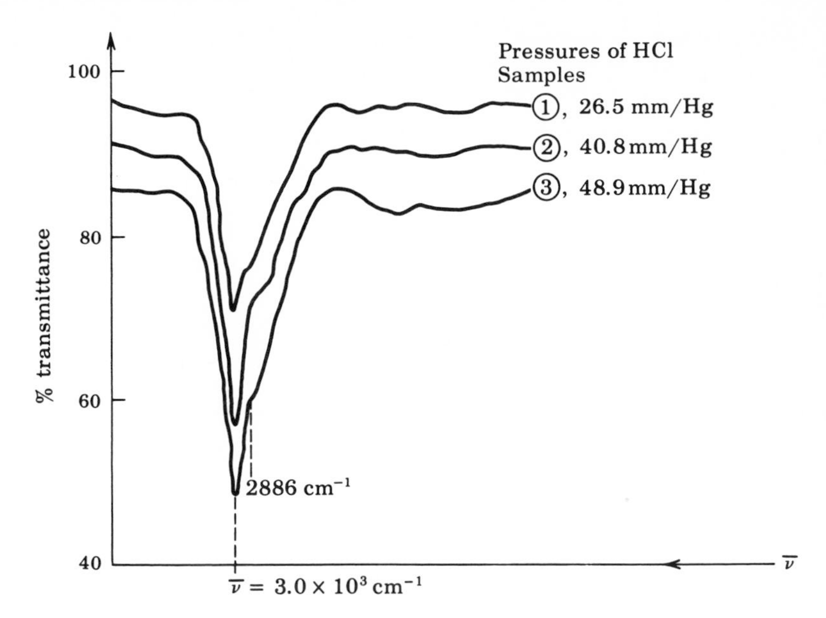

Fig. II-6 Concentration dependence of spectra.

and subtract this background absorbence from the absorbence found above for $\bar{\nu} = 3.0 \times 10^3 \text{ cm}^{-1}$. The result is the true absorbence.]

PROBLEM 3-6

Using the results of Prob. 3-5, find the extinction coefficient ε for HCl.

PROBLEM 3-7

Using the fact that the % transmittance depends on the concentration, sketch the absorption spectrum of a gaseous mixture: 40 mole % HCl, 60 mole % DCl. (Again assume that the deuterium substitution does not significantly alter the molecule, except for mass, so that ε is the same for both species. Let the cell be the same as that of Prob. 3-5 with a total pressure of 50 mm/Hg.)

(iii) The rigid rotor

(a) *Introduction*

In the previous section the motion of two masses along a line was discussed, and the results were applied to the vibration of two nuclei in a molecule. In much the same way the rotation of two masses held rigidly at the ends of a rod will now be investigated, and the results will be applied to rotation of nuclei held "rigidly" by a bond in a molecule. The treatment of this system draws upon the previous discussion of the separation of the hamiltonian and introduces a further set of coordinates, the so-called *angular* coordinates.

Where the system as a whole is located is not of great interest; rather, it is the *rotation* of the system that is of importance. Thus, just as for the harmonic oscillator, the cartesian coordinates of the two masses should be replaced by two new sets. The details of the procedure required here are given in Appendix II. The results are essentially the same as those of the harmonic oscillator, but they are complicated by the fact that this is a three-dimensional problem. The new center-of-mass coordinates X, Y, Z describe the system as a whole, and the internal coordinates R, θ, and ϕ describe the motion of a "reduced-mass particle" of mass μ located a fixed distance R from the center of mass. The coordinates θ and ϕ, specifying the orientation of the line joining the center of mass and μ, are taken as providing the description of the rotor. The transformation is illustrated in Fig. II-7. As indicated in Appendix II, these coordinates allow the energy of the system to be separated into two terms:

$$E = \underbrace{\tfrac{1}{2}M\left[\left(\frac{dX}{dt}\right)^2 + \left(\frac{dY}{dt}\right)^2 + \left(\frac{dZ}{dt}\right)^2\right]}_{\text{Center-of-mass coordinates}} + \underbrace{\tfrac{1}{2}\mu R^2\left[\sin^2\theta\left(\frac{d\phi}{dt}\right)^2 + \left(\frac{d\theta}{dt}\right)^2\right]}_{\text{Internal coordinates}}$$

Since the energy is separated into two independent terms, we can separate the SE into two separate equations (compare this to the separation of the SE into two equations in the case of the separable hamiltonian of the particle in a two-dimensional box). We could write the two equations as

$$H_{\mathrm{CM}}(X,Y,Z)\chi(X,Y,Z) = E_{\mathrm{CM}}\chi(X,Y,Z)$$
$$H_{\mathrm{rot}}(R,\theta,\phi)\psi(R,\theta,\phi) = E_{\mathrm{rot}}\psi(R,\theta,\phi)$$

These two equations are the equivalent, for the rigid rotor, of Eqs. (II-12) and (II-13) for the harmonic oscillator. Once again it is the second of these equations, the internal—in this case rotational—description that is of interest.

(b) *The solution*

Since R is constant, the variables in this final description are only θ and ϕ. Since potential energy is a constant (V is set to zero), the solution of the

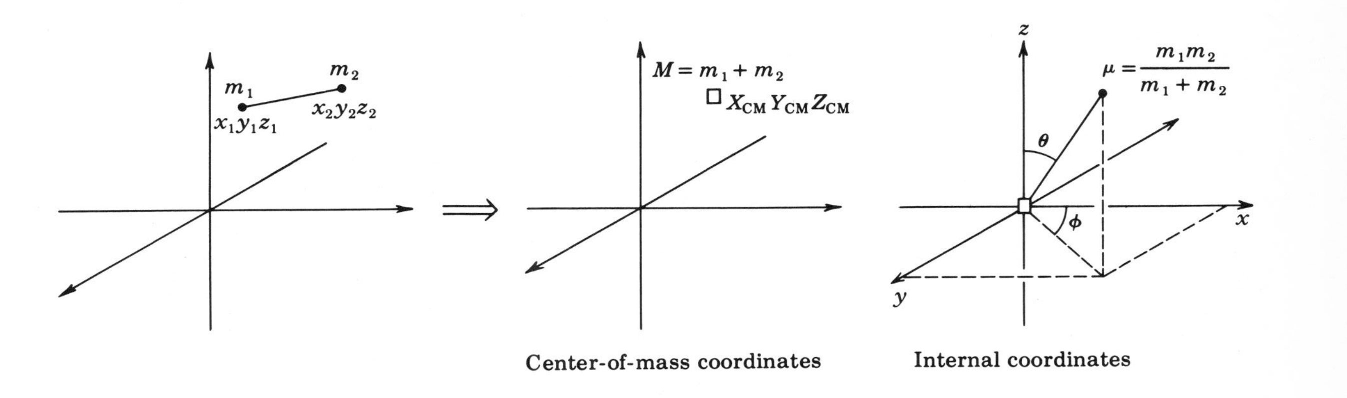

$$\Psi(x_1y_1z_1\ x_2y_2z_2) \Longrightarrow \chi(XYZ)\psi(R\,\theta\,\phi)$$

$$H(x_1y_1z_1\ x_2y_2z_2) \Longrightarrow H_{\mathrm{CM}}(XYZ) + H_{\mathrm{rot}}(R,\theta,\phi)$$

$$H(x_1y_1z_1\ x_2y_2z_2)\Psi(x_1y_1z_1\ x_2y_2z_2) = E\Psi(x_1y_1z_1\ x_2y_2z_2) \Longrightarrow \left\{ \begin{array}{l} H_{\mathrm{CM}}(XYZ)\chi(XYZ) = E_{\mathrm{CM}}\chi(XYZ) \\ H_{\mathrm{rot}}(R\theta\phi)\,\psi(R\theta\phi) = E_{\mathrm{rot}}\,\psi(R\theta\phi) \end{array} \right\}$$

Fig. II-7 Center-of-mass and relative coordinates for the rigid rotor.

SE has much in common with the case of the particle in a two-dimensional box, where there were two variables and a constant potential. The difference lies in the fact that θ and ϕ are angular coordinates, and, when the second derivative in the kinetic energy is expressed in these coordinates, the result is a rather more complicated hamiltonian. Indeed, the SE cannot be separated directly, but, as shown in Appendix II, if one sets $\psi(R,\theta,\phi) = T(\theta)S(\phi)$, the SE can be transformed, after some algebra, into two separate and simpler equations:

$$[\text{Operator in } \theta]T(\theta) = ET(\theta) \tag{II-17}$$

$$[\text{Operator in } \phi]S(\phi) = (\text{number})S(\phi) \tag{II-18}$$

The solution of Eq. (II-18) and the first few solutions of Eq. (II-17) are obtained in Appendix II. When the boundary condition on ϕ is imposed on $S(\phi)$, a quantum number $m = 0, \pm 1, \pm 2, \ldots$ is introduced. The solution of Eq. (II-17) gives the energy as $E = (h^2/8\pi^2 I)[l(l+1)]$, where l is the quantum number associated with $T_l(\theta)$. As shown in Appendix II, the solution $T_l(\theta)$ restricts the values of m to $m = 0, \pm 1, \pm 2, \ldots, \pm l$. Hence one generally writes

$$\psi(R,\theta,\phi) = T_{lm}(\theta)S_m(\phi)$$

The first few allowed solutions, along with their energy and associated quantum numbers, are given in Table II-6. The solutions, for example, $T_{lm}(\theta) = \cos\theta$ for $l = 1$, $m = 0$, and $S_m(\phi) = 1$ for $m = 0$, are to be taken in the same way as the solution $\psi_n(r) = e^{-ar^2}$ for $n = 0$ in the harmonic oscillator. They are just the solutions obtained on solving the pertinent Schroedinger equation, and although $T_{lm}(\theta)$ and $S_m(\phi)$ have not been worked out in detail as was the case in the two earlier systems, they are found in a similar fashion and play the same role. The $T_{lm}(\theta)S_m(\phi)$ are, of course, different functions from those for the particle-in-a-box and vibrational descriptions. But this is what one expects, for the system and the interactions they describe are different. In the same way that the solutions are different in form, so also is the statement of the energy levels different. Furthermore, although there are two quantum numbers l and m, the energy depends on only the quantum number l. Thus

$$E_l = \frac{h^2}{8\pi^2 I}\, l(l+1) \tag{II-19}$$

where $I = \mu R^2$ is the moment of inertia of the reduced mass about the position of the center of mass.

In the *classical* description of the rotation of a mass μ about the origin, the energy[1] is proportional to the square of the angular momentum (p_{angular} = distance × velocity) as $E_{\text{rot}} \sim p^2_{\text{angular}}$. The quantum treat-

[1] D. Halliday and R. Resnick, "Physics," Wiley, 1966.

Table II-6 Rigid-rotor description

Quantum numbers			*Function*	
l	m	*Energy*	$\psi(R,\theta,\phi) = T_{lm}(\theta)$	$S_m(\phi)$
0	0	0	1	1
1	0	$\left(\frac{h^2}{8\pi^2 I}\right)2$	$\cos\theta$	1
1	−1	$\left(\frac{h^2}{8\pi^2 I}\right)2$	$\sin\theta$	$e^{-i\phi}$
1	+1	$\left(\frac{h^2}{8\pi^2 I}\right)2$	$\sin\theta$	$e^{i\phi}$
2	0	$\left(\frac{h^2}{8\pi^2 I}\right)6$	$(3\cos^2\theta - 1)$	1

ment gives $E_{\text{rot}} \sim l(l + 1)$, and so the rotational quantum number l is also called the *angular-momentum quantum number*, and $\sqrt{l(l + 1)}$ is characteristic of the angular momentum. Furthermore, in the classical case the angular motion

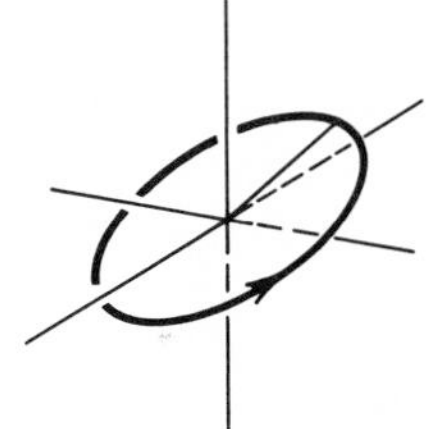

would have the same energy as the angular motion

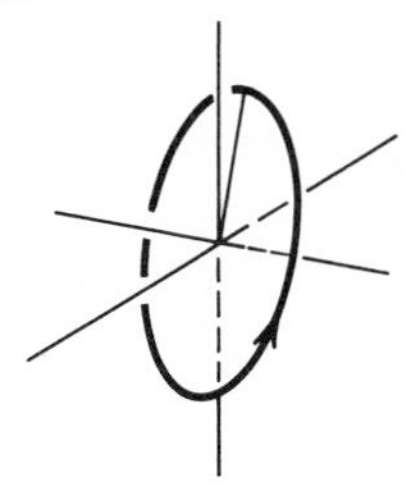

In other words the *energy is independent of the orientation* of the "orbit." Since, in the quantum-mechanical description of the rigid rotor, the *energy is independent* of the *quantum number m*, this number is taken as indicative of the orientation. (In more sophisticated treatments it can be shown[1]

[1] L. Pauling and E. B. Wilson, "Introduction to Quantum Mechanics," McGraw-Hill, 1935.

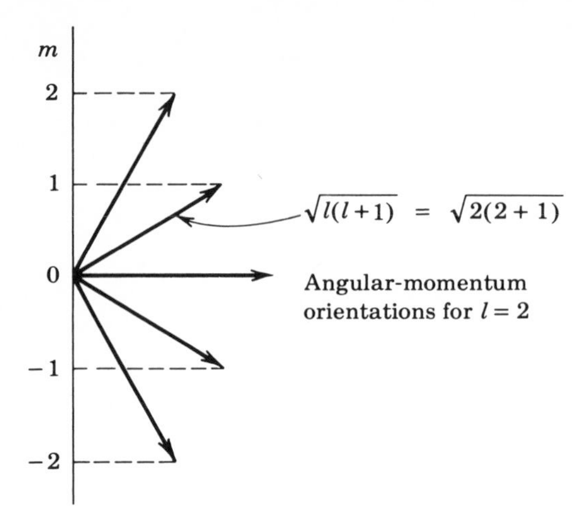

Fig. II-8 Projection of angular momentum.

explicitly that the m is proportional to the component of angular momentum in, for example, the z direction.)

It must, of course, be emphasized that since the quantum-mechanical treatment allows only certain values of l, the rotational energy (or angular momentum) is quantized, and since m is allowed only certain values, the orientation of the angular motion is restricted. This is sometimes emphasized by using a vector [of magnitude $\sqrt{l(l+1)}$] to represent the angular momentum. The orientation of a vector can be represented by its projection, and since the orientation is related to m, the projection, or allowed orientations, of this vector in a given direction are related to the m values as in Fig. II-8.

(iv) Project 4. The elementary spectroscopy of rotational transitions

(a) *Introduction*

If the internuclear separation R in HCl is considered fixed, then the rotation of the molecule HCl is formally the same as that of a rigid rotor. The rotational energy levels are simply given by Eq. (II-19). The change in rotational energy for the transition from $l = 0$ to $l = 1$ would be registered in a spectroscopy experiment by the absorption of radiation of a certain frequency $\nu_{0\to1}$.

Using this frequency and the formula for an energy change,

$$\Delta E_{\text{system}} = E_{l=1} - E_{l=0} = \left(\frac{h^2}{8\pi^2 I}\right)[1(1+1) - 0(0+1)]$$

one could find the internuclear separation of HCl as follows: $\nu_{0\to1} = (\Delta E_{\text{system}}/h) = (h/8\pi^2 I)2$, or, on rearranging, $I = (2h/8\pi^2\nu_{0\to1})$; but $I = \mu R^2$, giving $R = (h/4\pi^2\mu\nu_{0\to1})^{\frac{1}{2}}$. Again the spectroscopy experiment and a simple model of the system have provided information about the molecule—this time a value of the internuclear separation.

In general, for a transition from a state with the angular-momentum quantum number l_i to a state with the angular-momentum quantum number l_f, the energy change is given by

$$\Delta E_{\text{system}} = \frac{h^2}{8\pi^2 I}[l_f(l_f + 1) - l_i(l_i + 1)]$$

and, if the radiation is quoted in terms of $\bar{\nu}$ rather than ν, the value of $\bar{\nu}$ for the photon emitted or absorbed is given by

$$\bar{\nu} = \left(\frac{\Delta E_{\text{system}}}{hc}\right) = \frac{h/c}{8\pi^2 I}[l_f(l_f + 1) - l_i(l_i + 1)]$$

PROBLEM 4-1

Given that the $\bar{\nu}$ for the $0 \rightarrow 1$ rotational transition of CO is $\bar{\nu} = 3.83\ \text{cm}^{-1}$, find the internuclear separation.

PROBLEM 4-2

If the internuclear separation of HF is 0.917 Å, predict the frequency of absorption for the $l = 0 \rightarrow l = 1$ rotational transition.

(b) The spectrum

The absorption spectrum for the rotational transitions of HCl is given in Fig. II-9.

PROBLEM 4-3

Calculate the value of $\bar{\nu}$ corresponding to the absorption of energy for the transitions $l = 0 \rightarrow l = 1$, $l = 0 \rightarrow l = 2$, $l = 1 \rightarrow l = 2$, $l = 2 \rightarrow l = 3$, $l = 3 \rightarrow l = 4$, and $l = 4 \rightarrow l = 5$ in units of $h/8\pi^2 Ic$. For example, for $l = 1 \rightarrow l = 3$,

$$\bar{\nu}_{1\rightarrow 3} = \frac{h/c}{8\pi^2 I}[3(3 + 1) - 1(1 + 1)] = 10\left(\frac{h/c}{8\pi^2 I}\right)$$

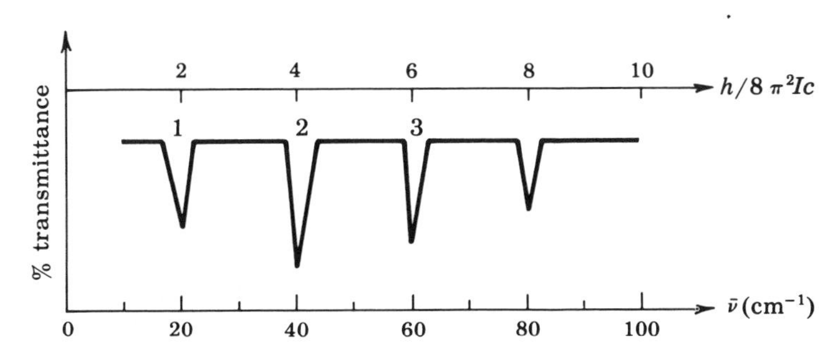

Fig. II-9 Rotational spectrum of HCl.

PROBLEM 4-4

Do any of the transitions in Prob. 4-3 have the same value of $\bar{\nu}$?

PROBLEM 4-5

The lowest absorption ① in Fig. II-9 has been assigned to the $0 \rightarrow 1$ transition. Using the results of Prob. 4-3, indicate the rotational quantum numbers for the next absorption ②.

The third absorption ③ occurs at a value of $\bar{\nu} = 6[(h/c)/8\pi^2 I]$. But the results of Prob. 4-4 indicate that this is the value of $\bar{\nu}$ corresponding to the energy change for *either* the $l = 0 \rightarrow l = 2$ *or* the $l = 2 \rightarrow l = 3$ transitions! Consequently the use of energy *alone* is not sufficient to enable the quantum numbers for all transitions to be assigned with certainty. However, with the assistance of what are known as *selection rules* that indicate which transitions are allowed, it is possible to assign the quantum numbers for each absorption. The "selection rule" for rotational transitions (to be developed in Chap. IV) states that the change in l must be unity; that is, $l = 1 \rightarrow l = 2$ $(\Delta l = 1)$ is allowed but not $l = 0 \rightarrow l = 2$ $(\Delta l = 2)$.

PROBLEM 4-6

The figure below is a combination of the spectrum of Fig. II-9 and an energy level diagram for rotational levels. Complete the figure by drawing the arrows appropriate to the observed absorptions (this has been done for the $0 \rightarrow 1$ transition).

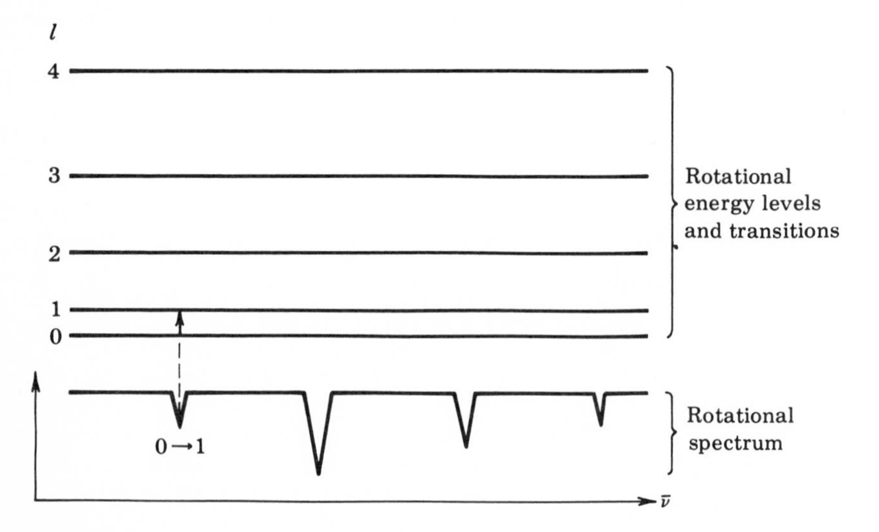

In many cases the determination of the initial and final quantum numbers appropriate to a particular absorption cannot be carried out with certainty. For example, the low-intensity $0 \rightarrow 1$ transition could be buried in the background noise, and one might mistakenly assign the first absorption observed at the low-frequency end as the $0 \rightarrow 1$ transition. Obviously any calculations based on this assignment would be in error. To avoid this possibility, we frequently extract information from the *change* in $\bar{\nu}$ from one transition to the next (i.e., we measure the *separation* of absorptions in the spectrum). Thus

$$\Delta\bar{\nu} = (\bar{\nu}_{l\rightarrow l+1}) - (\bar{\nu}_{l-1\rightarrow l}) = \left(\frac{h}{8\pi^2 Ic}\right)\{[(l+1)(l+1+1) - l(l+1)] - [l(l+1) - (l-1)(l-1+1)]\} = \left(\frac{h}{8\pi^2 Ic}\right)2$$

which is independent of l and, consequently, does not depend on assignment of quantum numbers.

PROBLEM 4-7

Using the $\bar{\nu}$ scale of Fig. II-9, obtain the value of separation between absorptions, and then use this value and the results of the previous paragraph to obtain the internuclear distance in HCl.

(c) The population of the energy levels

In the previous project the amount of radiation absorbed at a given frequency was related to the number of transitions taking place and, thus, to the concentration of the species. In Fig. II-9, which indicates several rotational transitions, some transitions appear to take place more often than others; e.g., the absorption for the $1 \rightarrow 2$ transition is more intense than that for the $0 \rightarrow 1$ transition. Since both transitions are rotational transitions of the same chemical species, this variation cannot be related to the concentration of the chemical species. There are two possible explanations—either the transition itself is more likely to occur, or there are more molecules in the $l = 1$ state available for the $l = 1 \rightarrow l = 2$ transition than there are molecules in the $l = 0$ state available for the $l = 0 \rightarrow l = 1$ transition. The first alternative is the subject of Chap. IV, and it has really been invoked by the requirement that only transitions from adjacent l's be considered.

The second alternative involves a discussion of the probability of the system being "in" a given level. From statistical mechanics the number of molecules in a state with energy E_l relative to the number with the lowest energy E_0 is given by the Boltzmann distribution[1] as

$$\frac{n_l}{n_0} = \frac{e^{-E_l/kT}}{e^{-E_0/kT}} = \frac{e^{-E_l/kT}}{e^{-0/kT}} = \frac{1}{e^{E_l/kT}}$$

Here k is the Boltzmann constant, and T is the temperature in degrees absolute. Certainly as the energy E_l increases, the relative occupancy, or population, of that level will decrease. However, the rotational energy levels are degenerate; for example, when $l = 1$ there are three possible states $m = -1$, 0, or $+1$, all equally possible, whereas for $l = 0$, $m = 0$ there is only one possible state. Since the energy for $l = 1$ is only slightly greater than that for $l = 0$, it might be possible that the three different possibilities would compensate for the slightly higher energy. In fact one should really include the degeneracy d_l as

$$\frac{n_l}{n_0} = d_l e^{-E_l/kT} \qquad \text{but } d_l = 2l + 1$$

so that

$$\frac{n_l}{n_0} = (2l + 1)e^{-E_l/kT} = \frac{(2l + 1)}{e^{E_l/kT}}$$

PROBLEM 4-8

Calculate the relative probability n_l/n_0 for the first five levels of HCl at room temperature.

PROBLEM 4-9

Sketch the dependence of n_l/n_0 on l from the results of Prob. 4-8.

II-3 DESCRIPTION OF THE MOTION OF ELECTRONS

The simple two-body systems of the previous two sections have introduced the quantum-mechanical description of the motion of *nuclei* in diatomic molecules, and to continue, a description of the *electrons* must be obtained. The exact description of the many electrons in even a diatomic molecule such as HCl is impossible; however, the electronic description of the one-electron atom can be obtained and used as the basis for the electronic description in more complex and more important systems.

(i) The hydrogenic atom

Consider the solution of the SE for the hydrogenic atom. As in the two previous sections the first step in the procedure is a separation into center-

[1] See sec. 5-2 of D. F. Eggers et al., "Physical Chemistry," Wiley, 1964.

of-mass (X,Y,Z) coordinates and relative coordinates. In this case the mass of the nucleus m_n is so much greater than the mass of the electron m_e that the center of gravity will be almost the position of the nucleus. Further, the reduced mass will be almost the mass of the electron [as $\mu = [m_e m_n/(m_e + m_n)] \simeq (m_e m_n/m_n) = m_e$]. Thus the relative coordinates can be considered to give the position of the mass m_e, i.e., the position of the electron, with the nucleus as the origin. A judicious choice of internal coordinates may be made if it is noted that the form of potential energy is $-e^2/r$ (where $r = \sqrt{x^2 + y^2 + z^2}$ is the distance from the electron to the nucleus). This would suggest that, instead of the relative coordinates x, y, and z, the new set of coordinates r, θ, ϕ indicated in Fig. II-10 would be more useful. Thus the potential would be dependent on only one coordinate! The separation into internal and external coordinate systems is illustrated in Fig. II-10. Of the two separated Schroedinger equations indicated in this figure, only

$$H_e(r,\theta,\phi)\psi(r,\theta,\phi) = E_e\psi(r,\theta,\phi)$$

which describes the electron, is of interest. As with the rigid rotor this equation can be separated relatively simply, and, although the general solution is complicated, the first few solutions can be examined from the point of view of the energy, the quantum numbers, and the interdependence of quantum numbers. The analysis is given in detail in Appendix III and is summarized as follows.

Applying the principles developed earlier, one can write $\psi(r,\theta,\phi)$ as a product $\psi(r,\theta,\phi) = R(r)T(\theta)S(\phi)$, allowing the SE to be separated into three equations, each involving only one variable:

$$\begin{aligned} [\text{Operator in } r]\, R(r) &= ER(r) \\ [\text{Operator in } \theta]\, T(\theta) &= l(l+1)T(\theta) \\ [\text{Operator in } \phi]\, S(\phi) &= m^2S(\phi) \end{aligned}$$

In the same fashion as for the previous systems, the general form for the solution to each of these equations may be found, the respective boundary conditions imposed, and, finally, the allowed solutions $R_{nl}(r)$ in r, $T_{lm}(\theta)$ in θ, and $S_m(\phi)$ in ϕ obtained. The total description is then a product $\psi_{nlm}(r,\theta,\phi) = R_{nl}(r)T_{lm}(\theta)S_m(\phi)$, where n, l, and m are the quantum numbers restricted by $n = 1, 2, \ldots ; l = 0, 1, \ldots, n - 1$, and $m = 0, \pm 1, \ldots, \pm l$. These solutions are the familiar atomic orbitals of hydrogen.

Since the only difference in other *one*-electron systems, such as He^+, Li^{++}, etc., is that the potential would be $(-Ze^2/r)$, where Ze is the nuclear charge, the same procedures would apply. The solutions obtained would

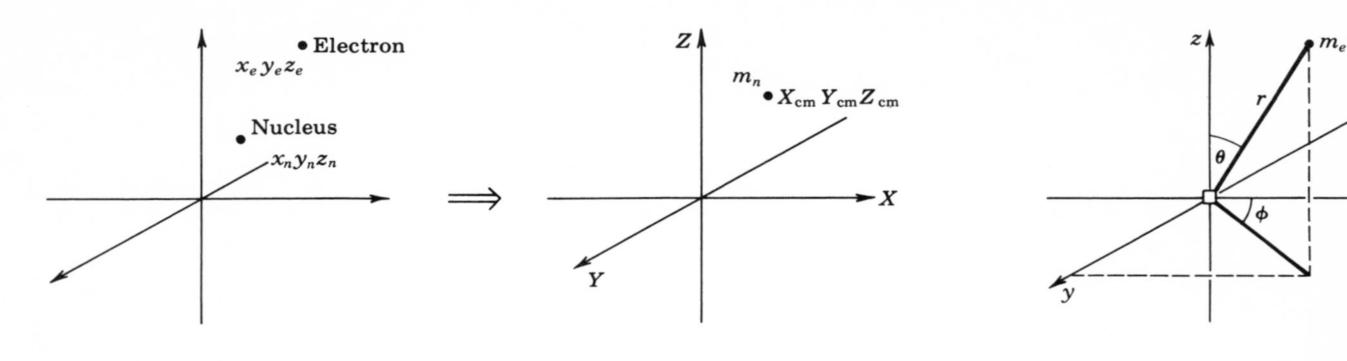

Cartesian coordinates $\Longrightarrow$ Center-of-mass coordinates nucleus position — Relative coordinates electron position

Hamiltonian separability

$$\mathrm{H}\,(x_n y_n z_n,\, x_e y_e z_e) \Longrightarrow \mathrm{H}_n(XYZ) + \mathrm{H}_e(r\theta\phi) \qquad \text{(a sum of operators)}$$

Solution form

$$\Psi(x_n y_n z_n,\, x_e y_e z_e) \Longrightarrow \chi(XYZ)\;\psi(r\theta\phi) \qquad \text{(a product of functions)}$$

SE separability

$$\mathrm{H}\Psi = E\Psi \Longrightarrow \left\{ \begin{array}{l} \mathrm{H}_n(XYZ)\chi(XYZ) = E_n\chi(XYZ) \\ \mathrm{H}_e(r\theta\phi)\psi(r\theta\phi) = E_e\psi(r\theta\phi) \end{array} \right\} \qquad \text{(two simpler equations)}$$

Fig. II-10 Separation of the SE for hydrogen.

Table II-7 Hydrogenic solutions

Quantum numbers			Function	Function‡	Energy in units of $\frac{2\pi^2 m_e e^4}{h^2}$
n	l	m	designation	$R_{nl}(r)T_{lm}(\theta)S_m(\phi)$	
1	0	0	1s	e^{-Zr/a_0}	$\frac{-Z^2}{1}$
2	0	0	2s	$\left(2 - \frac{Zr}{a_0}\right) e^{-Zr/2a_0}$	$\frac{-Z^2}{4}$
2	1	0	$2p_z$	$re^{-Zr/2a_0} \cos \theta$	$\frac{-Z^2}{4}$
2	1	±1	$2p_x$§	$re^{-Zr/2a_0} \sin \theta \cos \phi$	$\frac{-Z^2}{4}$
2	1	±1	$2p_y$§	$re^{-Zr/2a_0} \sin \theta \sin \phi$	$\frac{-Z^2}{4}$
3	0	0	3s	$\left[27 - 18\left(\frac{Zr}{a_0}\right) + 2\left(\frac{Zr}{a_0}\right)^2\right] e^{-Zr/3a_0}$	$\frac{-Z^2}{9}$

‡ Here a_0 is shorthand for $(h^2/4\pi^2 m_e e^2)$ and has the numerical value 0.53 Å.
§ The $2p_x$ and $2p_y$ functions are, respectively, the combinations $(\psi_{2,1,1} + \psi_{2,1,-1})$ and $(1/i)(\psi_{2,1,1} - \psi_{2,1,-1})$, where the subscripts are the quantum numbers n, l, and m, respectively. Further, the product $r \sin \theta \cos \phi = x$ and $r \sin \theta \sin \phi = y$ — hence the labels p_x and p_y.

be for a general one-electron–one-nucleus system. Some of these hydrogenlike, or hydrogenic, functions are indicated in Table II-7. The allowed energies are given by the equation $E_n = (-2\pi^2 m_e e^4/n^2h^2)Z^2$, which, for $Z = 1$, is the same as the energy given by Bohr for the hydrogen atom.

(ii) The orbital approximation

For the previous two-body system of the electron and the nucleus, a judicious choice of coordinates allowed the hamiltonian to be broken into several parts and the SE reduced to a set of individual equations, each of which could be solved. However, when the system of interest involves the interaction of more than two bodies, such as in the several-electron atoms, *no choice* of coordinates allows the exact separation of the problem into manageable parts. For example, in helium there are two electrons and one nucleus. For this system $Z = 2$, and the interactions could be represented by the hamiltonian

$$H = \text{KE}(1) + V_2(1) + \text{KE}(2) + V_2(2) + V(1,2)$$

where $V(1,2)$ is the potential energy of the repulsion between the two electrons and depends upon r_{12}, the *distance* between the two electrons, as $V(1,2) = (e^2/r_{12})$. The symbol in brackets, for example 2 in KE(2), indicates that this is the kinetic energy of electron 2, whereas the subscript on $V_2(1)$ indicates that this is the attraction of electron 1 to a nucleus of charge $+2e$. One might hope, by proper choice of coordinates, to separate the interactions into two groups, one for each electron. This separation is impossible to do, for one of the interactions, $V(1,2) = (e^2/r_{12})$, *depends on both electrons.* An exact solution appears to be impossible.

(*a*) *Omitting the electron repulsion*

If the electron-repulsion term is ignored, the interactions as represented in H become a sum of two sets of terms, each set dealing with only one electron. Since this approximate H can be separated into two parts, each dealing with one electron, the description can also be written as a product of two parts, $\Psi(1,2) = \psi(1)\psi(2)$, each part $\psi(1)$ or $\psi(2)$ treating only one electron. The *approximate* SE becomes

$$[\mathrm{KE}(1) + V_2(1) + \mathrm{KE}(2) + V_2(2)]\psi(1)\psi(2) = E\psi(1)\psi(2)$$

which can be separated into two equations:

$$\left.\begin{array}{l}[\mathrm{KE}(1) + V_2(1)]\,\psi(1) = E_1\psi(1)\\ [\mathrm{KE}(2) + V_2(2)]\,\psi(2) = E_2\psi(2)\end{array}\right\} \qquad \text{where } E = E_1 + E_2$$

Each of these equations is identical to that for one electron in the presence of a nucleus with $Z = 2$. But such systems have already been dealt with in Sec. II-3(i). The functions $\psi(1)$ and $\psi(2)$ are thus just the hydrogenic functions with $Z = 2$. In summary, the three-body (nucleus + two electrons) problem of the helium atom has been approximated by *two* two-body (nucleus + electron) problems. This is illustrated in Fig. II-11.

The resulting description of the many-electron system in terms of a product of one-electron functions $\psi(1)$ and $\psi(2)$ is an *orbital description*, and the functions $\psi(1)$ and $\psi(2)$ are called *orbitals*. If, for the moment, it is assumed that each orbital can accept two electrons, the lowest state of the helium atom would be represented by

$$\psi(1)\psi(2) = 1s(1)1s(2) = 1s^2$$

(for helium, the atomic orbitals 1*s* would be those with $Z = 2$). But this representation is rather crude, for in arriving at the 1*s* description of an electron in the helium atom, the repulsion between the electrons has been completely ignored—these hydrogenic orbitals are a good first attempt at a description, but they could be improved!

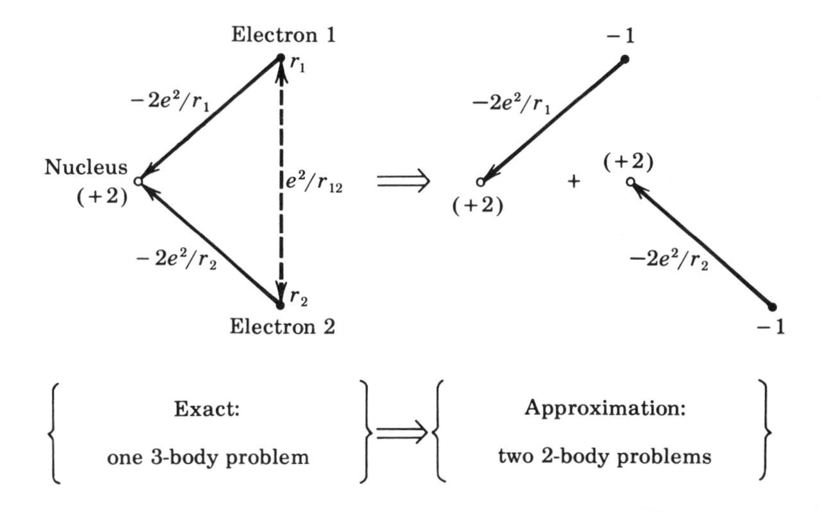

$$H(1,2) = \mathrm{KE}(1) + V_2(1) + \mathrm{KE}(2) + V_2(2) + V_{12} \Longrightarrow [\mathrm{KE}(1) + V_2(1)] + [\mathrm{KE}(2) + V_2(2)]$$

$$\Psi(1,2) \Longrightarrow \psi(1)\,\psi(2)$$

$$H(1,2)\Psi(1,2) = E\Psi(1,2) \Longrightarrow \begin{Bmatrix} H(1)\psi(1) = E_1\,\psi(1) \\ H(2)\psi(2) = E_2\,\psi(2) \end{Bmatrix}$$

Fig. II-11 Separation of the SE by ignoring the repulsion.

(*b*) *The averaged electron repulsion*

The attraction of the electron to the nucleus, which is the only force considered in the treatment above, is in part counteracted by the repulsion due to the other electron. For example, consider the arrangement indicated in Fig. II-12. Electron 1 will have a *net* force toward the nucleus that will be *less* than the force due to the nuclear attraction because of repulsion due to electron 2. One could think of this decreased net force as being due to a helium nucleus with a nuclear charge decreased by an amount σe to give an effective nuclear charge of $Z_{\mathrm{eff}}e = (Z - \sigma)e$. [The value[1] of σ would, of course, depend on the average position of the other electron]. In other words the electron behaves as if it were not experiencing the full charge of the nucleus—it is "*screened* from the nucleus by the other electron." Since both electrons are the same in helium, this argu-

[1] The values of σ may be found from the table of Z_{eff} in J. C. Slater, "Quantum Theory of Atomic Structure," vol. I, p. 369, McGraw-Hill, 1960.

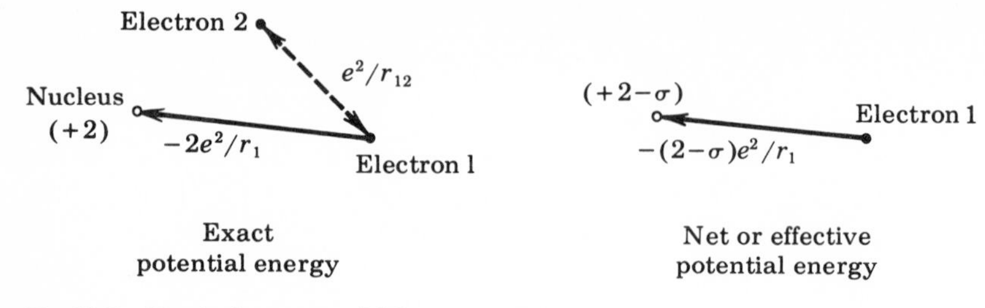

Fig. II-12 Equivalent potential by "screening."

ment replaces the three-body problem by the two approximately *equivalent two-body* problems, as illustrated in Fig. II-13.

The energy of the electrons would be the usual energy of a hydrogenic orbital but now with $Z_{\text{eff}} = (2 - \sigma)$ replacing $Z = 2$ for helium to give

$$E_n = -\frac{2\pi^2 m_e e^4}{n^2 h^2}(2 - \sigma)^2$$

Not only does the energy depend on n and on Z but it also depends on the value of σ! For example, because much of the electron density of a $2p$ orbital lies some distance from the nucleus, an electron in a $2p$ orbital would be more affected by screening than would a $2s$ electron. Consequently $Z_{\text{eff}} = Z - \sigma$ for a $2p$ orbital would be smaller than Z_{eff} for a $2s$ orbital, and a $2p$ orbital would have a higher energy than a $2s$ orbital. The result is the familiar ordering of orbitals for many-electron atoms, $1s < 2s < 2p$. Further, as the number of electrons increases, the effect of screening can dominate the principle quantum number, for example, the $3d$ orbital may be higher in energy than the $4s$. As the value of Z increases,

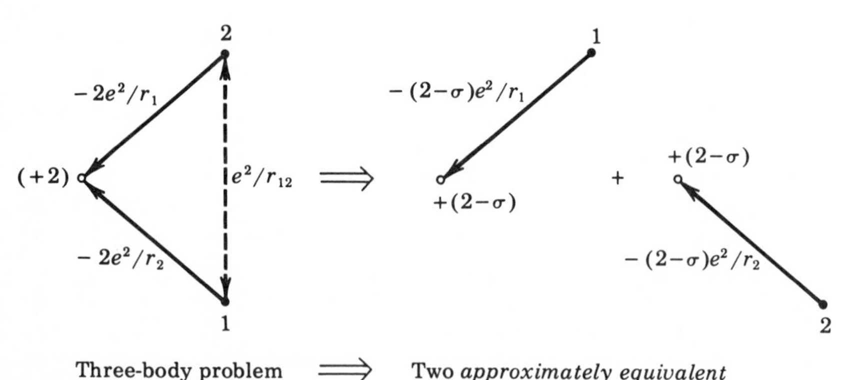

Fig. II-13 Separation of the SE by the equivalent potential.

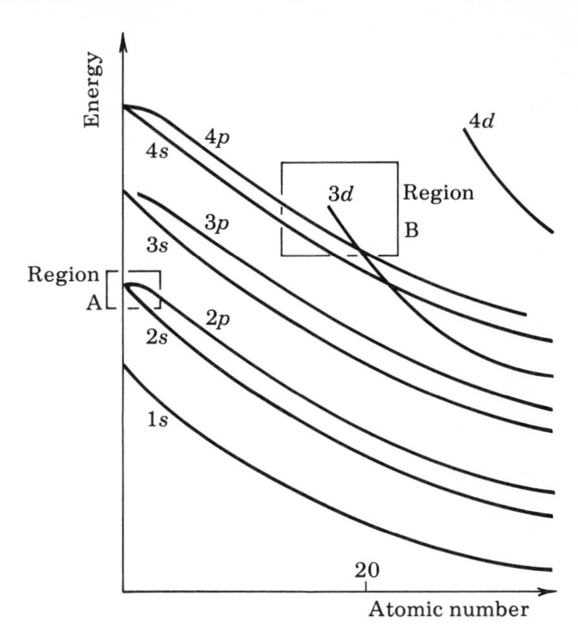

Fig. II-14 Change in energy level with atomic number.

the effective nuclear charge will change slowly, since the increasing nuclear charge is partly compensated by the increase in the number of electrons available for screening. The resulting gradual increase in Z_{eff} is reflected in Fig. II-14 in the downward trend of the orbital energies. That the screening is different for the *s*, *p*, and *d* orbitals can be seen by both the splitting within a shell and the difference in slope of the respective curves (see region *A* for *s* vs. *p* and region *B* for *p* vs. *d*). Such a simple discussion cannot be expected to give a completely adequate description of the electrons of all atoms, especially the transition element atoms. However, the use of Fig. II-14 and the Pauli principle[1] of a maximum of two electrons per orbital gives the configuration, i.e., orbital occupancy, for many of the atoms in the periodic table.

PROBLEM II-6

If the screening constant of the 1*s* orbital for helium is $\sigma = 0.31$, find the electronic energy of the helium atom.

PROBLEM II-7

Find the ionization energy for the removal of one electron from helium, i.e., for $He \rightarrow He^{+1} + e$. What would be the ionization energy for removal of the second electron, that is, $He^{+} \rightarrow He^{+2} + e$?

[1] This principle will be discussed in detail in Sec. II-4.

PROBLEM II-8

Draw an energy level diagram for the lithium atom if $\sigma = 0.3$ for the $1s$ orbital and $\sigma = 1.7$ for the $2s$ orbital. Predict the λ_{max} for a transition of an electron from $1s$ to $2s$, i.e., for $(1s)^2 (2s)^1 \rightarrow (1s)^1(2s)^2$. [The superscript indicates the occupancy of the orbital.]

PROBLEM II-9

Arrange the following configurations of the lithium atom from lowest to highest energy: $(1s)^2 (2p_x)$, $(1s)^2 (2s)$, $1s2s2p_y$, $1s2p_x2p_y$, $1s(2p_x)^2$.

(iii) Project 5. Atomic orbitals

(a) Introduction

Sketches of atomic orbitals and their probability functions are familiar.[1] Nevertheless, it would be instructive to investigate these functions in detail to become familiar with the functional dependence of the orbitals, the coordinates in which they are expressed, and the probability functions that they yield.

In Sec. I-4(iii) the product[2] $\psi^*(x)\psi(x) = \psi(x)\psi(x)$ was interpreted as representing the probability of finding the system with coordinate x, i.e., its "probability at a point." Similarly $\psi(x)\psi(x)\,dx$ in the integral $\int_{-\infty}^{\infty} \psi(x)\psi(x)\,dx$ was the probability that the system under consideration would be found with a coordinate between x and $x + dx$; it was a probability per unit length. In the case of the particle in a three-dimensional box, the equivalent function is $\psi(xyz)\psi(xyz)\,dx\,dy\,dz$, a probability per unit volume. The normalization condition is simply

$$1 = \int_{-\infty}^{\infty} dx \int_{-\infty}^{\infty} dy \int_{-\infty}^{\infty} dz\, \psi(xyz)\psi(xyz)$$

Thus the normalization and the concept of both the "point probability" and the probability per unit volume present no problem in the case of cartesian coordinates x,y, and z.

The problem is more difficult in the case of spherical polar coordinates r, θ, and ϕ. The principal difficulty is the determination of the element of volume to replace $dx\,dy\,dz$ above. However, if the basic relation between arc, angle, and radius

$$\text{angle} = \frac{\text{arc}}{\text{radius}}$$

Arc
Angle
Radius

[1] See, for example, sec. 2.3 in M. Sienko and R. Plane, "Chemistry," 3d ed., McGraw-Hill, 1966; E. A. Ogryzlo and G. B. Porter, *J. Chem. Ed.*, **40**:256 (1963).
[2] Only real functions will be considered here; consequently, $\psi^* = \psi$.

is used, the appropriate transformation can be found. The procedure is to consider sufficiently small angle increments $d\theta$ and $d\phi$ such that the "arc" is essentially straight. The volume element is then a product of the three sides of a "cube," as in Fig. II-15.

The "point probability" is still $\psi(r\theta\phi)\psi(r\theta\phi)$; but now the probability per volume element is $\psi(r\theta\phi)\psi(r\theta\phi)\, r^2 \sin\theta\, d\theta\, d\phi\, dr$, and the normalization becomes $1 = \int_0^r dr \int_0^\pi d\theta \int_0^{2\pi} d\phi\, \psi(r\theta\phi)\psi(r\theta\phi)\, r^2 \sin\theta$. Here, in addition to the change in $d\tau$ required for r, θ, and ϕ, the limits have been changed to those required for the spherical polar coordinates.

Suppose that the only information required is the probability ρ_R of having the r coordinate between r and $r + dr$. This means that θ and ϕ can have any value, and so the *probability for each and every value of θ and ϕ must be added* up by integrating:

$$\rho_R = \int_0^\pi d\theta \int_0^{2\pi} d\phi\, \psi^2(r\theta\phi)\, r^2 \sin\theta\, dr$$

If ψ is independent of θ and ϕ, one has

$$\rho_R = r^2\, dr\, \psi^2(r) \int_0^\pi d\theta \int_0^{2\pi} d\phi \sin\theta = 4\pi r^2 \psi^2(r)\, dr$$

Essentially this is the probability of finding the system anywhere in the volume of a thin spherical shell of thickness dr situated a distance r from the nucleus. It is called the *radial probability* and, for an s orbital, it is an obvious and useful characterization of the way the probability varies with distance from the nucleus.

(b) Units

The normalized $1s$ and $2s$ atomic orbitals for a nucleus of charge Ze are

$$\psi_{1s} = \frac{1}{\sqrt{\pi}}\left(\frac{Z}{a_0}\right)^{3/2} e^{-Zr/a_0}$$

$$\psi_{2s} = \frac{1}{4\sqrt{2\pi}}\left(\frac{Z}{a_0}\right)^{3/2} e^{-Zr/2a_0}\left(2 - \frac{Zr}{a_0}\right)$$

To simplify the numerical calculations, these functions are manipulated into a more suitable form. Thus

$$\frac{\psi_{1s}}{A'} = (Z)^{3/2} e^{-Zr/a_0} \qquad \text{where } A' = \frac{1}{\sqrt{\pi}}\left(\frac{1}{a_0}\right)^{3/2}$$

and $$\frac{\psi_{2s}}{A} = Z^{3/2} e^{-Zr/2a_0}\left(2 - \frac{Zr}{a_0}\right) \qquad \text{where } A = \left(\frac{1}{4\sqrt{2\pi}}\right)\left(\frac{1}{a_0}\right)^{3/2}$$

Since A is a constant, ψ_{2s}/A will adequately demonstrate the dependence of ψ_{2s} on r and Z. The value of r might just as well be quoted in units of a_0; for example, r could take the values $r = 1a_0$, $r = 2.3a_0$,

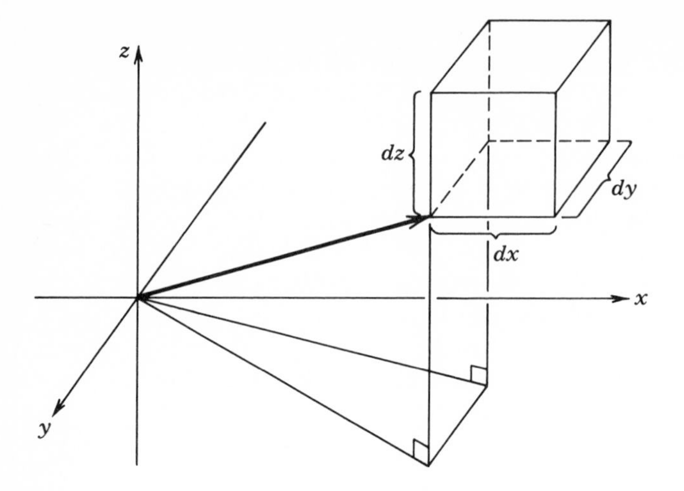

Cartesian coordinates
$d\tau$ = volume element = $dx\ dy\ dz$

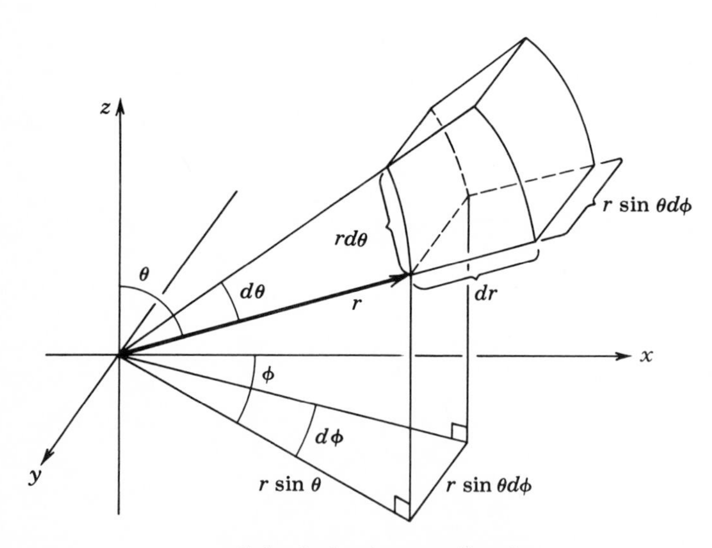

Spherical polar coordinates
$$d\tau = \text{volume element} = (r \sin \theta d\phi)\,(dr)\,(rd\theta) = r^2 \sin \theta d\theta d\phi\, dr$$

Fig. II-15 Volume elements.

$r = 3.01a_0$, etc., or, in general, $r = ua_0$, where u is the number of units of a_0. If this is done, then the dependence of the 2s hydrogen orbital ($Z = 1$) on r is

$$\frac{\psi_{2s}}{A} = e^{-u/2}(2 - u)$$

For example,

$$\frac{\psi_{2s}}{A} = e^{-1.5/2}(2 - 1.5) \qquad \text{for } r = 1.5a_0 \tag{II-20}$$

The exponentials $e^{-1.5/2}$, etc., can be readily found.[1] The same principles may be applied to the evaluation of the "point probability"

$$\rho(r) = \psi_{2s}\psi_{2s} = A^2e^{-u}(2 - u)^2$$

where now

$$\frac{\rho(r)}{A^2} = e^{-u}(2 - u)^2 \tag{II-21}$$

may be plotted to illustrate the dependence of the "point probability" of the 2s orbital. The radial probability for 2s can be treated in the same way:

$$\rho_R(r) = 4\pi r^2\psi_{2s}^2 = 4\pi u^2a_0^2A^2e^{-u}(2 - u)^2$$

where now

$$\frac{\rho_R(r)}{4\pi A^2a_0^2} = u^2e^{-u}(2 - u)^2 \tag{II-22}$$

may be plotted to illustrate the radial probability of the 2s orbital.

(c) *Calculations*

In this project a table of the values of the orbital ψ itself, its "point probability" $\rho = \psi^2$, and its radial probability $\rho_R = 4\pi r^2\psi^2$ is provided for a number of r values. Each set of numbers is incomplete and the calculation of the missing values should be undertaken to gain familiarity with the evaluation of those quantities.

PROBLEM 5-1

Calculate the missing quantities in Table II-8 for the 2s orbital of hydrogen.

PROBLEM 5-2

Indicate the dependence of the function ψ_{2s} on r by plotting ψ_{2s}/A against u [Eq. (II-20) and the values from Table II-8]. On the same graph indicate the dependence

[1] See the "Handbook of Chemistry and Physics," Chemical Rubber Publishing Company.

Table II-8 The 2*s* orbital of the H atom

Distance, in units of a_0	*Orbital* ψ_{2s}/A	*Point probability* $\rho(r)/A^2$	r^2, *in units of* a_0^2	*Radial probability* $\rho_R(r)/4\pi A^2 a_0^2$
0.2	1.6287	2.6527	0.04	0.1061
0.5	☐	1.3647	0.25	0.3412
0.8	0.8044	0.6471	0.64	0.4141
1.2	0.4390	0.1927	1.44	0.2775
2.0	0.0	0.0000	4.00	0.0000
3.0	−0.2231	0.0498	9.00	0.4482
4.0	−0.2706	0.0732	16.00	1.1712
6.0	☐	0.0396	36.00	1.4256
8.0	−0.1099	0.0121	64.00	0.7744
9.0	−0.0778	0.0061	81.00	0.4941
10.0	−0.0539	0.0029	100.00	0.2900

of the "point probability" and the radial probability on r by using, respectively, Eqs. (II-21) and (II-22) and Table II-8.

PROBLEM 5-3

For ψ_{2s}, what is the value of r where the electron density is greatest per unit volume? What is the most probable distance of the electron from the nucleus? Give this value in units of centimeters and angstroms. Explain why the most probable distance of the electron from the nucleus is different from the value of r where the electron density is greatest per unit volume. [Refer to Sec. II-3(iii) (*a*) and distinguish between point and radial probabilities.]

PROBLEM 5-4

Calculate the missing quantities in Table II-9 for the 2*s* orbital of the He^{+1} ion. Repeat Probs. 5-2 and 5-3 for the 2*s* He^+ orbital. Compare the results for H and He^+.

Table II-9 The 2*s* orbital of the He^+ ion

Distance, in units of a_0	*Orbital* ψ_{2s}/A	*Point probability* $\rho(r)/A^2$	r^2, *in units of* a_0^2	*Radial probability* $\rho_R(r)/4\pi A^2 a_0^2$
0.2	3.7045	13.7233	0.04	0.5489
0.5	☐	2.9419	0.25	☐
0.8	0.5082	0.2582	0.64	0.1652
1.2	−0.3406	0.1160	1.44	0.1670
2.0	−0.7652	0.5855	4.00	2.3420
3.0	−0.5632	0.3172	9.00	☐
4.0	−0.3102	0.0962	16.00	1.5392
6.0	☐	☐	36.00	☐
8.0	−0.0133	0.0002	64.00	0.0128
9.0	−0.0056	—	81.00	—
10.0	−0.0013	—	100.00	—

(d) Orthonormality

Two functions ψ_1 and ψ_2 are said to be *orthogonal* if the integral $\int \psi_1{}^* \psi_2 \, d\tau$ is zero. Essentially this means that the two functions are linearly independent of one another—their "overlap" is zero.

PROBLEM 5-5

For functions depending on only r, the overlap integral is $4\pi \int_0 \; \psi_1(r)\psi_2(r)r^2 \, dr$. Using the data of the tables, the values of $\psi_{1s}\psi_{2s}/AA'$ as a function of r (in units of a_0) for hydrogen can be found by forming the product of column 2 in Table II-8 and Table II-10. The integrand formed by multiplying r^2 (in units of a_0) times this function can then be plotted against r (in units of a_0). Comment on the sign of the integrand for various values of r. Make a rough estimate of the area with the positive sign and the area with the negative sign. Comment on the value of the overlap.

PROBLEM 5-6

The previous problem indicated graphically that, indeed, the 1s and 2s functions for hydrogen are orthogonal. By carrying out the integration mathematically show that the integral $\int$ 1s2s $d\tau$ is zero. Explicitly this integral is

$$\frac{1}{\sqrt{\pi}}\left(\frac{1}{a_0}\right)^{\frac{3}{2}} \frac{1}{4\sqrt{2\pi}}\left(\frac{1}{a_0}\right)^{\frac{3}{2}} \int_0^\infty e^{-r/a_0}e^{-r/2a_0}\left(2 - \frac{r}{a_0}\right) r^2 \, dr \int_0^\pi \sin\theta \, d\theta \int_0^{2\pi} d\phi$$

PROBLEM 5-7

Show that the 1s function is normalized, that is,

$$\int \psi_{1s}\psi_{1s} \, d\tau = \int_0^\infty \left(\frac{Z}{a_0}\right)^3 \frac{1}{\pi} e^{-2rZ/a_0} r^2 \, dr \int_0^\pi \sin\theta \, d\theta \int_0^{2\pi} d\phi = 1$$

Since ψ_{1s} and ψ_{2s} are *ortho*gonal and are *normal*ized, they are said to be *orthonormal.*

PROBLEM 5-8

By a graphical argument (i.e., looking at the magnitude and sign of the areas as in Prob. 5-5) show that ψ_{2p_x} and ψ_{1s} are orthogonal. [*Note:* the analytical form of ψ_{2p_x} is given in Table II-7, and, since $r \sin\theta \cos\phi = x$, ψ_{2p_x} can be sketched readily as a function of x.] Similarly show that ψ_{2p_x} and ψ_{2p_y} are orthogonal.

(iv) Molecular orbitals

In describing electrons in molecules, one is concerned with a description of electrons in the presence of several nuclei. As such the electron may

Table II-10 The 1s orbital for H atom

Distance, in units of a_0	*Orbital ψ_{1s}/A'*	*Distance, in units of a_0*	*Orbital ψ_{1s}/A'*
0.2	0.8187	3.0	0.0498
0.5	0.6065	4.0	0.0183
0.8	0.4493	6.0	0.0025
1.2	0.3011	8.0	0.0003
2.0	0.1353	9.0	0.0001

not be localized in the region of one nucleus but may have a description that encompasses the region of two or more nuclei.

(a) *The one-electron molecule*

The simplest example[1] is the H_2^+ molecule-ion consisting of hydrogen nuclei labeled a and b and a single electron. A description of the electron in the presence of these two nuclei is required. It would seem reasonable to give this molecular description in terms of the constituent *parts* of the molecule, namely, an electron in the region of one nucleus and a bare nucleus. There are at least two possibilities: $H_a \cdots H_b^+$, where the electron is in the region of nucleus a, and $H_a^+ \cdots H_b$, where the electron is in the region of nucleus b. The description of $H_a \cdots H_b^+$ is approximately that of a hydrogen atom a (with a proton b some distance away). Thus electron 1 in $H_a \cdots H_b^+$ can be described approximately by $\phi_a(1)$, and, for the lowest energy, $\phi_a(1)$ would be a $1s_a(1)$ orbital of hydrogen. Similarly $H_a^+ \cdots H_b$ could be described by $1s_b(1)$. The molecule is neither of these extremes but more probably some combination in between. Consequently the description of the electron by the molecular orbital ψ_{MO} could be written as a linear combination of the two possibilities

$$\begin{aligned}\psi_{\mathrm{MO}}(1) &= c_1\phi_a(1) + c_2\phi_b(1) \\ &= c_1 1s_a(1) + c_2 1s_b(1)\end{aligned} \tag{II-23}$$

In Eq. (II-23) the parenthetical (1) indicates that this is a description of electron 1, whereas c_1 and c_2 are a mathematical way of saying that the molecular orbital has some of the character $1s_a(1)$ and some of the character $1s_b(1)$. The energy of this description of the electron could be given, following Eq. (I-15), by

$$E = \frac{\int \psi_{\mathrm{MO}} \mathrm{H} \psi_{\mathrm{MO}}\, d\tau}{\int \psi_{\mathrm{MO}}\psi_{\mathrm{MO}}\, d\tau} \qquad (\text{since } \psi_{\mathrm{MO}} \text{ is real, } \psi_{\mathrm{MO}}^* = \psi_{\mathrm{MO}})$$

[1] The H_2^+ molecule-ion can be solved exactly if the internuclear separation is *assumed* to be fixed.

Since ψ_{MO} depends on the coefficients c, the energy depends on the c's. Therefore, to obtain the lowest energy of the electron, one would have to carry out a "variational treatment," i.e., vary the c's until values are found that make the energy expression above take its minimum value. A general way to do this is outlined in Appendix IV. This involves taking the derivative with respect to c_1, that is, $\partial E/\partial c_1$, and the derivative with respect to c_2, that is, $\partial E/\partial c_2$, setting both derivatives equal to zero (the condition for a minimum), and solving for the c's. However, for highly symmetric molecules such as H_2^+, the following simple argument for finding the c's suffices.

Because the nuclei in H_2^+ are the same, the interactions of the electron with both nuclei are identical, so that one would expect the lowest energy to be given by an electron distribution that was the same about both nuclei. Hence the coefficients of $\phi_a(1)\phi_a(1)$ and $\phi_b(1)\phi_b(1)$ in the distribution function from the MO would be equal, i.e., in

$$\rho = \psi_{MO}^2(1) = (c_1\phi_a + c_2\phi_b)^2 = c_1^2\phi_a(1)\phi_a(1) + 2c_1c_2\phi_a(1)\phi_b(1) + c_2^2\phi_b(1)\phi_b(1)$$

one would expect $c_1^2\phi_a(1)\phi_a(1) \equiv c_2^2\phi_b(1)\phi_b(1)$. But since $\phi_a(1)\phi_a(1)$ and $\phi_b(1)\phi_b(1)$ are identical, except for the center to which they refer, one has $c_1^2 = c_2^2$, giving $c_1 = c_2$ or $c_1 = -c_2$. The molecular orbitals are thus

$$\psi_1(1) = c_1[\phi_a(1) + \phi_b(1)] \qquad \text{for } c_1 = c_2$$

and

$$\psi_2(1) = c_1[\phi_a(1) - \phi_b(1)] \qquad \text{for } c_1 = -c_2$$

On normalizing [since the electron must be found somewhere, $\int\psi_{MO}(1)\psi_{MO}(1)\,d\tau = 1$] the value of c_1 is found as $c_1 = 1/\sqrt{2(1+S)}$ for ψ_1 or $c_1 = 1/\sqrt{2(1-S)}$ for ψ_2, and so the MO's are:

$$\psi_1 = \frac{1}{\sqrt{2(1+S)}}(\phi_a + \phi_b) \qquad \text{or} \qquad \psi_1 = \frac{1}{\sqrt{2(1+S)}}(1s_a + 1s_b)$$

where $S = \int\phi_a\phi_b\,d\tau$

and

$$\psi_2 = \frac{1}{\sqrt{2(1-S)}}(\phi_a - \phi_b) \qquad \text{or} \qquad \psi_2 = \frac{1}{\sqrt{2(1-S)}}(1s_a - 1s_b)$$

The probability functions for ψ_1 and ψ_2 are then

$$\rho_1 = \psi_1^2 = \frac{1}{2(1+S)}[\phi_a^2(1) + 2\phi_a(1)\phi_b(1) + \phi_b^2(1)] \tag{II-24a}$$

and

$$\rho_2 = \psi_2^2 = \frac{1}{2(1-S)}[\phi_a^2(1) - 2\phi_a(1)\phi_b(1) + \phi_b^2(1)] \tag{II-24b}$$

The term $\phi_a(1)\phi_b(1)$ in Eqs. (II-24) is the "overlap" and will be large only in the region where ϕ_a and ϕ_b are *both* large, namely, between the nuclei. The first orbital gives a term $+2\phi_a(1)\phi_b(1)$ in ρ_1, tending to increase electron density between the nuclei—thus ψ_1 is the bonding orbital ψ_B. The second orbital produces a term $-2\phi_a(1)\phi_b(1)$ in ρ_2, tending to decrease the electron density between the nuclei—thus ψ_2 is the antibonding orbital ψ_A. The procedure is summarized by Fig. II-16, where the solid lines refer to the orbitals. The dashed lines connect the molecular orbital with its parent atomic orbitals, and the lower energy of the bonding orbital is indicated by placing the line representing ψ_B below the level of the parent atomic orbitals $1s_a$ and $1s_b$. Similarly the line representing ψ_A is raised above the energy of the atomic orbitals.

PROBLEM II-10

The argument of the preceding section and the sketch of Fig. II-16 would suggest that the molecular orbital ψ_B has as much bonding character, i.e., lowering of the energy, as the orbital ψ_A has antibonding character. Show that this is true only if the overlap S is small. [*Hint*: Refer to the treatment of Appendix IV, particularly Eqs. (AIV-9) and (AIV-10).]

For fixed values of c_1 and c_2, the energy of the molecule will depend on the separation of the nuclei in the molecule. Thus in Eqs. (II-24) the attraction of the electron density represented by $\phi_a^2(1)$ to the nucleus b will certainly depend on *how close* the distribution $\phi_a^2(1)$ on nucleus a is to nucleus b. In other words the interaction energy will depend on the separation R of the nuclei. Indeed, the dependence of the energy of the molecule on R for the two MO's can be represented as in Fig. II-17 (see Appendix IV for a detailed discussion).

These molecular orbitals, made up of $1s$ orbitals, have spherical symmetry if one looks *along* the internuclear axis (i.e., they have cylin-

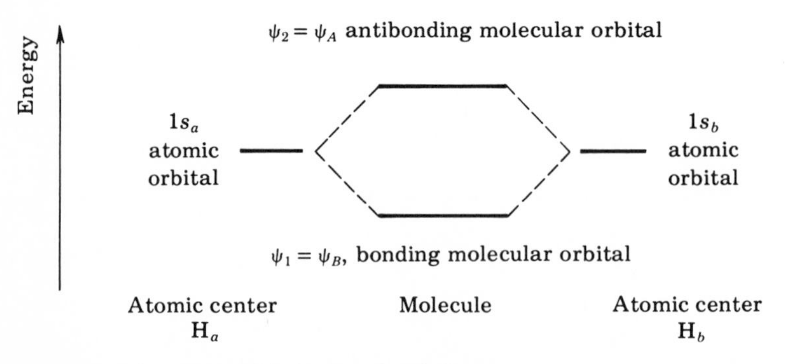

Fig. II-16 Molecular orbital energy level diagram.

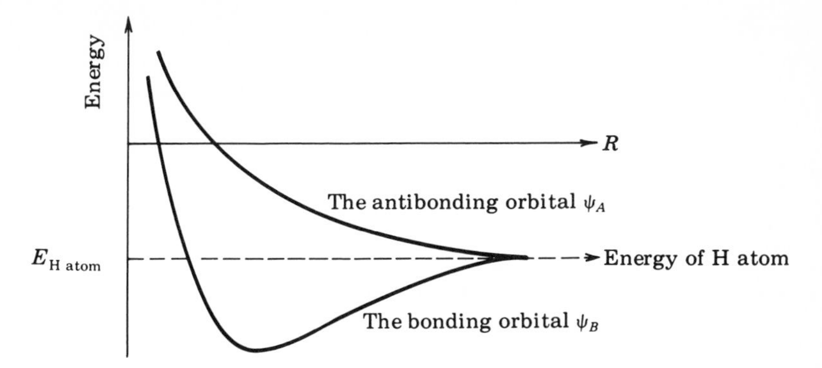

Fig. II-17 Dependence of the energy of the molecular orbitals on the internuclear separation R.

drical symmetry). They are designated $\sigma 1s$ for the bonding and σ^*1s for the antibonding. If the molecular orbitals had been generated from a linear combination of the $2s$ orbitals, the resulting molecular orbital would have the same symmetry, and the designation would be $\sigma 2s$ for the bonding and σ^*2s for the antibonding.

When the $2p$ orbitals are used to form the molecular orbitals, there are two possibilities. The end-on overlap of, say, the $2p_{za}$ and $2p_{zb}$ again results in an axially symmetric electron distribution with the designation $\sigma 2p$ and σ^*2p for the two MO's. Explicitly the MO's are

$$\sigma 2p = c(2p_{za} - 2p_{zb})$$

and $\sigma^*2p = c'(2p_{za} + 2p_{zb})$, where the minus sign is now required in the *bonding* orbital to generate positive overlap, that is,

$$\underset{2p_{za}}{\ominus\ \oplus} - \underset{2p_{zb}}{\ominus\ \oplus} = \underset{2p_{za}}{\ominus\ \oplus} + \underset{2p_{zb}}{\oplus\ \ominus} = \underset{\sigma 2_p}{\ominus\ \oplus\!\oplus\ \ominus}$$

Side-by-side combination of the $2p_{xa}$ and $2p_{xb}$ *may* allow a lesser degree of overlap above and below the internuclear axis, and the molecular orbitals so generated are designated $\pi 2p_x$, π^*2p_x, $\pi 2p_y$, π^*2p_y, where

$$\pi 2p_x = c(2p_{xa} + 2p_{xb}) \qquad \pi^*2p_x = c'(2p_{xa} - 2p_{xb})$$
$$\pi 2p_y = c(2p_{ya} + 2p_{yb}) \qquad \pi^*2p_y = c'(2p_{ya} - 2p_{yb})$$

The molecular orbitals are sketched in Fig. II-18.

Given that a bonding orbital has a lower energy than an antibonding orbital, the energy of a molecular orbital depends on the energy of the

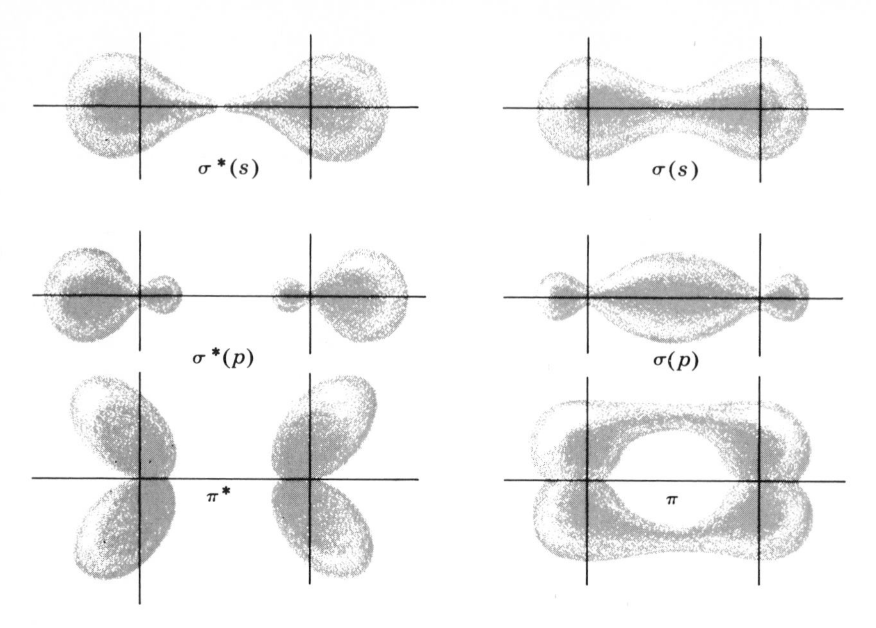

Fig. II-18 Representation of the molecular orbitals.

atomic orbitals of which it is composed. On this basis a relative ordering of the molecular orbitals can be suggested as either

$$A\colon \sigma 1s < \sigma^* 1s < \sigma 2s < \sigma^* 2s < \underbrace{\sigma 2p < \pi 2p_x, \pi 2p_y} < \pi^* 2p_x, \pi^* 2p_y < \sigma^* 2p$$

or

$$B\colon \sigma 1s < \sigma^* 1s < \sigma 2s < \sigma^* 2s < \overbrace{\pi 2p_x, \pi 2p_y < \sigma 2p} < \pi^* 2p_x, \pi^* 2p_y < \sigma^* 2p$$

The choice of A or B may vary from system to system, depending on whether the $\sigma 2_p$ or $\pi 2_p$ is the more bonding, i.e., has the greater degree of overlap (see Project 6). Figure II-19 illustrates the energy level diagram for the two possibilities.

(b) *Homonuclear diatomics*

The discussion of the molecular problem of one electron in the presence of several nuclei has introduced the concept of molecular orbitals. This method will now be applied to the description of a molecule with several electrons. In going to this more complex system, we are faced with the same situation as in going from the one-electron atom to the many-electron atom—there are the electron-repulsion terms to be considered. The solution is the same—either drop them or find their average value.

Thus for H_2 the complete electronic hamiltonian

$$H = [\mathrm{KE}(1) + V_{1a}(1) + V_{1b}(1)] + [\mathrm{KE}(2) + V_{1a}(2) + V_{1b}(2)] + V(1,2)$$

can be approximated by dropping $V(1,2)$ to give

$$H \simeq [\mathrm{KE}(1) + V_{1a}(1) + V_{1b}(1)] + [\mathrm{KE}(2) + V_{1a}(2) + V_{1b}(2)]$$

which is clearly separated into two parts, each describing only one electron and each being the same as for the H_2^+ problem. Thus $\Psi(1,2)$ for H_2 is approximated by $\Psi_{H_2}(1,2) = \psi(1)\psi(2)$, where, for the lowest state, $\psi(1) = \sigma 1s$, giving $\Psi_{H_2}(1,2) = \sigma 1s(1)\sigma 1s(2) = (\sigma 1s)^2$. For molecules with more electrons the same principles apply; for example, the molecular orbital configuration of O_2 is

$$\begin{aligned}\Psi_{O_2}(1,2,3, \ldots ,16) &= \psi(1)\psi(2)\psi(3) \cdots \\ &= (\sigma 1s)^2(\sigma^*1s)^2(\sigma 2s)^2(\sigma^*2s)^2(\sigma 2p)^2(\pi 2p_x)^2(\pi 2p_y)^2(\pi^*2p_x)^1(\pi^*2p_y)\end{aligned}$$

(The superscript indicates the number of electrons in the orbital.) The only difference is that the atomic orbitals used in the molecular orbitals are appropriate to the nuclei involved. Thus the $\sigma 1s$ molecular orbital for oxygen is made up of oxygen atomic orbitals $\sigma 1s_{O_2} = 1s_a + 1s_b$,

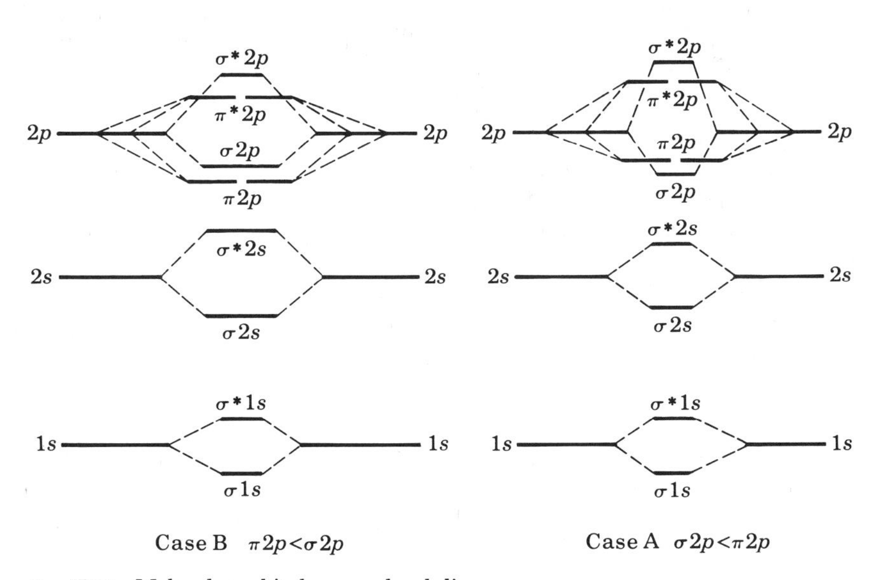

Fig. II-19 Molecular orbital energy level diagram.

where, for example, $1s_a = (1/\sqrt{\pi})(Z_{\text{eff}}/a_0)^{\frac{3}{2}}e^{-Z_{\text{eff}}r/a_0}$, and $Z_{\text{eff}}e$ is the effective nuclear charge for oxygen. Similarly the $\sigma 2s$, $\sigma 2p$, etc., will be generated from atomic orbitals of oxygen.

PROBLEM II-11

Give the molecular orbital configuration of the N_2 molecule.

PROBLEM II-12

On the basis of the bonding and antibonding character of the occupied molecular orbitals, compare the bond strengths of O_2 and N_2.

(c) *Heteronuclear diatomics*

When the nuclei of the molecule are different, e.g., as in CO or HF, the molecular orbitals might still be written as $\psi = c_1\phi_a + c_2\phi_b$, where ϕ_a and ϕ_b are atomic orbitals centered, respectively, on carbon and oxygen in the case of CO, or on hydrogen and fluorine in HF. However, the argument of the previous sections, that $c_1^2 = c_2^2$, will no longer apply. Indeed, one would expect that the molecular orbital would contain *unequal* contributions since the ability of the two nuclei to attract negative charge is different. Hence c_1 will not equal c_2. One must resort to the variational treatment of Appendix IV to find the values of c_1 and c_2 that make the energy a minimum. The result of such a treatment is that c_1 and c_2 may be quite different; in fact, the more unlike are the energies of the atomic orbitals involved, the more unlike are c_1 and c_2. For example, in HF one might attempt to generate a molecular orbital from $1s$ orbitals on hydrogen and fluorine as $\sigma 1s = c_1 1s_{\text{H}} + c_2 1s_{\text{F}}$. The result is a value of c_2 so much greater than c_1 that the "molecular orbital" is essentially a $1s$ fluorine *atomic orbital*—no bond is formed. Indeed, it can be shown[1] that, unless the energies of the atomic orbitals are fairly close to one another, no true molecular orbital forms; rather, the electrons remain essentially in their own atomic orbitals. Thus in HF, if a molecular orbital is to form, one of the fluorine atomic orbitals of approximately the same energy as that of the $1s_{\text{H}}$ must be used. The $2p_{\text{F}}$ orbital of fluorine has an appropriate energy, and the result is a molecular orbital

$$\psi_{\text{MO}}{}^{\sigma} = c_1 1s_{\text{H}} + c_2 2p_{\text{F}}$$

The magnitudes of c_1 and c_2, although different, are still close enough that there is a build-up of electron density between the nuclei [i.e., in $(\psi_{\text{MO}}{}^{\sigma})^2 = c_1^2 1s_{\text{H}}^2 + 2c_1c_2 1s_{\text{H}} 2p_{\text{F}} + c_2^2 2p_{\text{F}}^2$] and consequent bond formation.

[1] See C. A. Coulson, "Valence," p. 76, Oxford University Press, 1961.

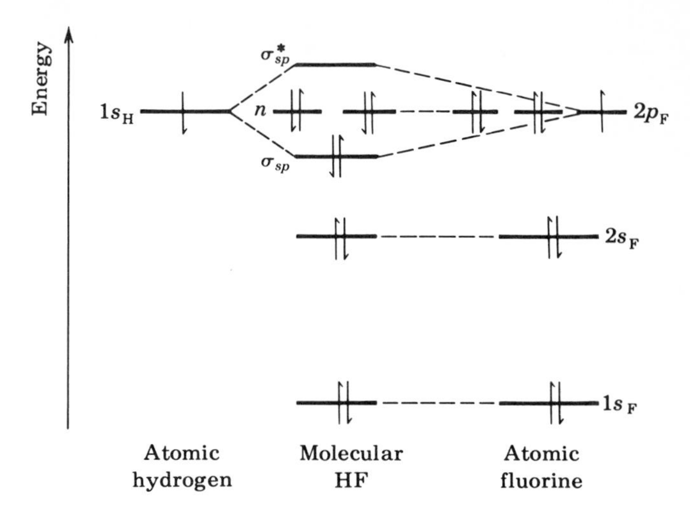

Fig. II-20 Molecular orbitals in HF.

The HF situation is illustrated in Fig. II-20, where arrows indicate the occupancy of the molecular orbitals in the molecule as well as the original occupancy of the orbitals in the parent atoms. Furthermore, the dashed lines connecting the atomic and molecular situations indicate not only the atomic orbitals of which a molecular orbital is composed but also the "fate," as the molecule forms, of the orbitals of the atoms. For example, the two molecular orbitals designated by n are, according to the dashed line, composed solely of $2p$ orbitals on the fluorine, so the two electrons originally in each of these atomic orbitals are essentially unchanged in the molecule. They are called *nonbonding electrons,* and the essentially $2p$ atomic orbital is designated by n, a nonbonding molecular orbital.

In CO the situation is similar but rather more complicated. The $1s$ orbitals on carbon and oxygen will be sufficiently different in energy that they need not be considered as forming molecular orbitals. [Even if the $1s$ orbitals in oxygen and carbon had very similar energies, they are so tightly bound that there is little $1s_O 1s_C$ overlap, and, consequently, the σ^*1s is only slightly antibonding and the $\sigma 1s$ only slightly bonding (see Project 6, Table II-11). In any case, since both $\sigma 1s$ and σ^*1s would be occupied, whatever bonding or antibonding tendency there was would cancel to give no net bond.] The energy of the $2s$ atomic orbital of oxygen is sufficiently different from the energy of any of the carbon atomic orbitals that it cannot enter into a true molecular orbital—these electrons remain essentially as a lone pair on the oxygen. However, the energy of the $2p_O$ oxygen orbitals is approximately that of both the $2s_C$ and $2p_C$

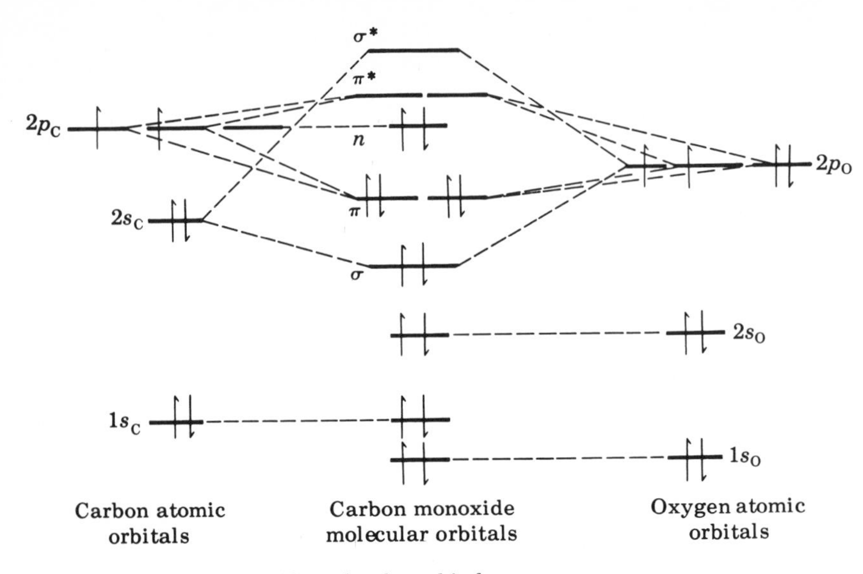

Fig. II-21 Carbon monoxide molecular orbitals.

carbon atomic orbitals. The result is that a σ-type molecular orbital may form from the $2s_C$ and $2p_{z,O}$ atomic orbitals, and two π-type molecular orbitals may form from the carbon and oxygen $2p$ atomic orbitals. Each of these last two molecular orbitals involves a $2p_C$ atomic orbital of carbon, leaving one $2p_C$ orbital not involved in bonding and its electrons essentially as "nonbonding (n) on the carbon." This situation is illustrated in Fig. II-21. In analyzing Fig. II-21, it should be remembered that it is not always possible to follow the electrons step by step from their atomic configuration to their molecular situation. For example, the two nonbonding electrons in the molecular orbital (n) certainly cannot be traced to a pair of electrons in any single atomic orbital. One might think of the atomic orbitals as spacial descriptions that can combine to give molecular orbitals. The resulting molecular orbitals are then filled up by the electrons of the constituent atoms.

(*d*) *Hybridization*

From the discussion of the one-electron molecule given earlier in this section, it was evident that bond formation was a result of the overlap electron density and that, the greater the overlap, the lower the energy of the bond. Consider a molecule such as methane CH_4, where as indicated in Fig. II-22 the four CH bonds are directed to the corners of a cube, and the four bonds are all equivalent. Since the four carbon-hydrogen bonds are known from experiment to be of identical energy, the overlap leading

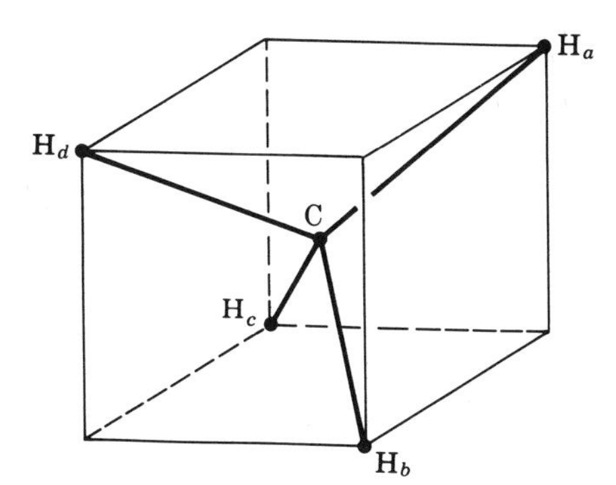

Fig. II-22 Tetrahedral structure of methane.

to bond formation must be identical for each bond. The atomic orbitals available for bond formation (i.e., those that have approximately the same energy as the atomic 1*s* orbital on hydrogen) are the three carbon 2*p* atomic orbitals and the one carbon 2*s* atomic orbital. The carbon 2*p* atomic orbital is certainly rather different in its spacial description from that of the carbon 2*s* orbital; hence, one would not expect the 2*p* and 2*s* to "overlap" to the same degree with a hydrogen 1*s* orbital. The only possible way out of this dilemma is that the atomic orbitals from the carbon must somehow be "combining" to give four "atomic" orbitals. For this molecular situation these orbitals must be *identical* as far as the hydrogens are concerned—they must give the *same* overlap and the same bond with the 1*s* orbitals on the four hydrogens. The "combined atomic orbitals" are referred to as *hybridized atomic orbitals t*, and the phenomena is called *hybridization*. Since they are a combination of one "*s*" orbital and three "*p*" orbitals, they are sp^3 hybrids. Further, since the *p* atomic orbitals have directional character, the hybrids will have directional character. The correct combination of *s* and *p* and the method of their determination is given in detail in Appendix V. With the formation of the appropriate hybrids, the molecular orbitals are

$$\sigma_{CH_a} = c_1 t_1 + c_2 1s_{H_a} \qquad \sigma_{CH_b} = c_1 t_2 + c_2 1s_{H_b}, \text{ etc.} \qquad \text{for } \sigma_{CH_c} \text{ and } \sigma_{CH_d}$$

The procedure is illustrated in Fig. II-23, where the first two columns serve to indicate the combination of several *orbitals on one atom* to give hybridized atomic orbitals. The third column then indicates the combination of a hybridized orbital on *one atom* with an orbital on *a different atom*, which results in the formation of molecular orbitals.

Similarly for other molecules, the atomic orbitals form hybrids that have the appropriate directional character and energy. Thus in ethylene, the 2*s* and two of the 2*p* atomic orbitals on carbon form sp^2 hybrids. The result is the formation of three σ molecular orbitals (that is, σ_{CC}, σ_{CH_a}, and

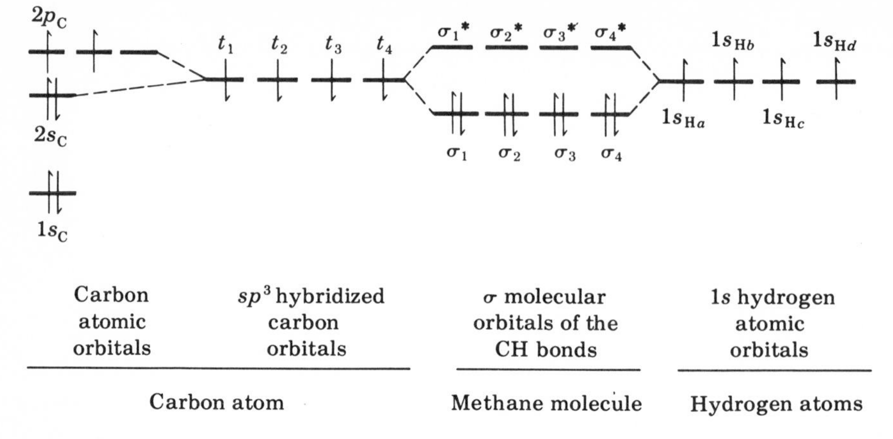

Fig. II-23 CH molecular orbitals of methane.

σ_{CH_b} bonds), whereas the remaining p orbitals on the carbons form a π bond. It should be emphasized that, for some cases, the hybridized set of orbitals will not all have identical energy or directional character, as was the situation in the sp^3 case. (See, for example, the hybridization discussed in Project 6 and the orbitals illustrated in Fig. II-24.)

(*e*) *Delocalized bonds*

The descriptions discussed thus far in this section have been concerned with molecular orbitals that encompassed the region of only two nuclei. In an earlier section (Chap. I, Project 2) a situation was described in which a given electron could be found anywhere in a region that encompassed *several* nuclei. It was clear from the simple particle-in-a-box model with the energy levels given as $E_n = (h^2/8mL^2)n^2$ that the larger L, the lower the energy—or in other words the more "delocalized" the electron, the lower the energy (other factors, e.g., potential energy, being equal). Thus in a molecule such as benzene [benzene ring structure], where the potential energy is the same from carbon to carbon, one would *expect* that the π electrons would have a lower energy if they were spread out over several carbons rather than confined to the region between the two nuclei, as the double bonds would indicate. Consequently a more appropriate designation would be [hexagon with dotted inner circle], where the dotted line indicates that any one of the six π electrons is delocalized over the entire ring. If this were to be so, the molecular orbital description of one of the electrons would not need to be given by atomic orbitals $2p_z$ from just *two centers*. Instead they could be given in terms of a contribution from each center as

$$\psi_{MO}^{\pi} = c_1 2p_{z1} + c_2 2p_{z2} + c_3 2p_{z3} + c_4 2p_{z4} + c_5 2p_{z5} + c_6 2p_{z6}$$

The coefficients c_1 through c_6 would then be determined as in Appendix IV so as to give the lowest energy. The three lowest orbitals, doubly occupied, would give the description of the six "π electrons" of benzene. The same procedure can be extended to other conjugated molecules.

(v) Project 6. Molecular orbitals and electronic transitions

In this Project some of the concepts just introduced will be modified and refined for particular molecular systems. The results will then be applied to the molecular orbital description and the spectroscopy of the molecules.

(*a*) *Homonuclear diatomics*

As indicated in the previous sections, atomic orbitals may, in some cases, form hybrids that, in turn, combine with other atomic orbitals to form molecular orbitals. Further, it has been pointed out that for significant "combination" of two orbitals to take place, the two orbitals must have approximately the same energy; i.e., two atomic orbitals on the *same atom* may combine to form hybrids if they have approximately the same energy. If a $2s$ atomic orbital on a nitrogen atom were to be combined with a small amount of the $2p_z$ atomic orbital of the *same* atom, the resulting hybrid[1] orbital, with some directional character along the internuclear axis, could well have a greatly increased overlap with the orbital from another nitrogen, resulting in a more bonding molecular orbital. Consequently the $\sigma 2s$ molecular orbital, previously considered as made up of only $2s$ atomic orbitals, may well have some $2p$ character. The insertion of this $2p$ character into the $\sigma 2s$ means that the previously designated $\sigma 2p$ will have some $2s$ character, less overlap, and hence less bonding—for a higher $\sigma 2p$ molecular orbital energy. Thus, as indicated in Fig. II-19(*b*), when *the $2p$ and $2s$ atomic orbitals are close together, the $\sigma 2p$ molecular orbital could have a higher energy than $\pi 2p$.* That the $\sigma 2p$ is indeed usually higher in energy than the $\pi 2p$ is indicated by the molecular orbital energies of Table II-11. The hybridization scheme and the resulting molecular orbitals are illustrated in Fig. II-24.

[1] Although the more familiar "*sp* hybrids" of carbon are usually taken as being a pair of equivalent orbitals (just as the sp^3 hybrids are taken as four equivalent orbitals), there is no necessity for this; the two hybrids of the pair may be quite different in both energy and in directional properties.

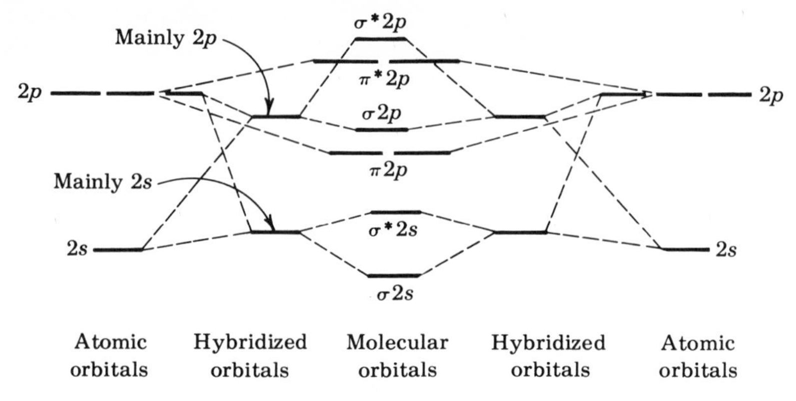

Fig. II-24 Hybridization and molecular orbital energies.

PROBLEM 6-1

Draw a molecular orbital energy level diagram, including hybridization, for N_2.

PROBLEM 6-2

Using the calculated molecular orbital energies shown in Table II-11 for N_2, give the ionization energy when an electron is ionized from the highest-occupied orbital and when it is ionized from the second-highest-occupied orbital. The experimental results are 0.574 au and 0.624 au, respectively.

PROBLEM 6-3

Would the lowest-energy transition of N_2 be a $\sigma \rightarrow \pi^*$ or a $\pi \rightarrow \pi^*$ type of transition?

(b) *Heteronuclear diatomics*

The argument presented above on hybridization in homonuclear diatomics can also be applied to the CO molecular orbitals, and recent calcula-

Table II-11 Molecular orbital energies‡ in diatomics

Molecule	$\sigma 1s$	$\sigma^* 1s$	$\sigma 2s$	$\sigma^* 2s$	$\pi 2p$	$\sigma 2p$	$\pi^* 2p$	Ref.
Li_2	−2.4267	−2.4265	−0.1789					1
Be_2	−4.7052	−4.7053	−0.4269	−0.2193				1
B_2	−7.677	−7.676	−0.673	−0.350	−0.3412	0.0086		2
C_2	−11.366	−11.364	−1.0334	−0.4898	−0.4358	−0.0498		1
N_2	−15.722	−15.720	−1.452	−0.7396	−0.5795	−0.5445		1
O_2	−20.595	−20.593	−1.522	−0.9782	−0.5499	−0.5564	−0.3944	3
F_2	−26.218	−26.217	−1.5841	−1.3173	−0.5645	−0.5037	−0.4318	1

‡ Energies are in atomic units (1 au = 4.36×10^{-11} erg).

1. B. J. Ransil, *Rev. Mod. Phys.*, **32**:239, 245 (1960).
2. A. A. Padgett and V. Griffing, *J. Chem. Phys.*, **30**:1286 (1959).
3. M. Kotani, Y. Mizuno, K. Kayama, and E. Ishiguro, *J. Phys. Soc. Japan*, **12**:707 (1957).

tions[1] indicate that the nonbonding orbital "n" in Fig. II-21 is not a pure $2p$ orbital but also includes some $2s$ character.

PROBLEM 6-4

Redo the energy level diagram for CO in Fig. II-21, taking into account the "sp" hybridization of the atomic orbitals. [The hybridized nonbonding orbital (the lone pair) will be slightly lower in energy than the atomic $2p$ but higher than the π molecular orbital.]

PROBLEM 6-5

On the energy level diagram for CO obtained in Prob. 6-4, indicate the transitions $n \longrightarrow \pi^*$, $\pi \longrightarrow \sigma^*$, $\pi \longrightarrow \pi^*$.

PROBLEM 6-6

Arrange the transitions of Prob. 6-5 in order of the energy change involved; which transitions are indicated by a λ_{max} of shorter wavelength, which by an intermediate λ_{max}, and which by a λ_{max} of longer wavelength?

PROBLEM 6-7

Draw a contour (i.e., the *outline* of the "charge-cloud representation" in Fig. II-18 is a contour diagram) of the highest nonbonding (n) orbital in Fig. II-21 and the same orbital as hybridized for Prob. 6-4. Comment on its directional character.

PROBLEM 6-8

Explain the origin of the Lewis-base character of CO.

PROBLEM 6-9

If CO were to lose its highest-energy electron (i.e., ionize), on which "end" of CO would most of the residual positive charge be found?

As indicated in Sec. II-3(iv), the molecular orbitals of CO will have unequal contributions from the contributing atomic orbitals of carbon and oxygen. Thus in the molecular orbital $\psi_{MO^\pi} = c_1 2p_C + c_2 2p_O$, c_2 is found to be somewhat greater than c_1; hence, the electron-density expression

$$\rho = (\psi_{MO^\pi})^2 = c_1^2(2p_C)^2 + 2c_1c_2(2p_O)(2p_C) + c_2^2(2p_O)^2$$

will certainly have the last term $c_2^2(2p_O)^2$ appreciably greater than the first term $c_1^2(2p_C)^2$. The antibonding molecular orbital is

$$\psi_{MO^{\pi*}} = c_1' 2p_C + c_2' 2p_O$$

[1] H. H. Jaffe and M. Orchin, *Tetrahedron*, **10**:212 (1960).

If $\psi_{MO}{}^{\pi*}$ and $\psi_{MO}{}^{\pi}$ are to be orthogonal, and if the overlap of the atomic orbitals $2p_C$ and $2p_O$ is not too large, then $c_1/c_2 \simeq -c_2'/c_1'$. Hence if $c_1{}^2 > c_2{}^2$, then $(c_2')^2 > (c_1')^2$.

PROBLEM 6-10

Predict the "end" of the CO molecule that will be most positive in the ground state. Would the dipole of the excited state (after $\pi \rightarrow \pi^*$) be the same as in the ground state?

PROBLEM 6-11

Explain the formation of nickel-carbon monoxide complexes. (*Hint:* consider the bonding properties of both the lone pair and the availability of the $\psi_{MO}{}^{\pi*}$ as a site for the d electrons of the nickel atom.)

(c) *Polyatomic molecules*

The carbonyl group $>C=O$ appears in many organic species, e.g., formaldehyde $H_2C=O$ (H and H bonded to C) and acetone $(CH_3)_2C=O$ (CH₃ and CH₃ bonded to C). Since the bond angles are taken to be 120°, the atomic orbitals of carbon are involved in sp^2 hybridization [following the discussion of Sec. II-3(iv) (d)]. Thus two of the $2p$ and the $2s$ atomic orbitals of the carbons form hybrids, leaving one $2p$ orbital untouched so far (see Fig. II-25 where the three hybrids are considered equivalent, although it is essential that only two of them be equivalent). In formaldehyde, H_2CO, one of the hybrids, g_3, is available for formation of a molecular orbital involving a $2p_O$ orbital from the oxygen, whereas the remaining two hybrids each form a σ bond with a hydrogen. The remaining $2p_C$ carbon atomic orbital is available to form the π bond with a $2p_O$ orbital from oxygen. The situation is illustrated in Fig. II-26 and the result is a σ and a π bond between the carbon and oxygen leaving two lone pairs on the oxygen, a low-lying $2s$ lone pair and a higher $2p$-type lone pair n.

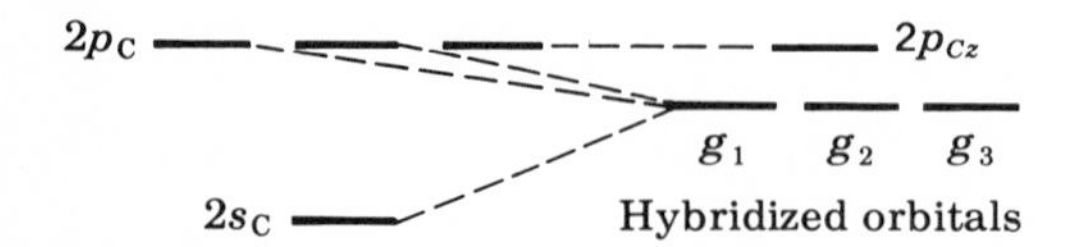

Fig. II-25 Carbon sp^2 hybridization.

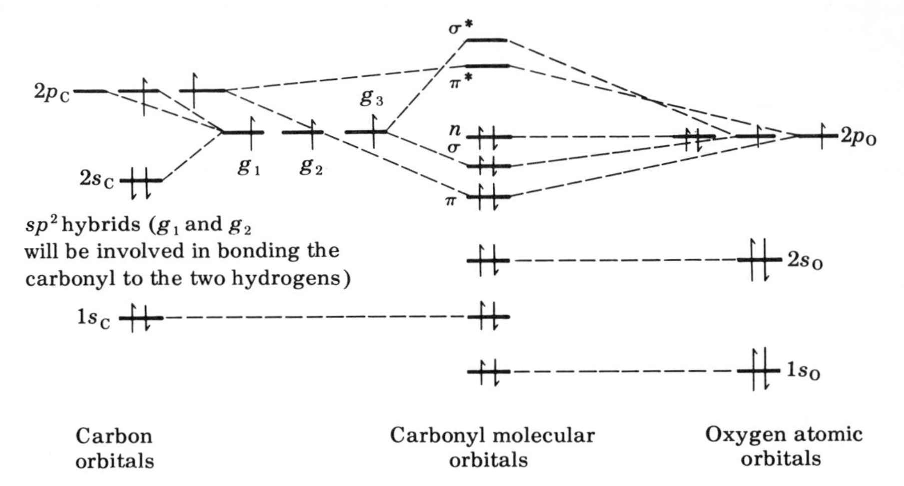

Fig. II-26 Molecular orbitals of carbonyl.

PROBLEM 6-12

Indicate the $n \longrightarrow \pi^*$, $\pi \longrightarrow \pi^*$, and $\pi \longrightarrow \sigma^*$ transitions in Fig. II-26. Arrange them in order of increasing λ_{max}.

The λ_{max} for the more probable transitions (the $n \longrightarrow \pi^*$ and $\pi \longrightarrow \pi^*$) of the carbonyl in acetone are indicated in the spectrum in Fig. II-27.

PROBLEM 6-13

Which λ_{max} in Fig. II-27 corresponds to the $n \longrightarrow \pi^*$ transition and which to the $\pi \longrightarrow \pi^*$ transition?

The $n \longrightarrow \pi^*$ absorption corresponding to 2790 Å in acetone is shifted to 2930 Å in acetaldehyde and to 2350 Å in acetylchloride.

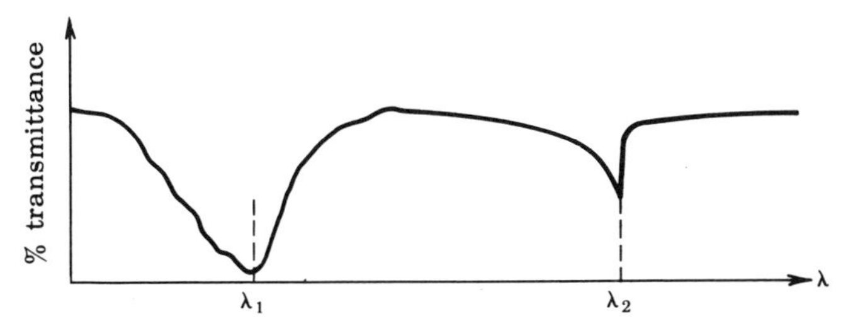

Fig. II-27 Spectrum of acetone.

PROBLEM 6-14

Compare the energy of the π^* molecular orbitals in the three compounds acetone, acetaldehyde, and acetylchloride. (*Hint:* Remember that the $n \to \pi^*$ transition involves the energy difference between the n and π^* molecular orbitals. The π^* level involves the carbon center at which the substitutions in acetone were made, that is, H for CH_3 to give acetaldehyde and Cl for CH_3 to give acetylchloride. The nonbonding level does not involve this center and should be affected much less by the substitution.)

II-4 SPIN AND SYMMETRY

(i) Spin

Within the orbital approximation (as developed in the previous sections), it would be possible to account for the many electrons in an atom or molecule by having each electron described by an orbital. Such a method would give the space description, i.e., the position relative to the center of mass, for each of the electrons in the system. It has been found, however, that a description of an electron in terms of just space coordinates does not adequately explain the behavior of the electrons in a magnetic field. Rather, in addition to the energy due to the usual kinetic and electrostatic contributions, the electron appears to contribute a small amount of energy in a way that would indicate an *intrinsic magnetic dipole;* i.e., it behaves as a small magnet. Since a circulating electric charge is known to produce a magnetic dipole, the term *spin of the electron* has come into use for the intrinsic magnetic property of the electron. Whether or not the electron spins, i.e., *is* a spinning charge, is not the point; it is just convenient to treat it that way. (It is to be emphasized that this is an intrinsic magnetic property of the electron, not a magnetic property due to "circulation" about the nucleus.) There appear to be two possible descriptions of electron spin states α and β that correspond to small, equal, and opposite magnetic dipoles.

The same situation applies to nuclei, where the intrinsic magnetic character of the nucleus is given the name "nuclear spin." For a hydrogen nucleus there are two possible descriptions, again called α and β, but with magnetic properties of different magnitude from those of α and β for the electron. For other nuclei there may be more than two possible descriptions; for example, there are three possible descriptions for the spin states of a deuteron.

(ii) Description of indistinguishable particles

With spin in mind the electronic description of the ground state of helium might be written

$$\Psi(1,2) = \psi(\text{space part})\psi(\text{spin part}) = [1s(1)1s(2)][\alpha(1)\beta(2)] \quad \text{(II-25}a\text{)}$$

where the electrons share the *same* space part but have opposite spins. This, of course, is the Pauli principle, which requires that no two electrons may have the same values of the four quantum numbers n, l, m, and m_s (here m_s is a spin quantum number $+\frac{1}{2}$ for α and $-\frac{1}{2}$ for β). The description of the helium atom given by Eq. (II-25*a*) implies that electron 1 has spin α and electron 2 has spin β. It could equally well be that electron 1 has spin β and electron 2 spin α, that is,

$$\Psi(1,2) = [1s(1)1s(2)][\beta(1)\alpha(2)] \qquad \text{(II-25}b\text{)}$$

is also a possible description of the system. To be realistic, one must recognize this and write the description as a combination of the two possibilities:

$$\Psi(1,2) = c_1[1s(1)1s(2)\alpha(1)\beta(2)] + c_2[1s(1)1s(2)\beta(1)\alpha(2)]$$

Since each of the descriptions [Eqs. (II-25*a*) and (II-25*b*)] is equally possible, then, in the probability description,

$$\rho = \Psi^2(1,2) = c_1^2[1s(1)1s(2)\alpha(1)\beta(2)]^2 + c_2^2[1s(1)1s(2)\beta(1)\alpha(2)]^2 + \text{cross terms}$$

there must be an equal "probability" of each of these descriptions. Hence c_1^2 must equal c_2^2, giving $c_1 = \pm c_2$, and a possible description is either

$$\Psi_1(1,2) = c_1[1s(1)1s(2)\alpha(1)\beta(2) - 1s(1)1s(2)\beta(1)\alpha(2)] \qquad \text{for } c_1 = -c_2 \qquad \text{(II-26)}$$

or

$$\Psi_2(1,2) = c_1[1s(1)1s(2)\alpha(1)\beta(2) + 1s(1)1s(2)\beta(1)\alpha(2)] \qquad \text{for } c_1 = c_2 \qquad \text{(II-27)}$$

For the configuration $1s2s$ of helium, where one electron has been excited to a $2s$ orbital, the description would be $\Psi(1,2) = \psi(\text{space part})\,\psi(\text{spin part})$. The space part could be thought of as simply $1s(1)2s(2)$; but again, this is saying more than one should, for the electrons are indistinguishable and electron 1 could be in the $2s$ orbital and electron 2 in the $1s$ orbital. The space part must be written as $[c_1 1s(1)2s(2) + c_2 2s(1)1s(2)]$ and since each description is equally possible, one finds $c_1 = \pm c_2$ and the two possible space descriptions

$$\psi_{\text{space}} = c_1[1s(1)2s(2) - 2s(1)1s(2)] \qquad \text{(II-28)}$$

$$\psi_{\text{space}} = c_1[1s(1)2s(2) + 2s(1)1s(2)] \qquad \text{(II-29)}$$

One of the spin descriptions for this configuration could be $\alpha(1)\alpha(2)$, where now, since the space parts of the two electrons are different, it is possible to have the same spin description for each electron. Similarly $\beta(1)\beta(2)$ is a possible spin description. The spin description $\alpha(1)\beta(2)$ must be combined as before with $\beta(1)\alpha(2)$ for the two further spin descriptions $\alpha(1)\beta(2) \pm \beta(1)\alpha(2)$. The four possible spin descriptions are then

$$\alpha(1)\alpha(2), \qquad \beta(1)\beta(2), \qquad [\alpha(1)\beta(2) + \beta(1)\alpha(2)] \tag{II-30}$$
$$[\alpha(1)\beta(2) - \beta(1)\alpha(2)] \tag{II-31}$$

Since there are two possible space descriptions [Eqs. (II-28) and (II-29)], each of which might be combined with the four spin descriptions [Eqs. (II-30) and (II-31)], it would appear that there would be *eight* possible descriptions of this excited configuration of helium. However, as we will show, the results of spectroscopic measurements indicate that the excited state of helium does not exist in all eight descriptions but only in descriptions of a certain "symmetry"!

(iii) Symmetry

Symmetry is familiar in the sense that a function $y = x^2$ is symmetrical (has the same sign) if x is replaced by $-x$, or that the function $y = 1/x$ is antisymmetrical (changes sign) if x is replaced by $-x$. In addition to the symmetry of changing $x \rightarrow -x$, there is the symmetry of interchanging variables; for example, the function $z = x + y$ is symmetrical, denoted by s, or unchanged on interchanging x and y, whereas the function $z = x - y$ changes to $-z$ or is antisymmetrical, denoted by a, when x and y are interchanged:

$$z = x - y \quad \underset{\substack{\text{Interchange} \\ x \text{ and } y}}{\longrightarrow} \quad y - x = -(x - y) = -z$$

Within the definition of the preceding discussion, we can see that the function given by Eq. (II-26) is antisymmetric to the interchange of the electrons, that is,

$$\begin{aligned} \Psi_1(1,2) &= c_1 1s(1)1s(2)[\alpha(1)\beta(2) \\ &\quad - \beta(1)\alpha(2)] \underset{\substack{\text{Interchange} \\ \text{electrons} \\ 1 \text{ and } 2}}{\longrightarrow} c_1 1s(2)1s(1)[\alpha(2)\beta(1) - \beta(2)\alpha(1)] \\ &= c_1 1s(1)1s(2)[-\alpha(1)\beta(2) + \beta(1)\alpha(2)] \\ &= -c_1 1s(1)1s(2)[\alpha(1)\beta(2) - \beta(1)\alpha(2)] \\ &= -\Psi_1(1,2) \end{aligned}$$

However, the description provided by Eq. (II-27) is symmetric. In the excited state $1s2s$ there are eight possible combinations of space and spin parts that can again be classified as symmetric or antisymmetric. For example, the antisymmetric space part in Eq. (II-28) may be combined with the antisymmetric spin part in Eq. (II-31) to give

$$\Psi_3 = [1s(1)2s(2) - 2s(1)1s(2)][\alpha(1)\beta(2) - \beta(1)\alpha(2)]$$

Table II-12 The space-spin descriptions of the helium atom

Ψ_n	*Space function*	*Space-function symmetry*	*Spin function*	*Spin-function symmetry*	*Total symmetry of space-spin function*
1	$1s(1)1s(2)$	s	$\alpha(1)\beta(2) - \beta(1)\alpha(2)$	a	$sa = a$
2	$1s(1)1s(2)$	s	$\alpha(1)\beta(2) + \beta(1)\alpha(2)$	s	$ss = s$
3	$1s(1)2s(2) - 2s(1)1s(2)$	a	$\alpha(1)\beta(2) - \beta(1)\alpha(2)$	a	$aa = s$
4	$1s(1)2s(2) - 2s(1)1s(2)$	a	$\alpha(1)\beta(2) + \beta(1)\alpha(2)$	s	$as = a$
5	$1s(1)2s(2) - 2s(1)1s(2)$	a	$\alpha(1)\alpha(2)$	s	$as = a$
6	$1s(1)2s(2) - 2s(1)1s(2)$	a	$\beta(1)\beta(2)$	s	$as = a$
7	$1s(1)2s(2) + 2s(1)1s(2)$	s	$\alpha(1)\beta(2) - \beta(1)\alpha(2)$	a	$sa = a$
8	$1s(1)2s(2) + 2s(1)1s(2)$	s	$\alpha(1)\beta(2) + \beta(1)\alpha(2)$	s	$ss = s$
9	$1s(1)2s(2) + 2s(1)1s(2)$	s	$\alpha(1)\alpha(2)$	s	$ss = s$
10	$1s(1)2s(2) + 2s(1)1s(2)$	s	$\beta(1)\beta(2)$	s	$ss = s$

This is a product of two antisymmetric functions and hence is symmetric. The eight possible descriptions obtained on combining the space parts in Eq. (II-28) or (II-29) with the spin parts from Eq. (II-30) or (II-31) are indicated in Table II-12.

In the absence of an external magnetic field, the energy can be taken as depending on only the space part. Thus states Ψ_1 and Ψ_2 with space part $1s(1)1s(2)$ will have the lowest energy. In the configuration $1s2s$ the spacial parts given by Eq. (II-28) or (II-29) have the same values for the kinetic energy and nuclear-attraction terms.

PROBLEM II-14

Show that the spacial parts given by Eqs. (II-28) and (II-29) yield the same energy for the approximate hamiltonian obtained on *omitting* the electron repulsion [see Sec. II-3(ii)(*a*)].

However, when the interelectron-repulsion term is considered the spacial descriptions provided by Eqs. (II-28) and (II-29) do have different energies. For the spacial part $[1s(1)2s(2) - 2s(1)1s(2)]$, the expectation value of the electronic repulsion e^2/r_{12} would be

$$E_{\text{repulsion}} = \int [1s(1)2s(2) - 2s(1)1s(2)] \frac{e^2}{r_{12}} [1s(1)2s(2) - 2s(1)1s(2)]\, d\tau$$

which, on multiplying out, gives

$$e^2 \left\{ \int \frac{1s^2(1)2s^2(2)}{r_{12}}\, d\tau + \int \frac{2s^2(1)1s^2(2)}{r_{12}}\, d\tau - 2 \int \frac{[1s(1)2s(1)][2s(2)1s(2)]}{r_{12}}\, d\tau \right\}$$

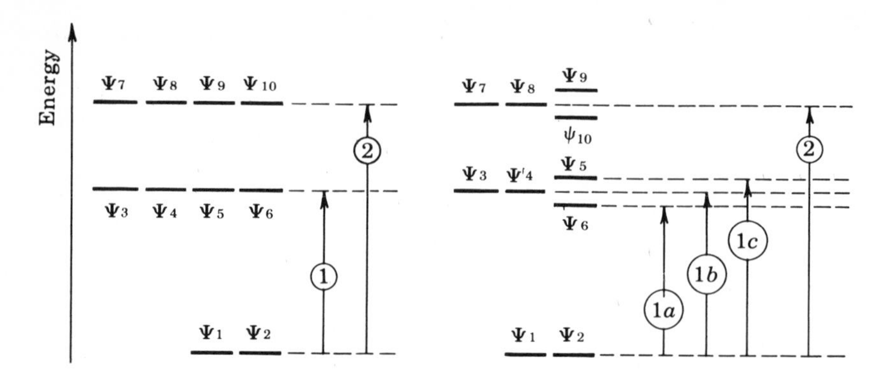

Energy with no magnetic field Energy with a magnetic field

Fig. II-28 Energies of the $1s^2$ and $1s2s$ helium configurations.

The first two terms are the coulombic terms—"coulombic" in the sense that an electron for which the probability description is $1s^2$ is experiencing *repulsion* due to another electron, whose probability description is given as $2s^2$. Repulsion is given a positive sign [attraction was negative—Sec. I-2(ii)], and so the repulsion *integrals* are positive. The last term is a so-called exchange term, where an electron, described by a product of two different orbitals as $1s2s$, is repelled by another electron, which is also "exchanged" between two orbitals. Since this last term enters with a negative sign, this "repulsion" really *lowers the energy for this antisymmetric space part.* However, for the *symmetric* space part $1s(1)2s(2) + 2s(1)1s(2)$, the exchange *raises* the energy.

The preceding discussion means that the functions Ψ_1 and Ψ_2 have the *lowest* energy. The functions Ψ_3, Ψ_4, Ψ_5, and Ψ_6 would all have the same *somewhat higher* energy, whereas Ψ_7, Ψ_8, Ψ_9, and Ψ_{10} would all have the same *even higher* energy. This situation is illustrated in the left-hand column of Fig. II-28. If the system is subjected to a magnetic field, the spin states $\alpha\alpha$ and $\beta\beta$ will have different energies from the spin states $\alpha\beta - \beta\alpha$ or $\alpha\beta + \beta\alpha$. This situation is illustrated in the right-hand column of Fig. II-28. When electronic transitions from the ground state are induced in the presence of the magnetic field, it is observed that the lower-energy transition ① of Fig. II-28 is split into a group of three closely spaced transitions (1a), (1b), and (1c). But the higher energy transition remains unchanged by the presence of the magnetic field. To give rise to the different energies of (1a), (1b), and (1c), it would appear that at least three different spin states must exist for the lower-energy excited state. Of these, two must be $\alpha\alpha$ and $\beta\beta$, giving, respectively, the slightly greater and slightly lower energies of the "triplet." Consequently the two *totally antisymmetric* descriptions

$$\Psi_5 = [1s(1)2s(2) - 2s(1)1s(2)]\alpha(1)\alpha(2)$$
$$\Psi_6 = [1s(1)2s(2) - 2s(1)1s(2)]\beta(1)\beta(2)$$

do exist. Since the energy of the transition to the higher excited state is not "split," we are led to the conclusion that the two totally *symmetric* states

$$\Psi_9 = [1s(1)2s(2) + 2s(1)1s(2)]\alpha(1)\alpha(2)$$
$$\Psi_{10} = [1s(1)2s(2) + 2s(1)1s(2)]\beta(1)\beta(2)$$

do not exist. This suggests that the electronic[1] descriptions must *always* be *totally antisymmetric.* Consequently the allowed descriptions of the helium atom are Ψ_1, Ψ_4, Ψ_5, Ψ_6, and Ψ_7!

In the absence of an external magnetic field, the three allowed descriptions of the lower-energy excited state, Ψ_4, Ψ_5, and Ψ_6, all have the same energy—i.e., are degenerate—and the state is said to be a *triplet.* However, there is only one possible totally antisymmetric description of the higher excited state, namely, Ψ_7, and this state is said to be a *singlet.* These results are summarized in Fig. II-29.

PROBLEM II-15

What spin functions are allowed for the inner pair of electrons ($1s^2$) in the $1s^22s$ configuration of Li? What spin functions are allowed for the outer electron ($2s$) in the same configuration?

PROBLEM II-16

Would the ground state of N_2 be a singlet, a doublet, or a triplet? Explain. [*Hints:* Find the lowest-energy space part first and see how this restricts the spin part. When

[1] It might be pointed out that whereas electrons or protons must always be described by an antisymmetric function, other particles, e.g., deuterons, must be described by a symmetric function.

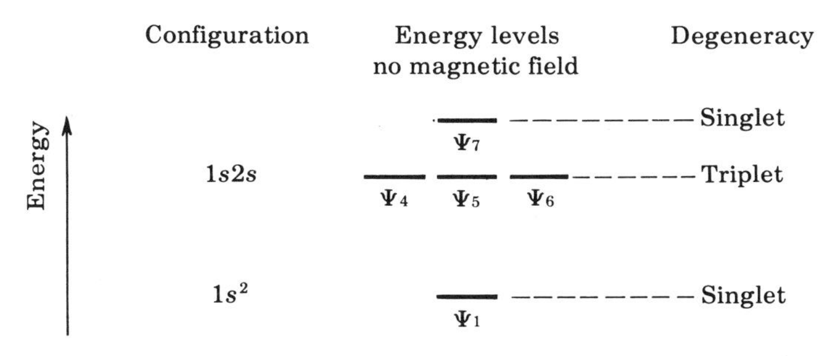

Fig. II-29 Singlets and triplets of helium.

naming the state as a singlet, a doublet, a triplet, etc., only the highest-energy electrons are of concern. Consequently, if the inner electrons are paired (requiring singlet spin functions), and, for example, the outer electron allows a doublet, then the state is called a *doublet*.]

PROBLEM II-17

Would the ground state of the lithium atom be a singlet, a doublet, or a triplet? Explain the answer.

PROBLEM II-18

Would the ground state of the oxygen molecule be a singlet, a doublet, or a triplet? Explain the answer.

III

The Complete Description and Energy of a Molecule

III-1 INTRODUCTION

In the previous chapter the basic method of "separation of variables" by which the quantum-mechanical description can be obtained has been outlined and applied to a number of systems, and a simple spectroscopic application of each solution has been included. Consequently the individual descriptions and their respective applications in spectroscopy should be familiar. However, this approach fails to do justice to the relation of one description or of one spectroscopy to another. For example, in H_2, if the electronic description is $\sigma 1s^2$, what is the vibrational description? What is the rotational description? If the descriptions are independent, what allows this independence? What approximations have been made? Or, from the spectroscopic point of view, in a transition from one state to another, which coordinates are changing and which are unchanged? For example, in a vibrational transition of HCl, what is happening to the electronic distribution? What about the rotational description?

These questions can be answered only if one has at hand the total energy in terms of the various motions, electronic, vibrational, etc., and the complete description of the molecule in terms of the various coordinates x_{el}, r_{vib}, etc. Clearly the solution of the complete Schroedinger equation must be investigated. An initial separation of the hamiltonian can be effected into the usual parts—the subsystems: center of mass, electronic, vibrational, rotational, and spin. Then the total description can be built up from the individual parts, and the relation of each of these to the whole can be emphasized. A clear overall description of the whole molecule can be maintained by quoting, where possible, the pertinent results obtained in the previous chapter. Finally, the coupling, or interaction, of one internal coordinate with another internal coordinate or with an external field can be examined.

III-2 COORDINATE SEPARABLE CONTRIBUTIONS

(i) The separation of variables

As an example, consider the molecule H_2. This is a four-particle system—two electrons and two nuclei, for a total of 12 coordinates in a space-fixed reference. It is advantageous to make an initial separation of these 12 coordinates into a center-of-mass set of three coordinates and an internal set of nine coordinates. Figure III-1 illustrates these coordinates.

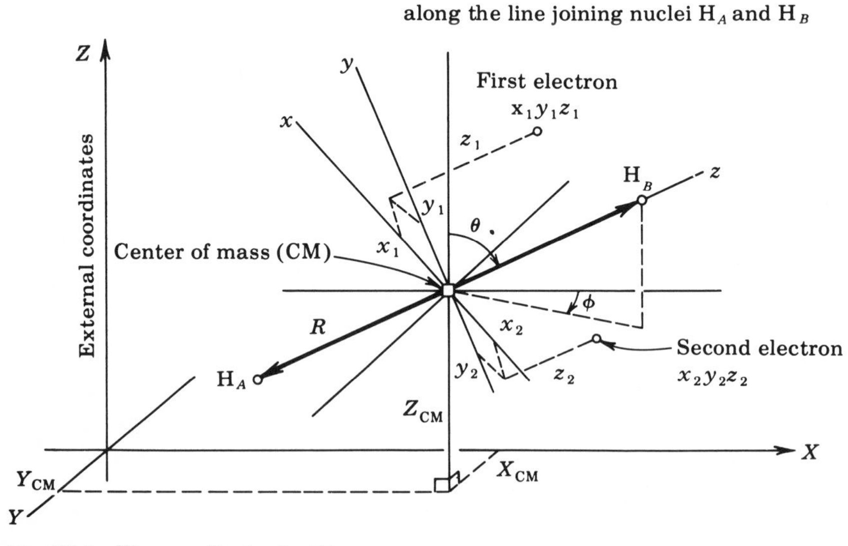

Fig. III-1 The coordinates for H_2.

The complete spacial description of the system is specified by coordinates of four different types:

1. Center-of-mass coordinates $X_{CM}Y_{CM}Z_{CM}$ that give the position of the system as a whole in an external reference system.
2. Electronic coordinates $x_1y_1z_1$ and $x_2y_2z_2$ that describe the electrons; these coordinates have the center of mass as their origin.
3. A linear coordinate R, or r, referring to the nuclei, but this time telling how far apart they are; as such, R speaks of a displacement of one nucleus relative to the other and is called a *vibrational coordinate.*
4. The angular coordinates θ, ϕ, which, although only partially describing the nuclei, at least describe the orientation of the line joining the nuclei; thus a change in θ, ϕ implies a rotation of this line.

In addition to these space coordinates, there are the spin coordinates of the electrons and nuclei, which will be given the general symbol σ_i.

The complete description of the system would be achieved by solving $H\Psi = E\Psi$. H contains the quantum-mechanical statement of the kinetic energy and interactions of the system, and, as such, is a function of the coordinates of the system $H = H(XYZx_1y_1z_1x_2y_2z_2R\theta\phi\sigma_1\sigma_2\sigma_A\sigma_B)$. Generally H is a complicated function of the coordinates—certainly too complex for present purposes. However, the analysis given above for the coordinates could suggest that the terms in H might be grouped according to the five types

$$H_{CM}(X,Y,Z) \qquad H_{el}(x_1y_1z_1x_2y_2z_2) \qquad H_{vib}(R)$$
$$H_{rot}(\theta,\phi) \qquad H_{spin}(\sigma_1\sigma_2\sigma_A\sigma_B)$$

Although such a grouping cannot be justified in its entirety, some rationalization can be given. The center-of-mass coordinates can be shown to be completely independent of all others [see Sec. II-2(i)]. Further, the nuclei are relatively massive compared to the electrons, so that their motions will be sluggish. They might be considered stationary when the electron motions are considered—such a justification is usually called the *Born-Oppenheimer approximation.* No ready justification for separating H_{rot} and H_{vib} can be given, and, indeed, their interdependence is considerable; in turn, the separation of H_{spin} cannot be justified, except, perhaps, on the grounds that its contribution is so small in itself that its effect on the other variables would be even smaller. The internal are not independent of each other. Therefore, one has only to consider that the description of changes in internuclear separation (vibration) will depend on the force constant (i.e., upon the bond defined by the electrons) or that the rotational description will depend on the moment of inertia and, thus, on R. Nevertheless, some such separation is essential to a meaningful analysis of the problem, and so the *hamiltonian is approximated by*

$$H \simeq H_{\text{CM}}(XYZ) + H_{\text{el}}(x_1y_1z_1,x_2y_2z_2) + H_{\text{vib}}(R) + H_{\text{rot}}(\theta,\phi) + H_{\text{spin}}(\sigma_1\sigma_2\sigma_A\sigma_B) \qquad \text{(III-1)}$$

Thus, as has been done before, the assumptions necessary to effect a *separation* will be made, the problem will be analyzed, and the results will be reassessed to see what effect the neglected interdependence could have. This is similar to dropping the interelectron repulsion in atoms to effect separation of the hamiltonian. This approximation was followed somewhat later by a reassessment that introduced screening to overcome the neglect of the repulsion in the original analysis [recall Sec. II-3(ii)].

As was shown in Sec. II-1, if the hamiltonian can be separated into parts, then the total energy can be written as a sum of parts, and the complete function can be written as a product of functions, each depending on only the coordinates of the separated part. Thus, the approximation implied by Eq. (III-1) allows one to have

$$E_{\text{total}} = E_{\text{CM}} + E_{\text{el}} + E_{\text{vib}} + E_{\text{rot}} + E_{\text{spin}} \qquad \text{(III-2)}$$

$$\Psi(XYZ,x_1y_1z_1x_2y_2z_2,R,\theta,\phi,\sigma_1\sigma_2\sigma_A\sigma_B) = \psi_{\text{CM}}(XYZ)\psi_{\text{elec space}}(x_1y_1z_1,x_2y_2z_2)\psi_{\text{vib}}(R)\psi_{\text{rot}}(\theta,\phi)\psi_{\text{spin}}(\sigma_1\sigma_2\sigma_A\sigma_B) \qquad \text{(III-3)}$$

The function ψ_{CM} describes the center of mass relative to a fixed frame, $\psi_{\text{elec space}}$ describes the electrons relative to an internal frame, ψ_{vib} describes the vibration of the nuclei, ψ_{rot} describes the rotation of the molecule, and ψ_{spin} describes the spin character of the electrons and nuclei. Then, having separated the hamiltonian as in Eq. (III-1) and having written the function as above, the complete SE breaks down into individual Schroedinger-type equations, each dealing with only one of the separated parts.

(ii) The separated systems

(a) The external, or center-of-mass, system

In this system X, Y, and Z, the center-of-mass coordinates, are independent of all others. The coordinate system is indicated in Fig. III-2. The separated "center-of-mass SE" is

$$H_{\text{CM}}\psi_{\text{CM}}(XYZ) = E_{\text{CM}}\psi_{\text{CM}}(XYZ)$$

where

$$H = \frac{-h^2}{8\pi^2 M}\left(\frac{\partial^2}{\partial X^2} + \frac{\partial^2}{\partial Y^2} + \frac{\partial^2}{\partial Z^2}\right) \qquad M = \text{total mass}$$

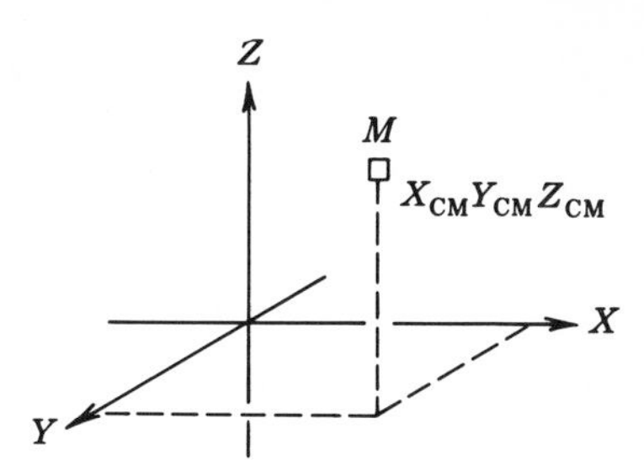

Fig. III-2 The center-of-mass coordinates.

This is the SE considered previously in the particle-in-a-box problem. The solutions to this equation are the familiar sine or cosine functions, and, because there are no boundary conditions, the energy is not quantized and can take any value, such as $E_{CM} = 0$, for convenience. ψ_{CM} describes only the center of mass relative to some external set of coordinates, e.g., those that indicate the position of the center of mass relative to the corner of a laboratory. Since only the internal features of the system are of interest, no further reference to ψ_{CM} need be made. However, this coordinate system will be used in a later section in the discussion of the imposition of external fields.

(b) The electronic system

For this system the description of the electrons in terms of $x_1y_1z_1x_2y_2z_2$ is considered independent of all the other coordinates, which are, for convenience, taken to be fixed. In particular the calculation is carried out for a fixed value of the internuclear separation R. The coordinate system is indicated in Fig. III-3. The Schroedinger equation for this system is then $H_{el}\psi_{\text{elec space}}(x_1y_1z_1,x_2y_2z_2) = E_{el}\psi_{\text{elec space}}(x_1y_1z_1,x_2y_2z_2)$, where

$$H_{el} = \text{KE}(1) + \text{KE}(2) + V_{1A}(1) + V_{1B}(1) + V_{1A}(2) + V_{1B}(2) + V_1(1,2)$$

Here KE(1) and KE(2) are the kinetic energies of electrons 1 and 2, respectively; $V_{1A}(1)$ is the attraction of electron 1 to nucleus A, $V(1,2)$ the repulsion between electrons 1 and 2, etc., for the other terms. As was pointed out in the previous chapter, it is necessary to make the further approximation of either neglecting $V(1,2)$ or finding its average value, so that the electronic hamiltonian may be separated into parts that involve only one electron. By such a procedure the *orbital* descriptions of the electrons can be obtained. Thus $\psi_{\text{elec space}} = \psi_{\text{elec space}}(1)\psi_{\text{elec space}}(2)$, where $\psi_{\text{elec space}}(1)$ might equal $[1/\sqrt{2(1+S)}][1s_A(1) + 1s_B(1)]$, and, for each $\psi_{\text{elec space}}$ an appropriate energy E_{el} can be given. In this way the different electronic descriptions and electronic energies can be obtained, all for "fixed" values of the other coordinates.

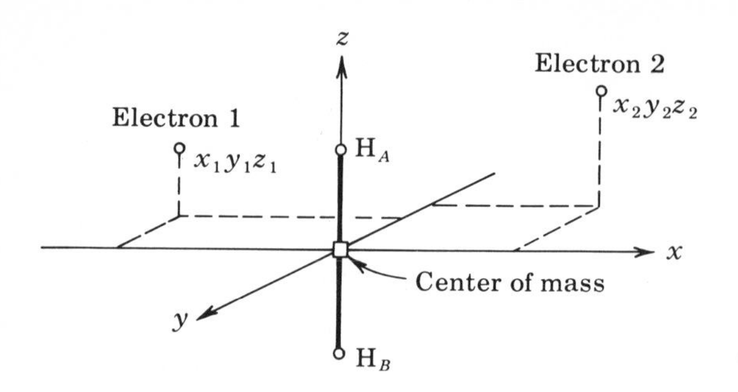

Fig. III-3 The electronic coordinate system.

It is to be emphasized that the H_{el} indicated above does not include a nuclear repulsion term e^2/R, so the energy obtained is purely an energy dependent on the motion and potential of the electrons. If the fixed value (R is fixed) for the repulsion energy of the nuclei is added, the so-called molecular energy E_M is obtained for the different $\psi_{\text{elec space}}$. The energy level diagram obtained depends, however, on the fixed value of R selected for the calculation. For example, when $R = R_e$ (the equilibrium distance for the ground state), the energy level diagram for the different states could be indicated as in Fig. III-4. Energies and descriptions for *different* values of the internuclear separation can be obtained, but *each* description is for a fixed value of R. Thus, from the electronic part, sketches of the molecular energy for various values of R can be obtained (see, for example, Appendix IV). Three such molecular energy vs. internuclear-separation curves are indicated in Fig. III-5.

(c) *The vibrational system*

Here only the description of the system in terms of the internuclear distance R is considered. It is "independent of the rest of the coordinates" of the system in that only the "average" description of the electrons need be considered in defining the bond holding the nuclei together. Effectively, then, all coordinates, save R, may be ignored. The vibrational motion of nuclei has already been treated as the analog of harmonic

Energy $E_M(R = R_e)$ Electronic description

———————— $\sigma 1s\sigma 2s$

———————— $(\sigma^* 1s)^2$

———————— $(\sigma 1s)^2$

Fig. III-4 The energy levels for a fixed internuclear separation.

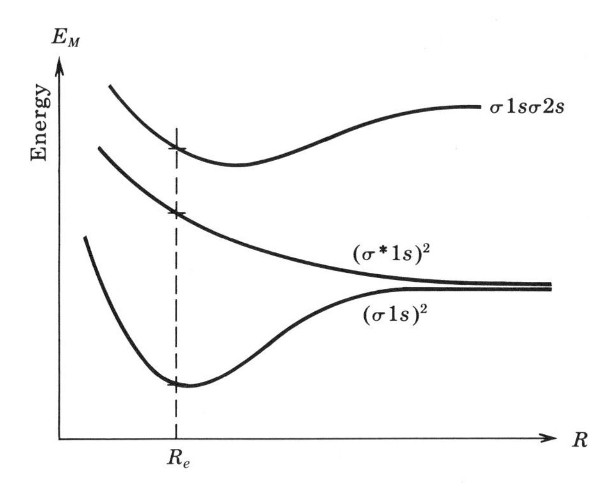

Fig. III-5 The energy E_M of electronic states of H_2 for various values of the internuclear distance R.

motion [see Sec. II-2(i)], although no justification was given. A justification can now be provided. It is evident from Fig. III-5 that, for a given electronic configuration, there is a most favorable internuclear separation and that any stretching or displacement from this position increases the energy. Since a system tends to the lowest possible energy, it should be clear that there would be a force tending to restore the internuclear separation to its optimum value. This restoring force is dependent, of course, on the molecular energy or the bond energy for the system, and it would be possible to indicate, by some function, the way this energy and the associated restoring force depended upon the internuclear separation R. It would, however, be a complicated function and, generally, only an *approximate but simple* statement for the restoring force is attempted.

The shape of the molecular energy curve near the minimum in Fig. III-6*b* is evidently very similar to that of a parabola, that is,

$$V(x) = \frac{k}{2} x^2 \text{ or } V = \frac{k}{2} (R - R_e)^2 \tag{III-4}$$

Equation (III-4) is the potential energy of a Hooke's law force $F = -k(R - R_e)$ already studied as the harmonic oscillator in Sec. II-2(i). Thus, it is expedient to say that the restoring force in the molecule approximates a Hooke's law and to treat the vibration of the nuclei as a harmonic oscillator. The resulting quantum-mechanical descriptions, as discussed in detail in Sec. II-2(i), are found by solving the Schroedinger equation $H_{\text{vib}}\psi_{\text{vib}}(r) = E_{\text{vib}}\psi_{\text{vib}}(r)$, where, for convenience,

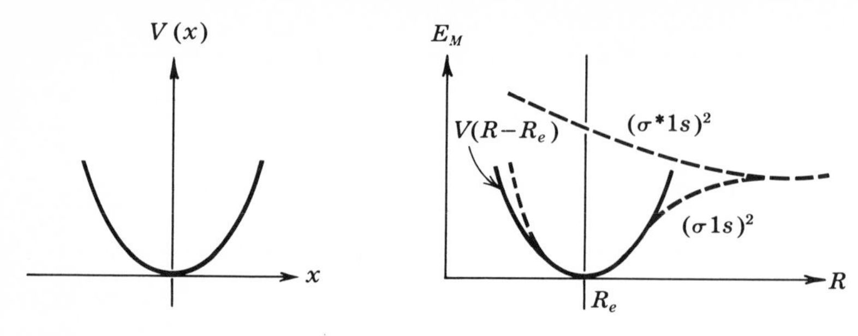

(*a*) Parabola of potential for a Hooke's Law Force

(*b*) Potential for the bond force

Fig. III-6 The harmonic potential in a diatomic molecule.

a displacement coordinate $r = R - R_e$ describes the internuclear separation. With the hamiltonian $H_{\text{vib}} = \text{KE} + (k/2)r^2$, the energy levels are found as $E_n = (n + \frac{1}{2})[(h/2\pi)\sqrt{k/\mu}]$, where k is the force constant and μ the reduced mass. The vibrational energy levels E_n for a given electron configuration, such as $(\sigma 1s)^2$, would look like Fig. III-7, where the vibrational energy of the molecule is added to the electronic energy of the system. The energy levels are given in terms of the "fundamental frequency" $\nu_0 = (1/2\pi)\sqrt{k/\mu}$.

The energy contained in a *classical* vibrational system is continually changing from potential to kinetic (i.e., it is all potential energy at maximum displacement $r = r_{\max}$ and all kinetic as the particle goes through zero displacement). In fact, if the vibrational energy is known, the maximum classical displacement $r_{\max}$ can be found by setting E_n = potential energy $= (k/2)r^2_{\max}$. Clearly the greater E_n, the greater $r_{\max}$. This relation might be represented pictorially as in Fig. III-8. A sketch of the potential energy of the system, i.e., of $V = (k/2)r^2$, may be drawn as in Fig. III-9*a*, where, if $r_{n,\max}$ is marked for a given value of energy E_n, say, $n = 3$, then the value of the ordinate is the value of the potential energy for $r_{\max}$. But this is also the vibrational energy. The dotted horizontal line therefore automatically represents the energy level,

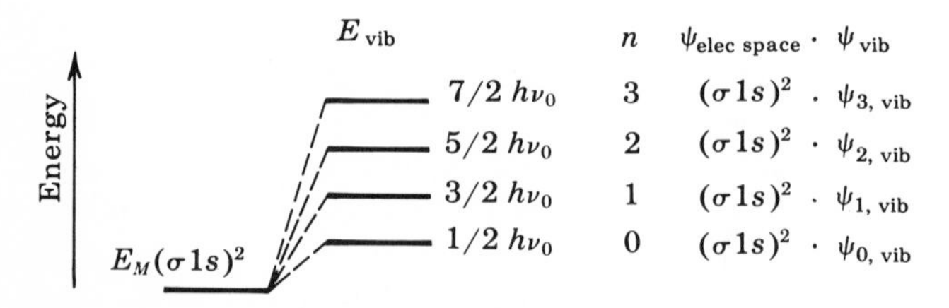

Fig. III-7 The electronic-vibration system.

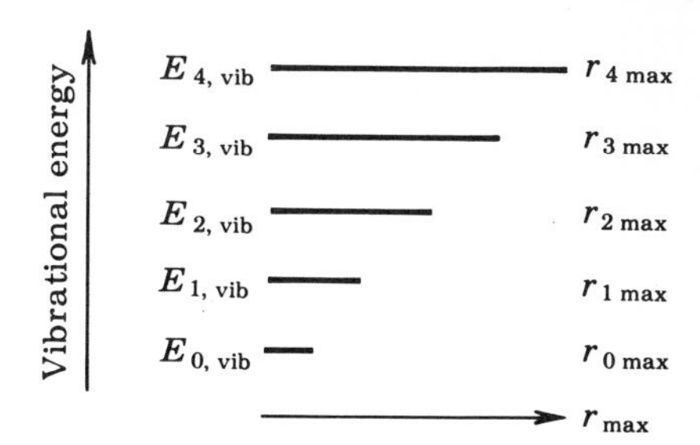

Fig. III-8 Classical energy vs. maximum displacement.

and its length automatically gives the classical value of r_{max} for that energy level. To talk in terms of the limit of displacement of the nuclei, the dotted line is extended to the other side, and a pictorial representation of the *energy level* combined with the classical value for the maximum *displacement* of the nuclei is generated as in Fig. III-9*b*. (It must be emphasized that this is a classical argument, and in the quantum mechanical description the limits on r are $\pm\infty$ for *all* energy states. However, the probability of the system having a value of r larger than the classical r_{max} is small.)

The potential energy term $(k/2)r^2$ in H_{vib} was simply an attempt to represent the potential of the restoring force due to the electronic bond of the molecule. It is a potential energy represented by the depression in the curve for the electronic energy as given in Fig. III-6*b*. Near the minimum it is very much like $(k/2)r^2$. Thus the classical "vibrational energy level-maximum displacement" representation of Fig. III-9*b* might be inserted into Fig. III-6*b*, as shown in Fig. III-10.

In all the diagrams for vibrational energy discussed so far, the energy levels have been given by $E_n = (n + \frac{1}{2})h\nu_0$, where $\nu_0 = (1/2\pi)\sqrt{k/\mu}$. Since k was taken as a constant for all levels,

$$\Delta E = (n + 1 + \tfrac{1}{2})h\nu_0 - (n + \tfrac{1}{2})h\nu_0 = h\nu_0$$

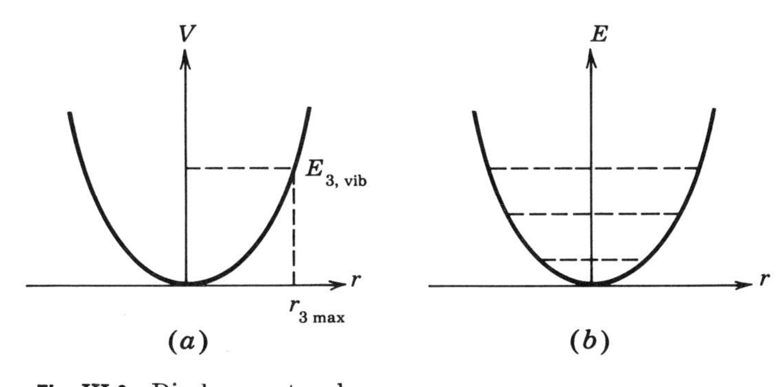

Fig. III-9 Displacement and energy.

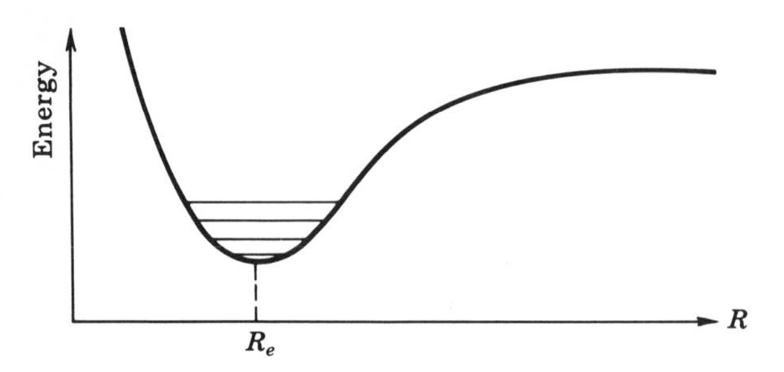

Fig. III-10 Lower-lying vibrational energy levels.

and all levels were evenly spaced. Obviously if k were a constant for all values of internuclear separation, then the potential energy curve of Fig. III-6*b* would be a parabola, as Fig. III-6*a*. But the potential certainly is not a parabola, although near the bottom it is rather a close approximation. We should now consider the implications of the parabolic approximation.

Even though the harmonic oscillator approximation is not really valid for higher vibrational energies, it would be possible to find functions as $V'(r) = (k'/2)r^2$ to describe the potential energy further up the scale. This is illustrated in Fig. III-11, where k' will be required to be smaller than k to give a good fit to the higher portion of the curve. The separation between energy levels is given by $\Delta E = h\nu_0 = h(1/2\pi)\sqrt{k/\mu}$, and, if k is *smaller*, then the separation between levels will be *smaller*. Consequently a more correct "vibrational energy level-maximum displacement" sketch would resemble that given in Fig. III-12, where the separation goes

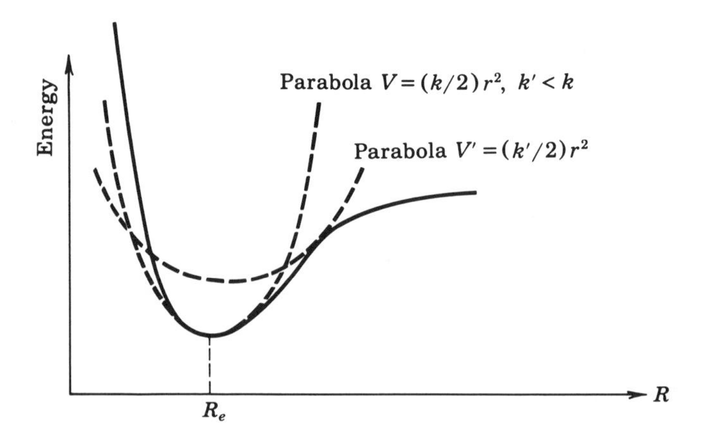

Fig. III-11 Parabolic potential-energy curve.

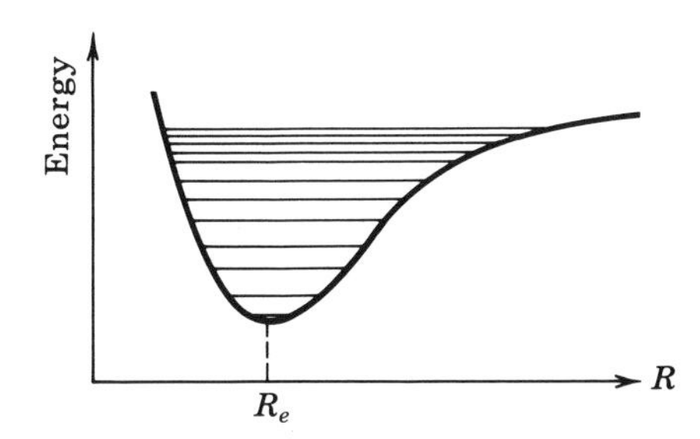

Fig. III-12 Vibrational energy level representation.

to zero when k' goes to zero (as the potential $V' = (k'/2)r^2$ attempts to fit an ever-widening curve at higher energies $k' \to 0$). Thus the "energy level-maximum displacement" representation of Fig. III-12 provides a pictorial representation of the way the vibrational states change with changing energy and helps, even if only indirectly, to give some feeling for what the different vibrational states are like. In a sense, it plays a role similar to that of the contour-diagram representations of electronic descriptions (see Fig. II-18).

(*d*) *The rotational system*

Here the description of the system in terms of the angles θ and ϕ is of interest, and only the average values of R and the electronic coordinates are considered. Consequently one is really discussing a system of two nuclei held rigidly at a "fixed" distance by the *bond* of the electronic distribution. Such a system is the rigid rotor discussed in Sec. II-2(iii).

The coordinates are indicated in Fig. III-13, and the energy levels were given in Sec. II-2(iii) as $E_{\text{rot}} = (h^2/8\pi^2 I)l(l+1)$, where I, the moment of inertia, is $I = [m_1 m_2 R^2/(m_1 + m_2)] = \mu R^2$, and $l = 0, 1, 2,$

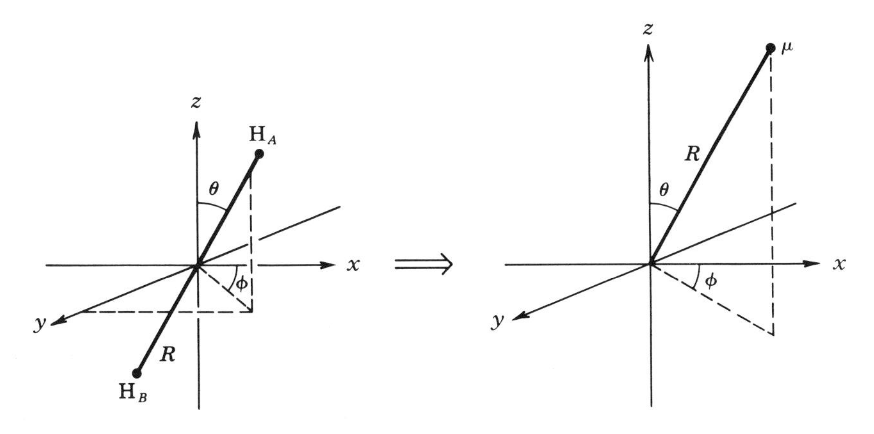

Fig. III-13 The rotational coordinates.

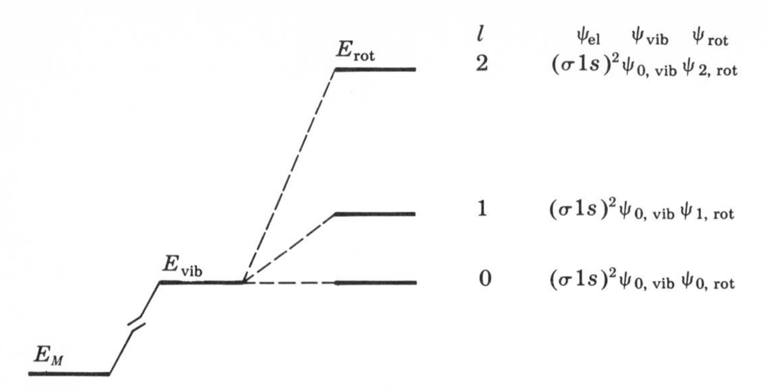

Fig. III-14 Electronic-vibrational-rotational system.

. . . . Since, for a given l, i.e., a given energy, there are $2l + 1$, $(-l, -l + 1, \ldots, -1, 0, 1, \ldots, l)$ values of m, the rotational energy level is $(2l + 1)$-fold degenerate.

For a given electronic description and a given vibrational description, the rotational energy level diagram could be depicted as in Fig. III-14. It must be emphasized that the broken line —⁄⁄— in Fig. III-14 is intended to indicate the *large* energy separation between the different *kinds* of energy levels. The separation between levels l and l' is given by

$$\Delta E_{rot} = E_{l',rot} - E_{l,rot} = \frac{h^2}{8\pi^2 I}[l'(l' + 1) - l(l + 1)]$$

For adjacent levels $l' = l + 1$ and

$$\Delta E = \frac{h^2}{8\pi^2 I}[(l + 1)(l + 2) - l(l + 1)]$$
$$= \frac{h^2}{8\pi^2 I} 2(l + 1)$$

It is worthwhile pointing out that the energy change given by this formula depends on the value of the moment of inertia I as well as on the quantum number l, but I, in turn, depends on the internuclear separation R. Clearly R may change for higher vibrational states, and so the spacing between energy levels will change.

(e) *The spin system*

Even though we may be able to separate the spin part of the hamiltonian from the rest, on the basis that its contribution to the total energy is so slight as to have really very little effect upon the other descriptions, this does not mean that the other coordinates do not affect spin. It was shown in Sec. II-4 that the complete function must be antisymmetric to the interchange of the coordinates of two electrons. From the discussion given in that section, it should be clear that there is a significant difference in energy between a symmetric and an antisymmetric electronic space description. Consequently if an antisymmetric electronic function is suggested by the overall energy requirements, then one *must* have a symmetric spin part. For example, the space part for the first excited state of H_2 is $\sigma 1s\sigma 2s = (1/\sqrt{2})[\sigma 1s(1)\sigma 2s(2) - \sigma 2s(1)\sigma 1s(2)]$, and the spin part would be one of $\alpha\alpha$, $\beta\beta$, $(1/\sqrt{2})(\alpha\beta + \beta\alpha)$ *not* $(1/\sqrt{2})(\alpha\beta - \beta\alpha)$, simply on the basis of symmetry considerations. Clearly even though the spin hamiltonian may be "separated" from the electronic part, the spin function is *not independent*. This interdependence is sometimes called a *manifestation of the Pauli force.*

Although the spin hamiltonian does not, by itself, dictate the spin functions, the expectation value of the spin hamiltonian for the various *allowed* functions can, nevertheless, be considered. Hence the electron spin energy will be given by the statement for the expectation value $E_{\text{elec spin}} = \int \psi_{\text{elec space}}\psi_{\text{elec spin}}[H_{\text{elec spin}}]\psi_{\text{elec space}}\psi_{\text{elec spin}}\, d\tau_{\text{el}}$ rather than by solving the SE $H_{\text{elec spin}}\psi_{\text{elec spin}} = E_{\text{elec spin-spin}}\psi_{\text{elec spin}}$.

An electron with spin α can be considered as having its magnetic vector (i.e., the vector from the south pole to the north pole) up and an electron with spin β as having its magnetic vector down. Two electrons could be represented as

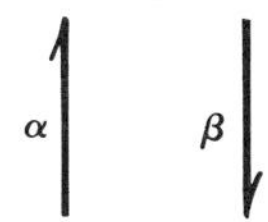

Case I

Another possibility would be both electrons with spin α:

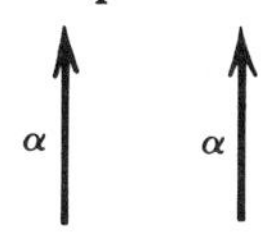

Case II

Certainly the interaction of the two "magnets" would be different in case I from that of case II. Therefore the first conclusion, a rather obvious one, would be that the spin interaction depends on the spin description. Nevertheless, one still does not know how *much* interaction there would be. From a classical point of view this would depend not only on the orientation of the "magnets" but also on *how close* they were to one another. In the quantum-mechanical description the spin is "tied" to the electron, i.e., the "position" of the electron spin is given by the position of the electron; consequently the proximity of the spin "magnets" is controlled by the space description $\psi_{\text{elec space}}$. Thus a statement of the spin-spin energy would contain a function $P = f(1,2)$ related to the *probability* of a given *separation* of spins and an operator $\hat{S}$ giving the value of the *interaction*[1] of the two "magnets" *at a given separation,* that is,

$$H_{\text{elec spin}} = P\hat{S}$$

The expectation value of the spin-spin energy for the two electrons would be

$$\begin{aligned} E_{\text{elec spin}} &= \int \psi_{\text{elec space}}\psi_{\text{elec spin}}[H_{\text{elec spin}}]\psi_{\text{elec space}}\psi_{\text{elec spin}}\, d\tau_{\text{space}}\, d\tau_{\text{spin}} \\ &= \int \psi_{\text{elec space}} P \psi_{\text{elec space}}\, d\tau_{\text{space}} \int \psi_{\text{elec spin}}\hat{S}\psi_{\text{elec spin}}\, d\tau_{\text{spin}} \end{aligned}$$

For $\psi_{\text{elec space}} = [\sigma 1s(1)\sigma 2s(2) - \sigma 2s(1)\sigma 1s(2)]$, an antisymmetric space part, there would be three possible spin functions, $\alpha\alpha$, $\beta\beta$, $(1/\sqrt{2})(\alpha\beta + \beta\alpha)$. Since all three cases have the same space part, the "spins" will have the same average separation. The difference in its energy will then depend only on the orientation, i.e., upon α or β in $\int \psi_{\text{elec spin}}\hat{S}\psi_{\text{elec spin}}\, d\tau_{\text{spin}}$. In the first case, for $\alpha\alpha$, the interaction of the magnets will be $\int \alpha\alpha\hat{S}\alpha\alpha\, d\tau_{\text{spin}}$ (interaction of parallel magnets $\uparrow\uparrow$) $= W$ units of energy; for $\beta\beta$ $\downarrow\downarrow$, the interaction not surprisingly gives W units, and it can be shown that the *same* value is obtained for $\int (1/\sqrt{2})(\alpha\beta + \beta\alpha)\hat{S}(1/\sqrt{2})(\alpha\beta + \beta\alpha)\, d\tau_{\text{spin}}$. However, there would be an interaction of the "paired spins" $\uparrow\downarrow$ in $(1/\sqrt{2})(\alpha\beta - \beta\alpha)$ that would certainly be different from the interaction of the unpaired spins. The electronic spin levels would be as depicted in Fig. III-15. [The magnetic moments of the electron could also interact with an external field, in which case the energy of the $\alpha\alpha$ and $\beta\beta$ states would separate. The effect of the external field on spin will be considered in Sec. III-3(ii).]

Frequently the spin interactions of the nuclei and electrons can be separated to allow the consideration of, for example, a fixed electron spin part and a nuclear spin part that is changing. Because of symmetry

[1] For many cases $\hat{s} \sim s_{1x}s_{2x} + s_{1y}s_{2y} + s_{1z}s_{2z}$; see H. Eyring, J. Walter, and G. Kimball, "Quantum Chemistry," chap. IX, Wiley, 1944 for the operators s_x, s_y, etc.

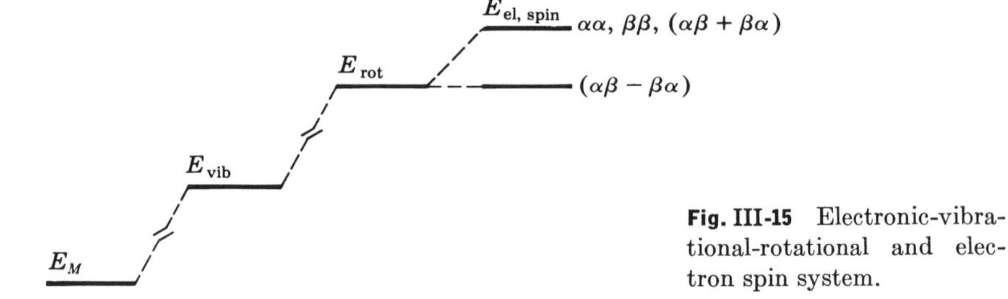

Fig. III-15 Electronic-vibrational-rotational and electron spin system.

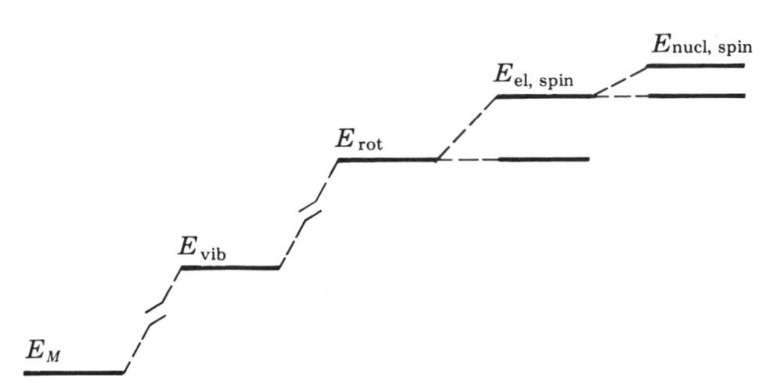

Fig. III-16 Electronic-vibrational-rotational spin system.

restrictions, the possible nuclear spin functions will depend on the descriptions given by $\psi_{rot}\psi_{vib}$ for the other nuclear coordinates.

When these restrictions are taken into account, the various possible energy contributions from the different combinations of electron and nuclear spin functions can be worked out. If, for example, the electron spin part is $\alpha(1)\alpha(2)$, and if the possible nuclear spin parts are $\alpha(A)\alpha(B)$, $\beta(A)\beta(B)$, $(1/\sqrt{2})[\alpha(A)\beta(B) + \beta(A)\alpha(B)]$, then the previous energy level diagram could be extended as in Fig. III-16. (The relative spacing of nuclear and electron spin contributions is dependent on H_{spin}, and Fig. III-16 is to be taken as only an illustration.)

(iii) A composite representation

The principal contributions to the total energy of the system within the approximation of the separable hamiltonian have now been considered. It would be worthwhile bringing these contributions together in some comparative table or schematic representation.

The relative contributions of these types of energy can readily be calculated (see, for example, Prob. III-1) and are shown in Table III-1. As Table III-1 indicates, the total energy is determined principally by the

Table III-1 The relative energy of the different "motions" of a molecule

Type of contribution	*Coordinate*	*Energy, kcal/mole (order of magnitude)*	*Comments*
Translational	XYZ	0–10	Thermal energies
Molecular-electronic	$x_1y_1z_1$	10^2	Includes nuclear repulsion for fixed R
Vibrational	R	10^0	
Rotational	θ,ϕ	10^{-1}	
Electron spin-spin	σ_1		Variable but generally small
Nuclear spin-spin	σ_A		

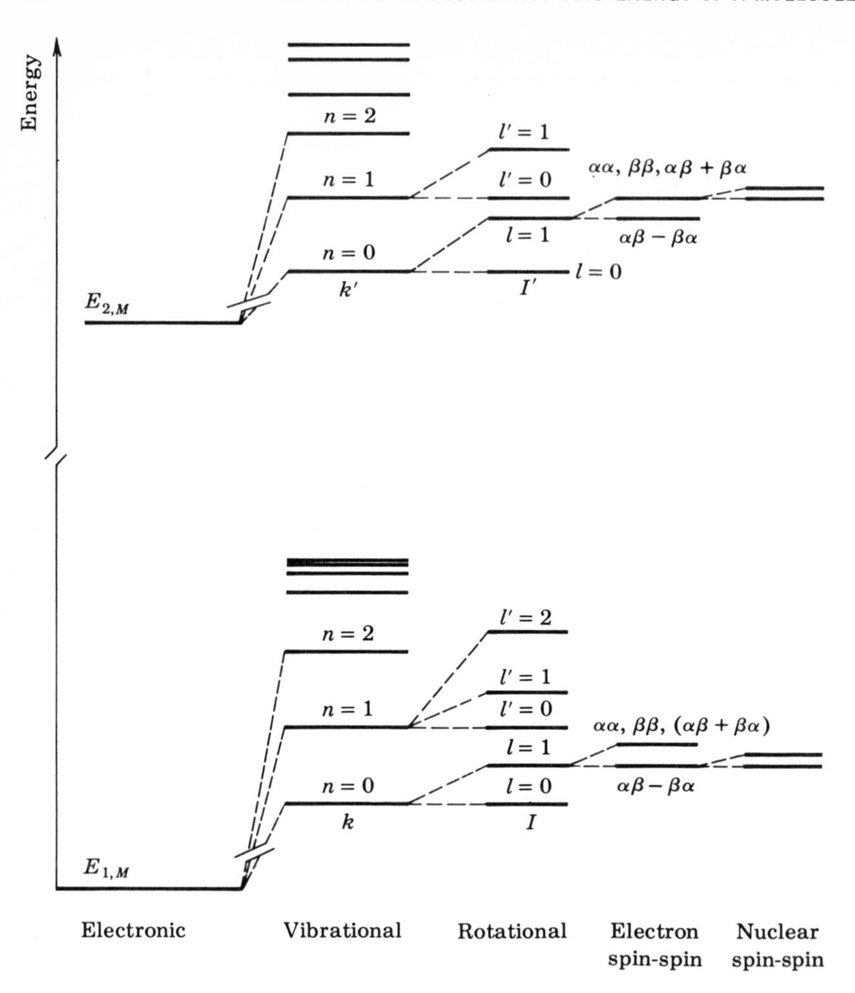

Fig. III-17 Composite energy level diagram.

electronic energy, with lesser contributions from the other types down to a very minute portion from the spin-spin interactions. Although it will not be possible to represent such wide variations exactly to scale, Fig. III-17 is an attempt to produce such a composite energy level diagram.

PROBLEM III-1

The energy of a rotational transition clearly depends on the reduced mass μ and on the internuclear separation R_e. Find the range of μ values for diatomics, for example, H_2, HI, N_2, O_2. Assuming a range of 1.0 to 2.0 Å for R_e, find the energy change for rotational transitions of diatomic molecules.

The molecular energy diagram (Fig. III-5) has already been used as a background for the vibrational energy level diagram. One might now attempt to represent not only vibrational energy levels but also the other levels on this backdrop. Figure III-18 is the result. The lines from one side of the potential well to the other are the *vibrational* energy levels of the indicated value of n for that particular electronic configuration. The remaining lines, in order of decreasing lengths, are the *rotational* levels for the given electronic and vibrational states; the *electronic spin* energy

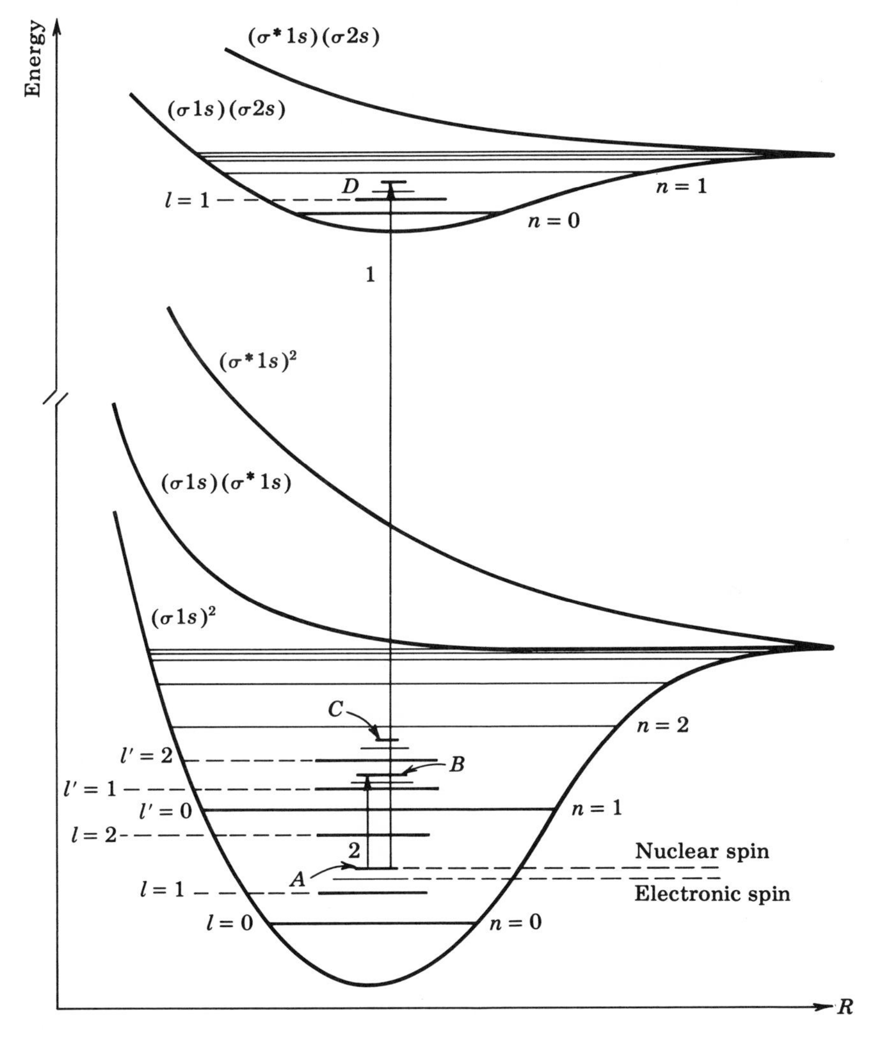

Fig. III-18 Composite energy level diagram on the background of E_M vs. R curve.

Table III-2 Molecular description and energies

$$\psi_A = \psi_{1,\text{elec space}} \cdot \psi_{0,\text{vib}} \cdot \psi_{1,\text{rot}} \cdot \psi_{1,\text{elec spin}} \cdot \psi_{1,\text{n spin}}$$
$$= N_A(\sigma 1s)^2 \cdot (e^{-ar^2}) \cdot (\cos\theta) \cdot (\alpha\beta - \beta\alpha) \cdot (\alpha\alpha)$$ where N_A is the normalizing constant

$$E_A = E_M(\sigma 1s)^2 + \frac{h\nu_0}{2} + \frac{h^2 2}{8\pi^2 I} + E_{\text{elec spin}}(\alpha\beta - \beta\alpha) + E_{\text{n spin}}(\alpha\alpha)$$

$$\psi_B = \psi_{1,\text{elec space}} \cdot \psi_{1,\text{vib}} \cdot \psi_{1,\text{rot}} \cdot \psi_{1,\text{elec spin}} \cdot \psi_{1,\text{n spin}}$$
$$= N_B(\sigma 1s)^2 \cdot re^{-ar^2} \cdot \cos\theta \cdot (\alpha\beta - \beta\alpha) \cdot (\alpha\alpha)$$
$$E_B = E_M(\sigma 1s)^2 + \tfrac{3}{2}h\nu_0 + \frac{h^2 2}{8\pi^2 I} + E_{\text{elec spin}}(\alpha\beta - \beta\alpha) + E_{\text{n spin}}(\alpha\alpha)$$

$$\psi_C = \psi_{1,\text{elec space}} \cdot \psi_{1,\text{vib}} \cdot \psi_{2,\text{rot}} \cdot \psi_{1,\text{elec spin}} \cdot \psi_{1,\text{n spin}}$$
$$= N_C(\sigma 1s)^2 \cdot re^{-ar^2} \cdot (3\cos^2\theta - 1) \cdot (\alpha\beta - \beta\alpha) \cdot (\alpha\alpha)$$
$$E_C = E_M(\sigma 1s)^2 + \tfrac{3}{2}h\nu_0 + \frac{h^2 6}{8\pi^2 I} + E_{\text{elec spin}}(\alpha\beta - \beta\alpha) + E_{\text{n spin}}(\alpha\alpha)$$

$$\psi_D = \psi_{2,\text{elec space}} \cdot \psi_{0,\text{vib}} \cdot \psi_{1,\text{rot}} \cdot \psi_{1,\text{elec spin}} \cdot \psi_{1,\text{n spin}}$$
$$= N_D(\sigma 1s)(\sigma 2s) \cdot (e^{-a'r^2}) \cdot (\cos\theta) \cdot (\alpha\beta - \beta\alpha) \cdot (\alpha\alpha)$$
$$E_D = E_M(\sigma 1s)(\sigma 2s) + \frac{h\nu_0'}{2} + \frac{h^2 2}{8\pi^2 I'} + E_{\text{elec spin}}(\alpha\beta - \beta\alpha) + E_{\text{n spin}}(\alpha\alpha)$$

levels for the given electronic, vibrational, and rotational description; and, finally, the *nuclear spin* levels. In addition to these graphical representations of the energy of the molecule, one could collect the individual descriptions by reference to the preceding sections and write out the complete eigenfunction and energy for the molecule. The eigenfunctions and energies for lines A, B, C, and D of Fig. III-18 are given in Table III-2. Such explicit descriptions of the system should leave no doubt as to the meaning of each line in Figs. III-17 or III-18.

III-3 OTHER CONTRIBUTIONS TO THE ENERGY

(i) Other internal contributions to the energy

To keep the discussion fairly tidy, only those terms that can be directly attributed to a recognized coordinate for the system have been given so far. There are, however, several other contributions of the nature of magnetic interactions that, one might say, are secondary to a given coordinate. For example, the *orbital* "motion" of the *electron* would be expected to generate a magnetic field that would, in turn, interact with the magnetic field from the spin of the electrons. Consequently there would be the interaction depicted in Fig. III-19—the so-called spin-orbit coupling H_{LS}, where L refers to the orbital source and S to the spin source.

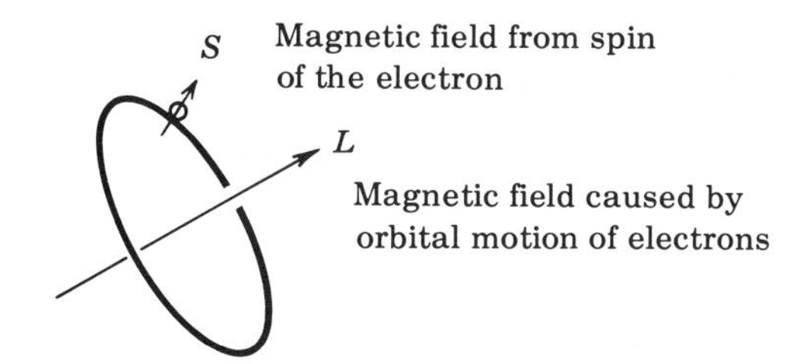

Fig. III-19 Spin-orbital interaction.

Similarly, other secondary magnetic interactions might be expected to contribute to the total energy, e.g., the interaction H_{LL} of the magnetic field from the orbital motion of one electron with the magnetic field due to the orbital motion of another. These terms will not be discussed in detail, but their presence should be noted.

(ii) External field-dependent energy contributions

(a) Dipole-external field interactions

All the terms considered thus far have been completely independent of external influences. Obviously external electric or magnetic fields would have an interaction with the system. For example, in the "Stark effect" a molecule with the electric dipole $\boldsymbol{\mu}$, shown in Fig. III-20, interacts[1] with an external electric field $\boldsymbol{\varepsilon}$. The resulting energy depends on the orientation, through θ, so that the rotational descriptions with different m values, i.e., different orientation, will have different energies. That some of the $(2l + 1)$-fold degeneracy of m values is removed is indicated by the new energy level diagram drawn up in Fig. III-21. The allowed transitions ($\Delta m = 0$) are also indicated. Certainly the energy of what was formerly an $l = 0 \rightarrow l = 1$ transition has changed, but, more significantly, the $l = 1 \rightarrow l = 2$ is split into two transitions with different energies. The sort of spectrum one would see with the field on and off is sketched in Fig. III-22.

It should not be difficult to see that the *shift* in the absorption frequency of the $0 \rightarrow 1$ transition will depend on the change in energy levels due to the external field, and since this change is dependent on the

[1] See E. M. Purcell, "Electricity and Magnetism," McGraw-Hill, 1963.

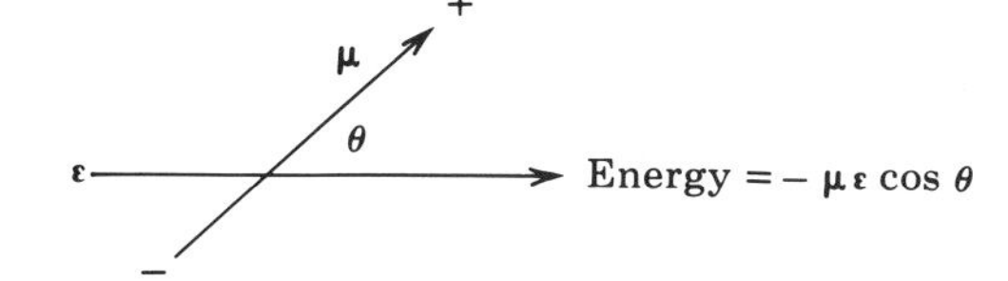

Fig. III-20 Field-dipole interaction.

Electric field off

Electric field on

$l = 2$, $m = -2\ -1\ 0\ +1\ +2$

$l = 1$, $m = -1\ 0\ +1$

$l = 0$, $m = 0$

$m = 0$, $m = \pm 1$, $m = \pm 2$ } $l = 2$

$m = 0$, $m = \pm 1$ } $l = 1$

$m = 0$ $l = 0$

Fig. III-21 Field-dependent Stark-effect splitting of energy levels.

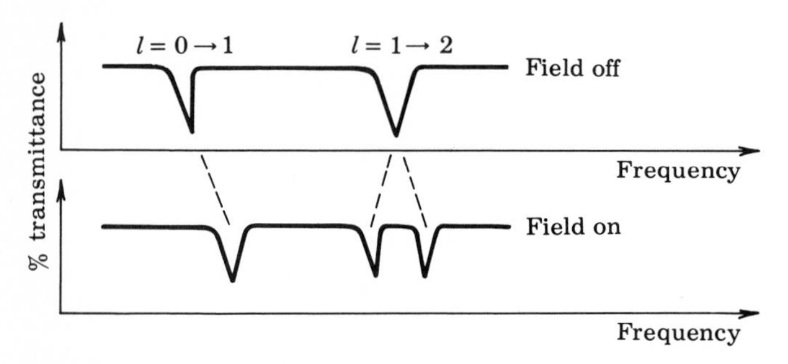

Fig. III-22 Field-dependent Stark-effect spectrum.

dipole moment, yet another property of the molecule can be found from its spectrum.

(b) Modification of the external field interaction by the internal features of the system

One would also expect interactions of an external magnetic field $\mathbf{H}_0$, with the magnetic moment of orbital motion, or with the intrinsic magnetic moment, the spin, of the electrons and nuclei.

The latter interaction has had considerable development in that branch of spectroscopy known as *nuclear magnetic resonance* (NMR). The magnetic dipole $\boldsymbol{\mu}_n$ of a bare nucleus, e.g., an isolated proton, will have an interaction energy E: $E = -H_0\mu_n \cos\theta$

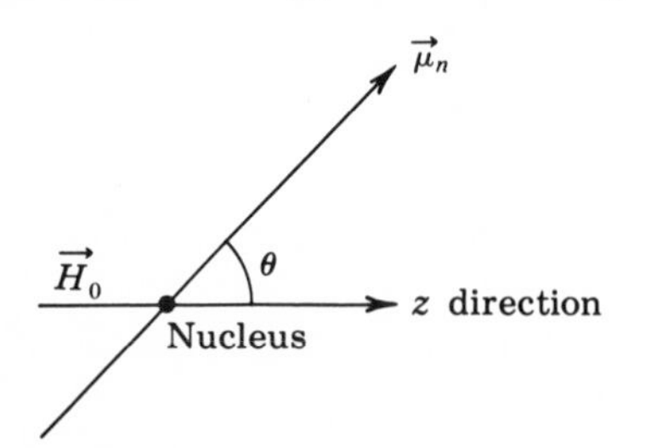

The component of $\boldsymbol{\mu}_n$ in the direction of the external field is simply $\mu_{nz} = \mu_n \cos\theta$, so the energy is simply $E = -H_0\mu_{nz}$. As pointed out when spin was introduced, there is a limited number of orientations of the spin magnetic moment; e. g. there are only two, α ($m_s = +\frac{1}{2}$) or β ($m_s = -\frac{1}{2}$), for a proton.[1] Thus there would be a limited number of possible energy states due to interaction with the external field. For a *proton* the two energies would be

$$E\ (\text{for}\ \overset{H_0}{\rightarrow} \nearrow_{\mu_n}) = -H_0(+\tfrac{1}{2})B_n \qquad \text{for spin } \alpha$$

$$E\ (\text{for}\ \overset{H_0}{\rightarrow} \swarrow_{\mu_n}) = -H_0(-\tfrac{1}{2})B_n \qquad \text{for spin } \beta$$

[Here $B_n = (eh/2\pi m_p c)g_n$ where $eh/2\pi m_p c$ is the nuclear magneton and g_n is the nuclear "g-factor" for the proton.] Thus the presence of the external field *creates* two energy levels

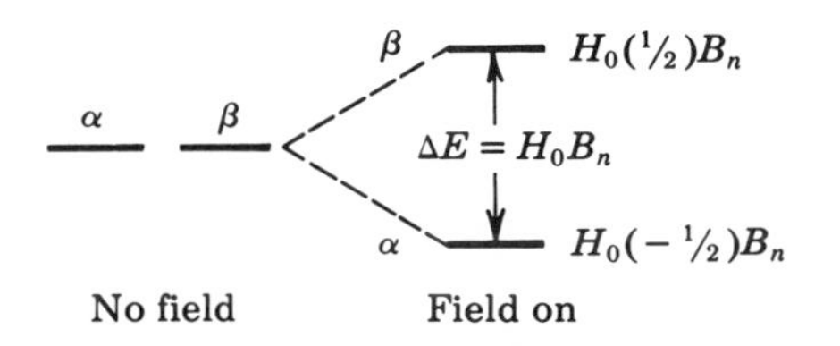

Since the nucleus could make a transition from one of these levels to the other, spectroscopic measurements are possible. Although the above formula for ΔE seems to provide very little information, it should be remembered that, in the molecule, the nuclei are not isolated but are surrounded by electrons. A magnetic field can induce motion of an electric charge (in this case motion of the electrons in the molecule) as

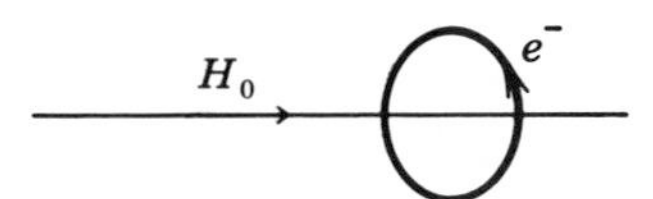

and a moving electric charge is known to produce a magnetic field (e.g., a solenoid loop). Consequently the induced motion of the electrons produces an opposing magnetic field

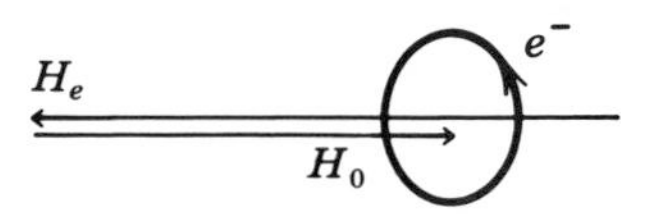

[1] In this and subsequent sections the word "proton" refers to the *hydrogen* nucleus, not to the protons in other nuclei.

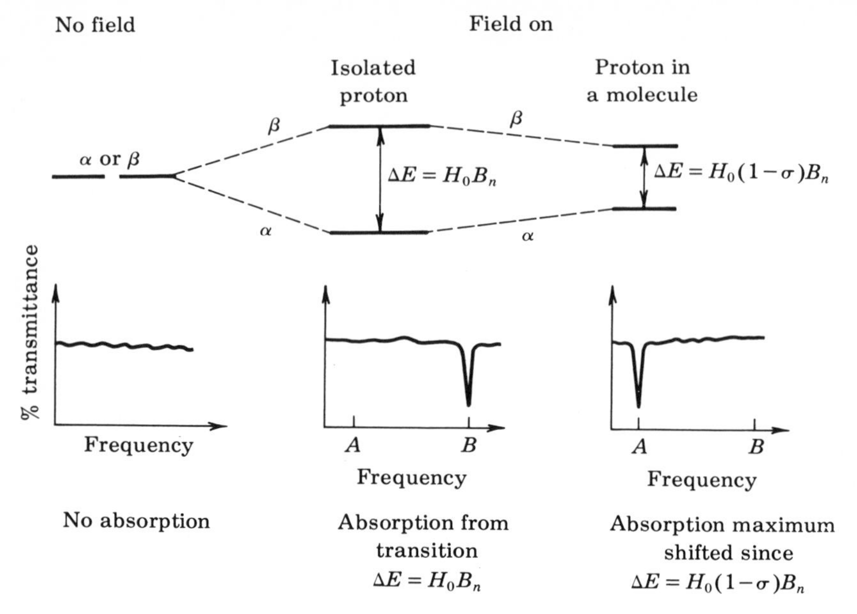

Fig. III-23 NMR chemical shift.

the field H_e will be proportional to the amount of electron motion, which, in turn, is proportional to the number (density) of electrons and to the external field. Thus $H_e = \sigma H_0$, where σ depends on the electron density in the region of the nucleus. Since H_e is opposite in direction to the external field H_0, the net field at the nucleus is less than H_0 by an amount $H_0\sigma$, and so one may say that the nucleus is "shielded" from the total external field. But the shielding depends on σ, which, in turn, depends on the electron density, and so one may say that the nucleus is shielded from the external magnetic field by the *electrons*. The energy levels of a proton are then

$$E = \tfrac{1}{2}B_nH_0(1-\sigma) \quad \text{or} \quad E = -\tfrac{1}{2}B_nH_0(1-\sigma) \quad \text{and} \quad \Delta E = B_nH_0(1-\sigma)$$

Since the separation ΔE has been *shifted* due to the chemical environment of the proton, the change is called the NMR *chemical shift*. Similarly, the frequency corresponding to the energy that would be absorbed in such a transition would be shifted. Thus one has energy levels defined principally by an external field but *modified by the internal features* of the system. The situation is illustrated in Fig. III-23. Clearly, the NMR shift would provide information on the electron density in the region of a nucleus. In fact NMR spectra should be *very* sensitive to the environment of a proton in complicated molecules.

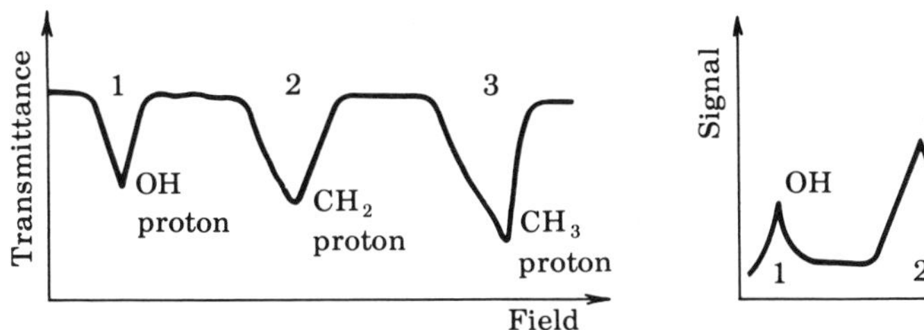

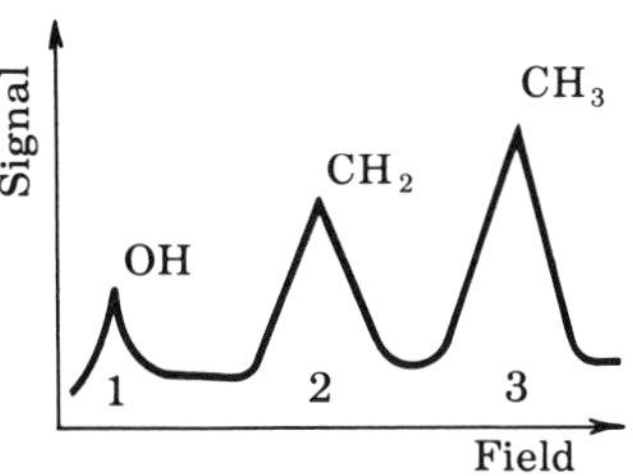

Fig. III-24 NMR chemical-shift spectrum of ethanol.

(iii) Project 7. NMR chemical shift

(a) Units

Because of instrumental difficulties the NMR transitions are usually not recorded as absorptions in a % transmittance vs. frequency spectrum. Rather, the electric field change generated as the nuclear magnetic moment "flips" (as $\alpha \to \beta$) is measured. Consequently, the signal spectrum shown in the right-hand half of Fig. III-24 is the more common. The spectra of Fig. III-24 three different environments for the protons in ethanol. But this is quite reasonable, for there are two protons on one carbon that should be the same, three on the other carbon that should have the same environment, and a single proton attached to the oxygen that should be different from the other two—there should be three peaks with relative intensities (areas) of 1:2:3.

The frequencies at which absorption occurs may be quoted in terms of a chemical-shift parameter Δ defined as

$$\Delta = -\frac{\text{frequency for sample} - \text{frequency for reference system}}{\text{frequency for reference system}} \times 10^6$$

Rather than vary the frequency, one may obtain NMR spectra by the equivalent procedure of holding the frequency constant and observing the value of the field H_0 at which absorption occurs. If the field H_0 is adjusted to make $H_0(1 - \sigma)$ match the fixed frequency, then certainly, when σ is relatively large $(1 - \sigma)$ will be relatively smaller than when σ is small. Consequently for a larger σ, a relatively larger value of H_0 will be needed to make the product $H_0(1 - \sigma)$ equal to the fixed frequency. Thus we expect that the magnetic field value required will be larger for highly screened protons. If the reference proton is very highly screened, then

$$\delta = \frac{[H_0(\text{reference}) - H_0(\text{sample})]}{H_0(\text{reference})} \times 10^6 \text{ (ppm) will be}$$

Table III-3 The NMR chemical shift of protons in various molecules

Molecule	τ	*Molecule*	τ
$-SO_3\underline{H}$	−2.0 to −1.0	TMS	10.0
$-CO_2\underline{H}$	−2.2 to −1.0	$-OC\underline{H_3}$	6.2 to 6.5
$RC\underline{H}O$	0.2 to 0.5	$-C\underline{H_2}X$	5.7 to 7.8
$RCON\underline{H_2}$	2.0 to 3.5	$\equiv C-\underline{H}$	6.9 to 7.6
$ArO\underline{H}$	2.3 to 5.5	$=\overset{\vert}{C}-C\underline{H_3}$	8.1 to 8.8
$Ar\underline{H}$	2.0 to 3.4	$-C\underline{H_2}-$	8.6 to 8.9
$=C\underline{H_2}$	4.3 to 5.4	$RN\underline{H_2}$	8.5 to 8.9
$RO\underline{H}$	4.8 to 7.0	$-\underset{\vert}{\overset{\vert}{C}}-C\underline{H_3}$	9.0 to 9.2

1. A small positive number, say, 1.0 ppm, for a sample in which the proton is highly screened.
2. A relatively large positive number, say, 10 ppm, for a sample in which the proton is not shielded.

It should be emphasized that all chemical shifts are small numbers, approximately 10^{-5}, but they are multiplied by 10^6 to give the value in parts per million (ppm). Hence "small" and "large" refer to ppm values. The chemical shift may also be reported in terms of a τ value (ppm), where $\tau = 10 - \delta$, and the protons in tetramethylsilane (TMS) are the reference protons (that is, $\tau_{TMS} = 10$). The τ values for protons in various types of compounds are indicated in Table III-3.

PROBLEM 7-1

Explain the relative order of the proton chemical shift of the following molecules: $CH_3I(\tau = 7.84)$, $CH_3Br(\tau = 7.32)$, $CH_3Cl(\tau = 6.95)$, $CH_3F(\tau = 5.74)$. (*Hint:* Electronegativity!)

PROBLEM 7-2

The proton NMR spectra for dimethyl ether, ethane, and methyl fluoride are indicated in Fig. III-25. Assign each spectrum to the appropriate molecule. Explain the relative order of their τ values. (*Hint:* What group is common to all these molecules and what part is changing?)

PROBLEM 7-3

Assign each of the four spectra in Fig. III-26 as that due to a molecule containing one of the following: acid, aldehyde, ether, and amide. (*Hint:* Refer to Table III-3.)

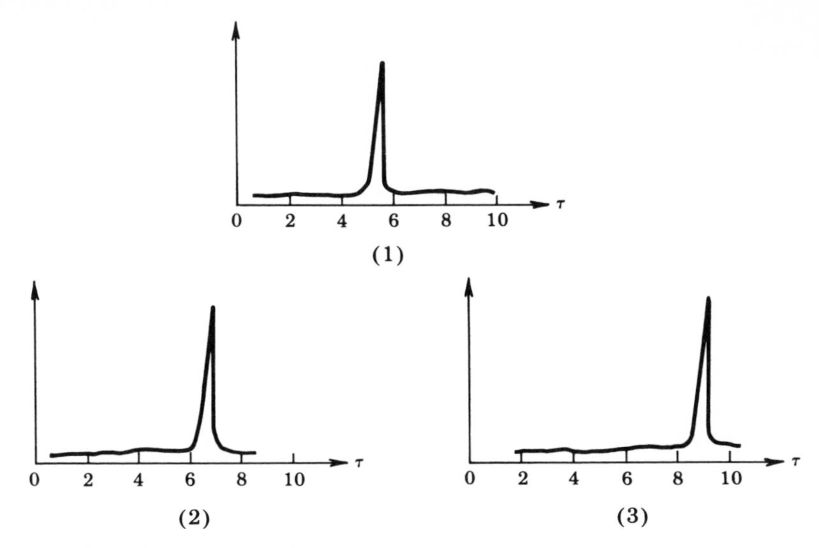

Fig. III-25 The effect of substituents on NMR spectra.

(b) Unknowns

The number of carbons, hydrogens, etc., in a molecule is usually readily determined. This, in conjunction with NMR chemical shift, can be used to indicate the structure of the molecule.

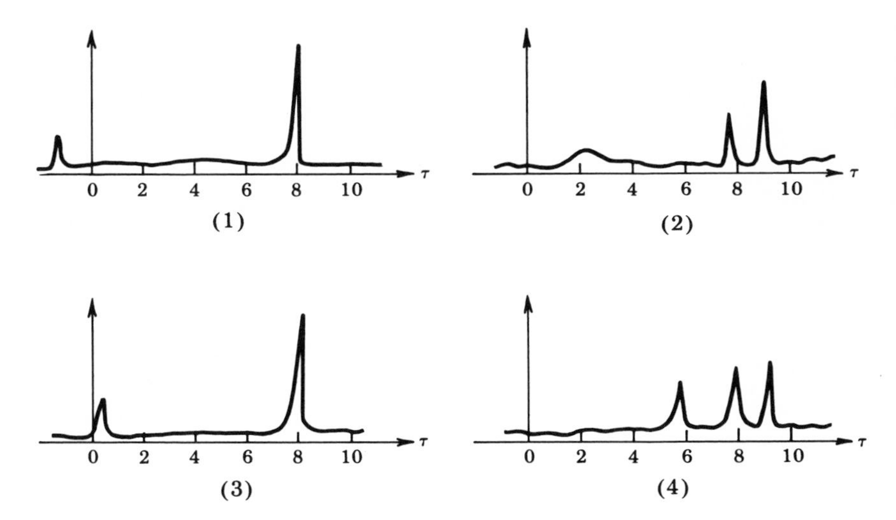

Fig. III-26 Functional groups.

PROBLEM 7-4

Give the structural formulas for the compounds having the NMR spectra and elemental analyses given in Fig. III-27.

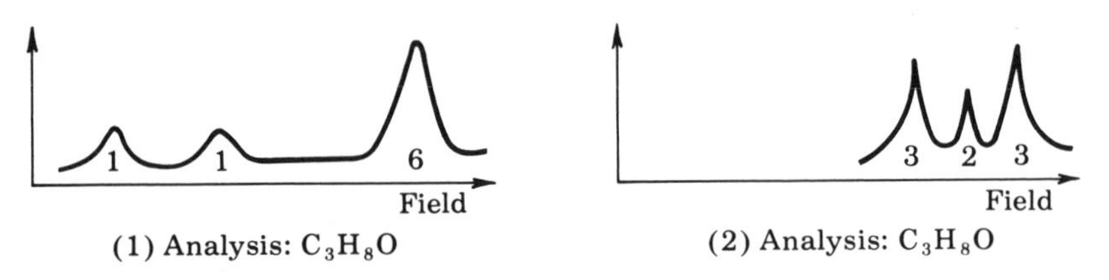

Fig. III-27 Unknown compounds.

PROBLEM 7-5

Find the structures corresponding to spectra (1) through (5) in Fig. III-28.

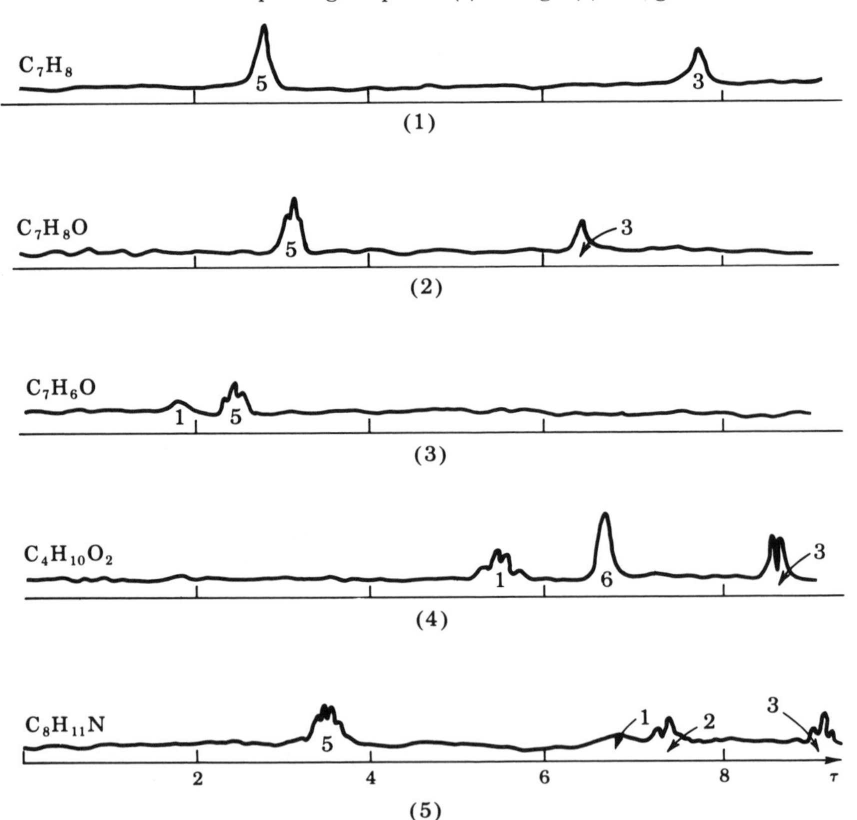

Fig. III-28 Chemical-shift structure analysis.

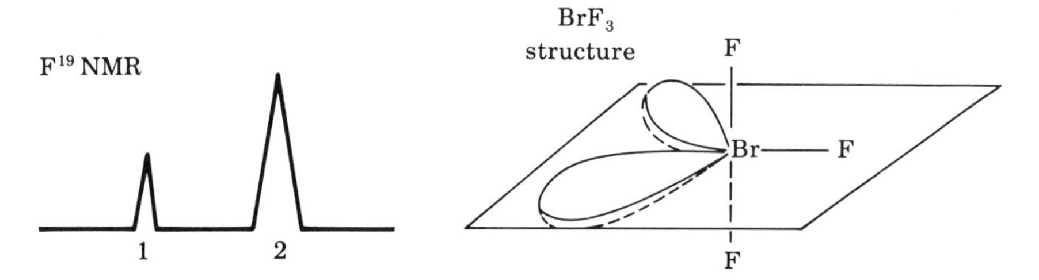

Fig. III-29 F^{19} NMR analysis.

PROBLEM 7-6

Sketch the NMR chemical-shift spectra of the following compounds:

Acetone	Acetaldehyde	*n*-Propanol
$(CH_3)_2C{=}O$	CH_3CHO	$CH_3CH_2CH_2OH$

(*c*) *Other nuclei*

The nucleus of the hydrogen atom is not the only nucleus to have magnetic properties. For example, the nuclei of both fluorine (F^{19}) and phosphorus (P^{31}) have spin states α or β. Consequently it is possible to observe the transitions between the nuclear spin states for these nuclei; for example, the F^{19} NMR spectrum of BrF_3 exhibits two peaks with relative areas 1:2. This suggests two types of F's as in the structure in Fig. III-29.

PROBLEM 7-7

Sketch the F^{19} NMR spectrum of TiF_4L_2 in the cis and trans forms (here L is a ligand, such as pyridine).

PROBLEM 7-8

The F^{19} NMR spectrum of $(CH_3)_2PF_3$ consists of two peaks of relative intensities 1:2. Suggest a structure and sketch the expected P^{31} NMR and proton NMR spectra.

PROBLEM 7-9

Sketch the P^{31} NMR spectrum of

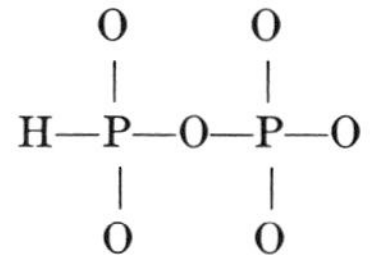

IV
Transitions

IV-1 INTRODUCTION

The previous chapter provided a molecular description in terms of the different types of coordinates. This method allows one to consider "pure" transitions in which the description of only one coordinate type changes. Thus the eigenfunctions of Table III-2 can be used to define a "pure" vibrational transition ($\psi_A \rightarrow \psi_B$) or a "pure" rotational transition ($\psi_B \rightarrow \psi_C$). From the data of Table III-1 it is clear that the energy change for the former transition would be quite different from that for the latter. Consequently the absorption maxima would occur in widely separate regions of the spectrum. Indeed, one could, using the information of Table III-1, confidently predict the type of "pure" transitions that would occur in each region of the spectrum. Table IV-1 contains the range of ΔE for the molecule and the range of λ, ν, and $\bar{\nu}$ for the photon emitted or absorbed for the various types of "pure" transitions. The common name for each range is also given. For example, an absorption

Table IV-1 The appropriate region for different types of transitions

Unit of measurement	*Type*		
	Rotational	*Vibrational*	*Electronic*
Ergs (ΔE system)	10^{-16}–10^{-15}	10^{-14}–10^{-13}	10^{-12}–10^{-9}
Wavelength λ, Å	10^{7}–10^{6}	10^{5}–10^{4}	10^{3}–10
Reciprocal centimeters $\bar{\nu}$, cm^{-1}	10–100	10^{3}–10^{4}	10^{5}–10^{7}
Frequency ν, sec^{-1}	10^{11}–10^{12}	10^{13}–10^{14}	10^{15}–10^{17}

Microwave | Far infrared | Infrared | Visible | Ultraviolet | X-rays

maximum in the infrared spectrum of a diatomic molecule would correspond to a vibrational transition.

PROBLEM IV-1

If the absorption maxima at each of the following is assumed to be due to a "pure" transition, suggest the type of transition taking place: $\lambda_{max} = 4250$ Å, $\bar{\nu} = 4070\ cm^{-1}$, $\nu = 1.15 \times 10^{11}\ sec.^{-1}$

Unfortunately the transitions that take place are not "pure" transitions but, rather, mixed transitions in which several coordinates are changing. The transition $\psi_A \rightarrow \psi_C$ of Fig. III-18 would be an example in which vibrational and rotational descriptions are both changing. The associated energy change would be

$$\begin{aligned} \Delta E_{AC} &= E_C - E_A = \Delta E_{\text{vib}} + \Delta E_{\text{rot}} \\ &= (E_{C,\text{vib}} - E_{A,\text{vib}}) + (E_{C,\text{rot}} - E_{A,\text{rot}}) \\ &= h\nu_0 + \frac{h^2}{8\pi^2 I} 4 \end{aligned} \tag{IV-1}$$

Thus if $h\nu_0$ corresponds to $\bar{\nu}$ of 2000 cm^{-1} (i.e., the $\bar{\nu}$ corresponding to the vibrational change $0 \rightarrow 1$), then $\bar{\nu}_{AC}$ corresponding to ΔE_{AC} would be $2000 + (h/8\pi^2 Ic)4$; but $(h/8\pi^2 Ic)4$ might be of the order of 40 cm^{-1} (a pure rotational change is 10–100 cm^{-1}), so that

$$\bar{\nu}_{AC} = 2000 + 40 = 2040\ cm^{-1}$$

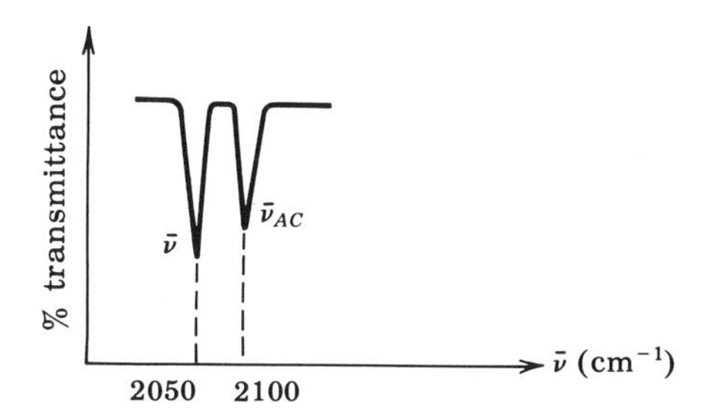

Fig. IV-1 Mixed vibration-rotation transitions.

There could have been *other* rotational changes *accompanying* the vibrational change. For example, a change from the lowest rotational state to the next highest would give an energy change $\Delta E = h\nu_0 + [(h^2/8\pi^2 I)2]$ with a corresponding $\bar{\nu}$ of $(2000 + 20)$ cm^{-1} = 2020 cm^{-1}. Consequently the spectrum (Fig. IV-1) would indicate a transition with $\bar{\nu}$ of 2020 cm^{-1} *as well as* the aforementioned transition with $\bar{\nu}_{AC}$ = 2040 cm^{-1}. There could be a multitude of such lines in the spectrum!

Even when there are only "pure" transitions, as in Fig. IV-2, the difficulties encountered in Project 4 (recall Prob. 4-4) would also suggest that energy alone is not enough to ensure proper assignment of spectra. More tools than have been presented so far will be needed! It will be necessary to know: which transitions, pure or mixed, are possible; the pattern of spacing for various combinations; and the pattern of intensities. Perhaps the key question would be simply: What transitions are possible? To answer this, the cause and the fundamental nature of transitions must be examined.

IV-2 THE NATURE OF TRANSITIONS

(i) The space- and time-dependent Schroedinger equation

The quantum-mechanical concepts discussed thus far have been concerned with the spacial description and not the time dependence. How-

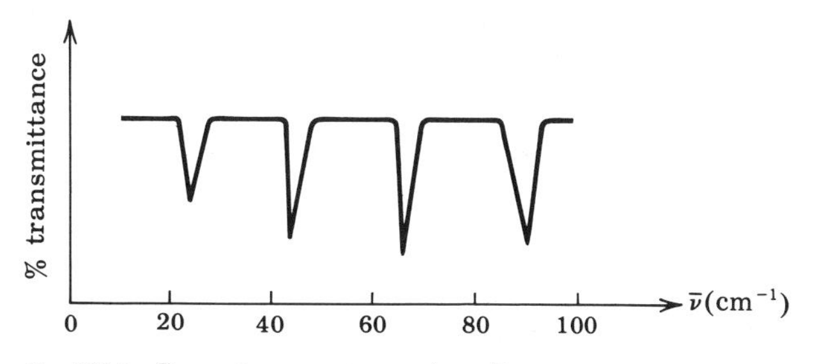

Fig. IV-2 Several pure rotation transitions.

ever, when transitions are considered, at some particular time t an initial state ψ_i changes to a new state ψ_f, and one *is* concerned with the time dependence.

(a) *Classical time dependence*

The general space and time *classical* wave equation is given in Appendix I as $[\partial^2 y(x,t)/\partial x^2] = (1/v^2)[\partial^2 y(x,t)/\partial t^2]$. The equation was separated into two parts, one in space, $[d^2\psi(x)/dx^2] = -(4\pi^2/\lambda^2)\psi(x)$, which was the starting point for the *spacial* quantum-mechanical Schroedinger equation, and one in time, $[d^2 g(t)/dt^2] = -(2\pi\nu)^2 g(t)$. The solutions to this latter equation are $g(t) = e^{-i2\pi\nu t}$ and $e^{+i2\pi\nu t}$. Of these solutions only $g(t) = e^{-i2\pi\nu t}$ will be taken in the discussion leading to the quantum-mechanical descriptions.[1] Since the selected form $g(t) = e^{-i2\pi\nu t}$ satisfies the simpler equation

$$\frac{dg(t)}{dt} = -i2\pi\nu g(t) \tag{IV-2}$$

this equation may be used as the starting point for the *time* dependence in quantum mechanics.

PROBLEM IV-2

Show that $g(t) = e^{-i2\pi\nu t}$ is a solution of Eq. (IV-2).

(b) *Quantum-mechanical time dependence*

In quantum mechanics the frequency ν is related to the energy by $E = h\nu$ or $\nu = E/h$, so that, on going to the quantum-mechanical case, Eq. (IV-2) becomes

$$\frac{d}{dt} g(t) = \frac{-i2\pi E}{h} g(t)$$

Both sides of this equation may be multiplied by $\psi(x)$ to give

$$\frac{\partial}{\partial t} g(t)\psi(x) = \frac{-i2\pi E}{h} g(t)\psi(x)$$

$$= \frac{-i2\pi E}{h} \psi(x)g(t)$$

Let us consider the quantum-mechanical case where the hamiltonian H depends on only space coordinates, i.e., the hamiltonian has no explicit

[1] A rigorous treatment of time dependence in quantum mechanics is beyond the scope of this text. However, for further discussion see E. C. Kemble, "Quantum Mechanics," pp. 15–18, Dover, 1958, and D. Bohm, "Quantum Theory," pp. 81–83, Prentice-Hall, 1951.

time dependence. We denote this hamiltonian by the symbol H^0 and its eigenfunctions by $\psi_n{}^0$. Hence $H^0\psi_n{}^0 = E_n{}^0\psi_n{}^0$, and $E\psi(x)g(t)$ may be replaced with $H_n{}^0\psi_n{}^0(x)g(t)$, giving

$$\frac{\partial}{\partial t}\Psi_n{}^0(x,t) = \frac{-i2\pi}{h}H^0\Psi_n{}^0(x,t)$$

where $\Psi_n{}^0(x,t) = \psi_n{}^0(x)g(t)$. This suggests[1] that *in general* the *space- and time*-dependent SE could be written as

$$\frac{\partial}{\partial t}\Psi(x,t) = \frac{-i2\pi}{h}H\Psi(x,t)$$

or

$$\boxed{\frac{ih}{2\pi}\frac{\partial}{\partial t}\Psi = H\Psi} \qquad \text{(IV-3)}$$

This, then, is the equation that we assume *all* quantum-mechanical descriptions must satisfy.

(c) *The steady-state description*

For the case $H = H^0$ the time-dependent SE can be separated into a time part and a space part as follows:

$$\Bigg(\underbrace{\frac{ih}{2\pi}\frac{\partial}{\partial t}}_{\text{Time}} - \underbrace{H^0}_{\text{Space}}\Bigg)\Psi = 0$$

As the previous section indicates, the solution Ψ may be written as a product $\Psi(x,t) = \psi^0(x)g(t)$ and the SE split into a space equation $H^0\psi_n{}^0(x) = E_n{}^0\psi_n{}^0(x)$ and a time equation

$$\frac{ih}{2\pi}\frac{\partial}{\partial t}g(t) = E_n{}^0g(t)$$

The solution to the time equation is $g(t) = e^{-i2\pi E_n{}^0t/h}$, and the complete solution is then $\Psi(x,t) = \psi^0(x)e^{-i2\pi E_n{}^0t/h}$ for this, the so-called steady-state system. It is worthwhile noting that, even though both the hamiltonian and the energy have no explicit time dependence, the function $\Psi(x,t)$ has an explicit imaginary (i.e., involving $i = \sqrt{-1}$) time dependence. However, in line with the "steady-state concept," it should

[1] Indeed, just as for the spacial Schroedinger equation there is no strict derivation of the time dependent case. Nevertheless the resulting equation has not been refuted.

be emphasized that the probability function

$$\begin{aligned}\rho &= \Psi^*(x,t)\Psi(x,t) = \psi^{0*}(x)e^{i2\pi E_n{}^0 t/h}\psi^0(x)e^{-i2\pi E_n{}^0 t/h} \\ &= \psi^{0*}(x)\psi^0(x)e^{(-i2\pi E_n{}^0 t/h)+(i2\pi E_n{}^0 t/h)} = \psi^{0*}(x)\psi^0(x)e^0 = \psi^{0*}(x)\psi^0(x)\end{aligned}$$

has no time dependence—hence the name *steady state.*

(ii) The space and time dependence of electromagnetic radiation

As indicated previously, transitions can be brought about by "beaming" a source of light (radiation) of proper frequency on the sample. The investigation of the interaction of this radiation with a molecule will illustrate a situation in which the hamiltonian is dependent on both space coordinates and time coordinates.

The electrical part of electromagnetic radiation is, in essence, simply an oscillating electric field. This means that a unit charge at a point in space through which the radiation is passing experiences an electric force that rises to a maximum value, decreases to zero and to a minimum, increases to zero, and rises to a positive maximum. The number of times this cycle is repeated per second is the frequency of the radiation. The *time* dependence of this interaction of the electric field with a molecule might be represented as in Fig. IV-3, or, analytically, as H_{pt} = (space part) (time part) = (H_p) $(\sin 2\pi\nu t)$ = $H_p(e^{i2\pi\nu t} - e^{-i2\pi\nu t})/2i$. Here the space part H_p depends on both the intensity of the radiation and the distribution of charge in the molecule; for example, the interaction with HCl depends on the electric field ε^0 of the radiation and the electric dipole μ of HCl.

(iii) The effect of "turning on" the radiation

If a molecule is in a region of space where there is *no* external field, the hamiltonian H^0 has no time dependence and the steady-state solutions

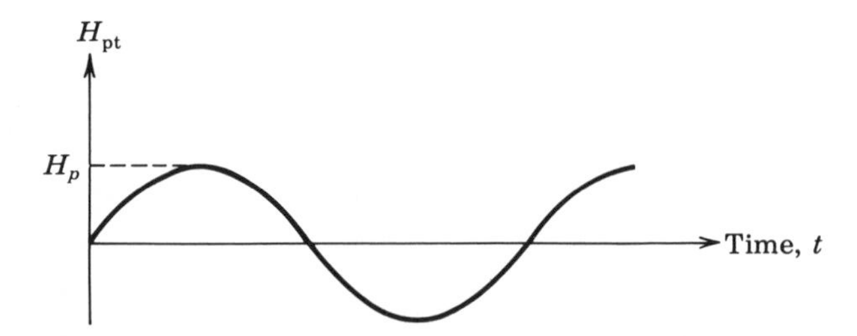

Fig. IV-3 Time dependence of the interaction of the molecule and radiation.

would be

$$\Psi_n{}^0 = \psi_n{}^0 e^{-i2\pi E_n{}^0 t/h} \qquad \text{where } H^0\psi_n{}^0 = E_n{}^0\psi_n{}^0$$

PROBLEM IV-3

Show that $\Psi_n{}^0 = \psi_n{}^0 e^{-i2\pi E_n{}^0 t/h}$ satisfies Eq. (IV-3).

If the external field is suddenly turned on, i.e., the "light beam" hits the system, the hamiltonian is no longer just H^0, but, since H must include *all* interactions, $H = H^0 + H_{pt}$. Here H_{pt} is *both* space- and time-dependent and, indeed, *cannot* be separated into a *sum* of two parts; it must remain as a product of a space and a time part. Consequently even though the first term H^0 is dependent on only space, the total hamiltonian H is not separable, and so the solution Ψ cannot be written as a product of space and time parts. A different approach from that used previously will be required.

The starting point is the recognition that the new description $\Psi(x,t)$ must be a solution of the time-dependent SE, that is, $\Psi(x,t)$ must satisfy the equation $(ih/2\pi)(\partial/\partial t)\Psi(x,t) = (H^0 + H_{pt})\Psi(x,t)$. If H_{pt} is small, then Ψ might be expected to look like some combination of the original functions $\Psi_n{}^0$. In fact, it should be most like $\Psi_1{}^0$, the description of the system just before the external field was turned on. Thus Ψ might be written $\Psi = C_1'(t)\Psi_1{}^0 + C_2'(t)\Psi_2{}^0 + C_3'(t)\Psi_3{}^0 \ldots$. The C_1',C_2', etc., are, of course, just a way of expressing mathematically the feeling that the new function will look like $\Psi_1{}^0$ plus a bit of $\Psi_2{}^0$, plus a bit of $\Psi_3{}^0$, etc.

(iv) The probability of a transition

This interpretation of the C's can be made more precise. On multiplying Ψ by Ψ^* and integrating over x, a probability function

$$\rho' = \int \Psi^*\Psi\, dx = C_1'^2(t)\int \Psi_1{}^{0*}\Psi_1{}^0\, dx + C_2'^2(t)\int \Psi_2{}^{0*}\Psi_2{}^0\, dx + \cdots$$

is obtained. Dividing by $C_1'^2(t)$ throughout gives

$$\frac{\rho'}{C_1'^2(t)} = \int \Psi_1{}^{0*}\Psi_1{}^0\, dx + \frac{C_2'^2(t)}{C_1'^2(t)}\int \Psi_2{}^{0*}\Psi_2{}^0\, dx + \cdots$$

and renaming the coefficients yields

$$\rho = \int \Psi_1{}^{0*}\Psi_1{}^0\, dx + C_2{}^2(t)\int \Psi_2{}^{0*}\Psi_2{}^0\, dx + \cdots \qquad \text{(IV-4)}$$

The first term in ρ may be considered as the *relative* probability that, at time t, the system "looks like" $\Psi_1{}^0$; similarly $C_2{}^2(t)\int \Psi_2{}^{0*}\Psi_2{}^0\, dx$ is the probability that it "looks like" $\Psi_2{}^0$. Since, at time $t = 0$, the system was described by *only* $\Psi_1{}^0$, yet, at time t, may look like $\Psi_2{}^0$, it would seem that there is a certain probability that the system has made a transition. Thus the transition probability at time t for $\Psi_1^0 \rightarrow \Psi_2^0$ would be proportional to $C_2^2(t)$, or the transition probability per unit time is

$$p_{1\rightarrow 2} = \frac{C_2^2(t)}{t}$$

PROBLEM IV-4

Show that $\Psi_2^{0*}\Psi_2^0$ in Eq. (IV-4) does not depend on time [i.e., the only time dependence in the second term of Eq. (IV-4) is in $C_2(t)$].

IV-3 THE CAUSE OF TRANSITIONS

(i) Dipole-induced transitions

As indicated previously, transitions are brought about by electromagnetic radiation of the proper frequency. Two questions immediately come to mind: What is the role of the *proper frequency?* What is the *interaction* of the radiation with the molecule that brings about the transition? With the development of the time dependence given in the previous section, these questions may now be examined. In particular the statement for the probability of a transition, that is, $p_{1\rightarrow 2} \sim C_2^2(t)/t$, should contain the necessary information. The problem is, of course, to find the coefficients $C_2(t)$, $C_3(t)$, etc.

(a) The role of the proper frequency

Consider the simple case where we assume that only Ψ_1^0 and Ψ_2^0 contribute significantly to Ψ, that is, $\Psi = \Psi_1^0 + C_2(t)\Psi_2^0$. Since Ψ is to be a solution to the new time-dependent SE, then

$$\frac{ih}{2\pi}\frac{\partial}{\partial t}[\Psi_1^0 + C_2(t)\Psi_2^0] = (H^0 + H_{pt})[\Psi_1^0 + C_2(t)\Psi_2^0]$$

Here H_{pt} is the interaction of the magnetic field with the molecule, and $C_2(t)$ is the unknown that we wish to find. To solve for $C_2(t)$, we first multiply out the terms in the preceding equation:

$$\frac{ih}{2\pi}\frac{\partial}{\partial t}\Psi_1^0 + \frac{ih}{2\pi}\frac{\partial}{\partial t}C_2(t)\Psi_2^0 = H^0\Psi_1^0 + C_2(t)H^0\Psi_2^0 + H_{pt}\Psi_1^0 + C_2(t)H_{pt}\Psi_2^0$$

Performing the differentiation on the left-hand side gives

$$\frac{ih}{2\pi}\frac{\partial}{\partial t}(\Psi_1^0) + \frac{ih}{2\pi}C_2(t)\frac{\partial}{\partial t}(\Psi_2^0) + \frac{ih}{2\pi}\Psi_2^0\frac{\partial C_2(t)}{\partial t} = H^0\Psi_1^0 + C_2(t)H^0\Psi_2^0 + H_{pt}\Psi_1^0 + C_2(t)H_{pt}\Psi_2^0$$

Since $(ih/2\pi)(\partial/\partial t)\Psi_1^0 = H^0\Psi_1^0$ and $(ih/2\pi)(\partial/\partial t)\Psi_2^0 = H^0\Psi_2^0$, the equation reduces to:

$$\frac{ih}{2\pi}\Psi_2^0\frac{\partial C_2(t)}{\partial t} = H_{pt}\Psi_1^0 + C_2(t)H_{pt}\Psi_2^0$$

Before the radiation was turned on the system was described completely by just Ψ_1^0. So we might expect that the new function will still look principally like Ψ_1^0, which implies that $C_2(t)$ is rather small. Since H_{pt} is not considered to be large, the product $C_2(t)H_{pt}$ will certainly be relatively small, and so the last term can be neglected, leaving only

$$\frac{ih}{2\pi}\Psi_2^0\frac{\partial C_2(t)}{\partial t} = H_{pt}\Psi_1^0$$

Multiplying this equation by Ψ_2^{0*}, integrating with respect to the general space coordinate $(d\tau)$, and remembering that $\int\Psi_2^{0*}\Psi_2^0\,d\tau = 1$ gives

$$\frac{\partial C_2(t)}{\partial t} = \frac{2\pi}{ih}\left(\int\Psi_2^{0*}H_{pt}\Psi_1^0\,d\tau\right)$$

Rearranging this as

$$dC_2(t) = \frac{2\pi}{ih}\left(\int\Psi_2^{0*}H_{pt}\Psi_1^0\,d\tau\right)dt$$

and integrating with respect to time from 0 to t yields

$$\int_0^t d[C_2(t)] = \frac{2\pi}{ih}\int_0^t\left(\int\Psi_2^{0*}H_{pt}\Psi_1^0\,d\tau\right)dt$$

Performing the integration on the left gives

$$C_2(t) - C_2(0) = \frac{2\pi}{ih}\int_0^t dt\left(\int\Psi_2^{0*}H_{pt}\Psi_1^0\,d\tau\right)$$

but since $C_2(t)$ was initially zero, that is, $C_2(0) = 0$, the result is

$$C_2(t) = \frac{2\pi}{ih}\int_0^t\left(\int\Psi_2^{0*}H_{pt}\Psi_1^0\,d\tau\right)dt \qquad \text{(IV-5)}$$

PROBLEM IV-5

Discuss the validity of Eq. (IV-5).

Clearly $C_2(t)$ involves both time and space integrations. But, since Ψ_2^{0*}, Ψ_1^0, and H_{pt} can all be split into space and time parts, the integral can be split in two parts, one for the space coordinates and one for the time, as

$$C_2(t) = \frac{2\pi}{ih}\int_0^t dt(\int \Psi_2^{0*} H_{pt} \Psi_1^0\, d\tau)$$
$$= \frac{2\pi}{ih}\int_0^t dt \int \psi_2^{0*} e^{i2\pi E_2^0 t/h}\left[(H_p)\left(\frac{e^{i2\pi\nu t} - e^{-i2\pi\nu t}}{2i}\right)\right]\psi_1^0 e^{-i2\pi E_1^0 t/h}\, d\tau$$
$$= \frac{\pi}{h}\left(\int \psi_2^{0*} H_p \psi_1^0\, d\tau\right)\left(\int_0^t dt(e^{(i2\pi/h)(E_2^0 - E_1^0 - h\nu)t} - e^{(i2\pi/h)(E_2^0 - E_1^0 + h\nu)t})\right)$$

Integration of the time-dependent integral

$$\int_0^t dt(e^{(i2\pi/h)(E_2^0 - E_1^0 - h\nu)t} - e^{(i2\pi/h)(E_2^0 - E_1^0 + h\nu)t})$$

gives

$$-\left\{\frac{1 - e^{(i2\pi/h)(E_2^0 - E_1^0 - h\nu)t}}{(i2\pi/h)(E_2^0 - E_1^0 - h\nu)} - \frac{1 - e^{(i2\pi/h)(E_2^0 - E_1^0 + h\nu)t}}{(i2\pi/h)(E_2^0 - E_1^0 + h\nu)}\right\}$$

The numerator of each fraction will always be relatively small but when $E_2^0 - E_1^0 = h\nu$, then the denominator of the first fraction goes to zero, and this *fraction* becomes large, giving a large value of the integral. In other words if $E_2^0 - E_1^0$ is approximately equal to $h\nu$, then the first term is large since its denominator is small. Indeed, if we expand the exponential (see Appendix VII) as

$$1 - e^{(i2\pi/h)(E_2^0 - E_1^0 - h\nu)t} = 1 - \left\{1 + \left[\frac{i2\pi}{h}(E_2^0 - E_1^0 - h\nu)t\right] + \frac{1}{2}\left[\frac{i2\pi}{h}(E_2^0 - E_1^0 - h\nu)t\right]^2 + \cdots\right\}$$

where squared and higher terms in the expansion may be neglected, since $(E_2^0 - E_1^0 - h\nu)$ is small, then the first term becomes

$$-\frac{1 - [1 + (i2\pi/h)(E_2^0 - E_1^0 - h\nu)t + \cdots]}{(i2\pi/h)(E_2^0 - E_1^0 - h\nu)} \simeq t$$

Hence $C_2(t)$ is directly proportional to t and the transition probability increases with time. Thus if $\nu = \Delta E/h = (E_2^0 - E_1^0)/h$, there will be a significantly large transition probability. The space integral $\int \psi_2^{0*} H_p \psi_1^0\, d\tau$ must still be investigated, but this, at least, settles the "role of the proper frequency."

PROBLEM IV-6

Show that the probability of a transition $\Psi_1 \rightarrow \Psi_2$ is the same as the probability of a transition $\Psi_2 \rightarrow \Psi_1$.

(b) The transition moment integral

Even having the correct frequency, the value for the integral

$$I_{21} = \int \psi_2^{0*} H_p \psi_1^0\, d\tau \quad \text{in} \quad C_2(t) \sim (\int \psi_2^{0*} H_p \psi_1^0\, d\tau)(t)$$

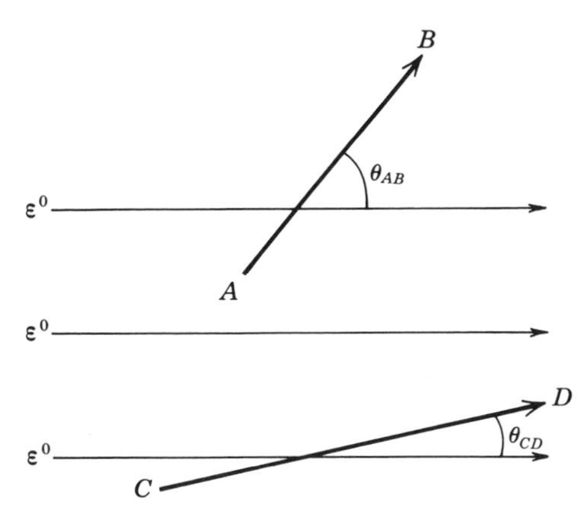

Fig. IV-4 Electric dipoles in an electric field.

must also be nonzero so that $C_2(t)$ be nonzero. This integral involves only space coordinates and is really the interaction of the initial and final states through the electric field. As such, this interaction can be considered to be the "mechanism for the transition" referred to in the preceding discussion. The *time-independent* effect of this interaction was written as H_p, and it was pointed out that H_p would probably be dependent on the electric field and on the particular molecule. For example, the electric dipole AB in Fig. IV-4 will have a certain energy in an electric field $\mathcal{E}^0$ that will be different from the interaction for CD. The difference will be dependent on both the orientation θ and the magnitude of the dipole. The interaction[1] of AB would be $H_{p,AB} = \mu_{AB}\mathcal{E}^0 \cos \theta_{AB}$, where μ_{AB} is the dipole AB. Thus it would be necessary to examine each system to find the interaction of the external field with the molecule and the way this interaction depended on the coordinates describing the system. Usually the electric field of the radiation is the same throughout the sample, and so it is necessary to see only how the interaction depends on the coordinates of the molecule. Having found the interaction and its coordinate dependence, the integration $\int \psi_f^{0*} H_p \psi_i^0 \, d\tau$ for given initial and final states of interest could be performed. First let us find an explicit statement of the interaction H_p.

(c) *The transition interaction*

Suppose, for the moment, that the nuclei of the molecule are fixed relative to one another. There will be a "center" of the *positive* charge, for example, in a homonuclear molecule H_2 this will be the center of the bond and will thus coincide with the center of mass. In Fig. IV-5 the center of positive charge is the origin of the set of coordinates x, y, z that describe

[1] See E. M. Purcell, "Electricity and Magnetism," McGraw-Hill, 1963.

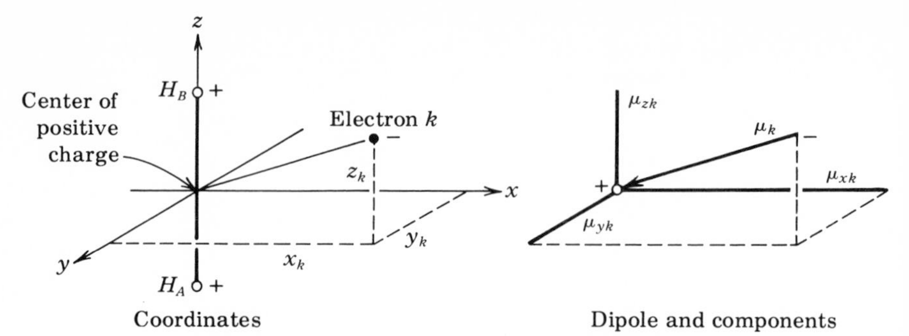

Fig. IV-5 The electric dipole.

the electrons. Electron k and the center of positive charge create an instantaneous dipole $\boldsymbol{\mu}_k$ with instantaneous components μ_{xk}, μ_{yk}, μ_{zk} (instantaneous in the sense that this is the dipole created at the instant when the "moving" electron is at this point). For example, the dipole component μ_{zk} = charge $\times$ separation $= -ez_k$. But the interaction of a dipole $\boldsymbol{\mu}_k$ in a field $\boldsymbol{\varepsilon}^0$ is $\boldsymbol{\varepsilon}^0\mu_k \cos w$, where w is the angle between field and dipole. If the field were in the z direction, w would be zero and the interaction would be simply $H_p = -\boldsymbol{\varepsilon}_z{}^0\mu_{kz} = \boldsymbol{\varepsilon}_z{}^0ez_k$. In general, the external field is defined in terms of the external coordinates, for example, $\boldsymbol{\varepsilon}^0$ might be along the external Z axis, as in Fig. IV-6. For the orientation in which the nuclei are, for the moment, considered fixed, the component of $\boldsymbol{\varepsilon}^0$ along z would be $\boldsymbol{\varepsilon}_z = \varepsilon^0 \cos \theta$. Thus the instantaneous contributions to H_p from μ_{zk}, μ_{yk}, μ_{xk} would be $H_p = H_{kz} + \cdots = \varepsilon^0 ez_k \cos \theta + \cdots$, where the $+ \cdots$ represents the contributions to the total interaction from instantaneous dipoles μ_{xk} and μ_{yk} in, the x and y directions.

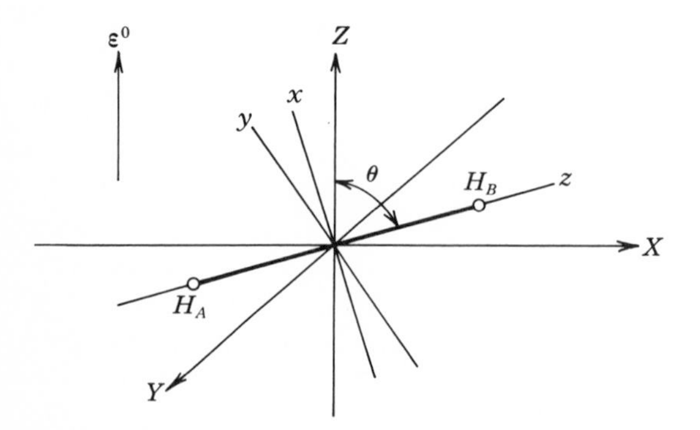

Fig. IV-6 Coordinates for the external field.

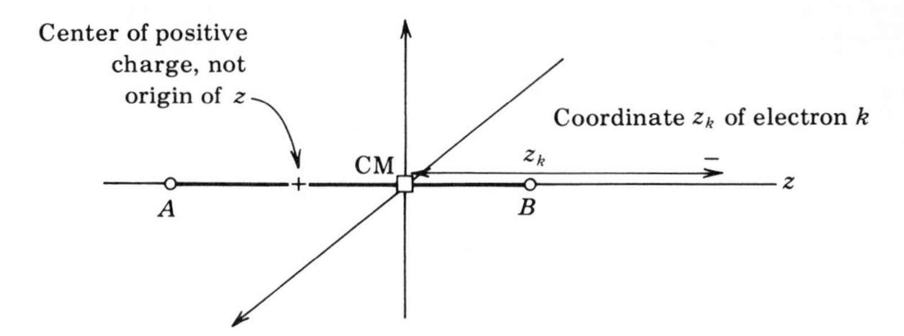

Fig. IV-7 The position of the center of positive charge.

Two points should immediately be obvious:

1. The magnitude of the instantaneous interaction depends on x_k, y_k, and z_k—the position coordinates of the electrons.
2. The magnitude of the instantaneous interaction depends on the orientation (relative to the external field) of the line joining the nuclei.

When a heteronuclear diatomic is considered, the magnitude of the instantaneous interaction will depend on the internuclear separation R. This is because the dipole depends on the distance between the electron and the center of positive charge. In a heteronuclear diatomic the position of the center of positive charge will be some position on the z axis that may *not* be the position of the center of mass (see Fig. IV-7).

If the internuclear separation were to change, the position of the center of positive charge relative to the position of the center of mass could change. One should thus replace z by $\mu_1 r + z$, where μ_1 is a proportionality constant indicating how much the center of positive charge is altered for a change in internuclear separation of r units. The interaction would then be written $H_{kz} = \varepsilon^0 e \cos\theta(z_k + \mu_1 r)$. The derivation including the x and y components would follow these same lines to give the total interaction

$$H_p = \varepsilon^0 e[(\cos\theta)\Sigma_k(z_k + \mu_1 r) + (\sin\theta\cos\phi)\Sigma_k x_k + (\sin\theta\sin\phi)\Sigma_k y_k] \qquad \text{(IV-6)}$$

where Σ_k indicates the sum of the interactions due to *all* the electrons.

Hence $$I_{21} = \int \psi_2^{0*}\{\varepsilon^0 e[(\cos\theta)\Sigma_k(z_k + \mu_1 r) + (\sin\theta\cos\phi)\Sigma_k x_k + (\sin\theta\sin\phi)\Sigma_k y_k]\}\psi_1^0\, d\tau$$

PROBLEM IV-7

The z component of H_p has been worked out in detail to give the first term in Eq. (IV-6). Use similar arguments to derive the x and y components, and show that they are the second and third terms in Eq. (IV-6).

(ii) The reduction of the transition probability integral

The transition probability integral

$$C_f = \int(\int \Psi_f^{0*} H_{pt} \Psi_i^0 \, d\tau) \, dt$$

for the transition $\Psi_i^0 \rightarrow \Psi_f^0$ has now been reduced[1] to

$$\begin{aligned} C_f &= (\int \text{space function } d\tau)(\int \text{time function } dt) \\ &= (\int \psi_f^{0*} H_p \psi_i^0 \, d\tau)[f(E_f^0 - E_i^0, \nu)] \\ &= (I_{if})[f(\Delta E, \nu)] \\ &= (\text{transition moment integral})(\text{line shape function}) \end{aligned}$$

Assuming the frequency $\nu = \Delta E/h$ required for the transition can be generated, the initial and final states could be inserted into the transition moment integral I_{if} and the integration carried out to determine the probability of a given transition. Considering the multitude of initial and final states and the resulting multitude of integrals, this would be a formidable task. It would seem appropriate to generate, if possible, a set of simple rules to obviate this task.

(a) *Symmetry*

In many cases an integral can immediately be said to be zero or nonzero simply on grounds of symmetry. This would certainly be useful, for, if the transition moment integral were known to be zero, then the probability of a transition would be zero. However, for a nonzero value of the transition moment integral, one could say that the transition was at least *possible.*

Consider the integral $k\int_{-a}^{a} x \, dx$ as an area. The integration limits are symmetric about $x = 0$, and the function x changes sign (x is odd) about this point. Consequently the integration includes an area with a negative sign for $x \leq 0$ and an equal area with positive sign for $x \geq 0$, the two canceling each other making the integral zero. But the integral $k\int_{-a}^{a} x^2 \, dx$ is not zero, for x^2 does not change sign about $x = 0$ (x^2 is even), and so the two areas for $x \leq 0$ and $x \geq 0$ do not cancel.

The argument can be extended to several variables, for example, the integral $\int\int kxy^2 \, dx \, dy$ can be split into $k\int x \, dx \int y^2 \, dy$ and each integral examined separately. Obviously if either of the integrals is zero, the product is zero. One might also note that an odd function times an odd function gives an even function, for example, $x \cdot x = x^2$, and odd times even is odd, for example, $x \cdot x^2 = x^3$, which changes sign.

In any case it would appear that, if the symmetry of the function $\psi_i[(z + \mu_1 r) \cos \theta + (\sin \theta \cos \phi)x + (\sin \theta \sin \phi)y]\psi_f$ appearing in the

[1] Here $\int \psi_f^{0*} H_p \psi_i^0 \, d\tau = \int \psi_i^{*0} H_p \psi_f^0$. Further, since all functions are "zeroth," the superscript will be dropped in subsequent sections.

transition moment integral could be determined, then it would be possible to say immediately whether or not the integral is zero. If, for example, the function has odd symmetry, then the integral would be zero, giving a transition probability coefficient of zero, and the transition would not occur—the "transition between the two states is forbidden by symmetry."

A simple example involves the harmonic-oscillator description. The first harmonic-oscillator function $n = 0$ was e^{-ar^2}, and the second one $n = 1$ was re^{-ar^2} (see Table II-4). Obviously the first function is symmetric (even), and the second function is antisymmetric (odd); however, the product of the second function and r (odd) will be even. Since the z component of I_{if}, that is, $\int \psi_i(z + \mu_1 r)\psi_f \, d\tau = \int_{-\infty}^{\infty} e^{-ar^2} (z + \mu_1 r) re^{-ar^2} \, dr$, contains an integral $\mu_1 \int_{-\infty}^{\infty} e^{-ar^2}(r)re^{-ar^2} \, dr$, where the integrand is even, I_{if} will be nonzero—the transition $\psi_{0,\text{vib}} \rightarrow \psi_{1,\text{vib}}$ will be possible. However, for $\psi_f = \psi_{2,\text{vib}}$, the integral $\int_{-\infty}^{\infty} e^{-ar^2}(r)(4ar^2 - 2)e^{-ar^2} \, dr$ will, by a similar argument, be zero, and so the transition $\psi_{0,\text{vib}} \rightarrow \psi_{2,\text{vib}}$ will be forbidden on the grounds of symmetry (at least within the harmonic-oscillator approximation). Another example, of use later, is the function in the integral $\int (\pi 2p_x) x (\sigma 1s) \, d\tau$. The integrand is symmetric and the corresponding transition is allowed. It should be pointed out that just because the integrand is symmetric does not mean that the integral *is* nonzero (the integral could be zero in both halves of the integration range). Nevertheless a symmetric integrand means the integral *could* be nonzero.

(b) *Orthogonality*

In some cases the transition moment integral may involve functions for which the symmetry is not immediately obvious. For example, in the integral $\int \alpha(1)\beta(1) \, d\tau_{\text{spin}}$ no analytical form has been given for α and β. Another instance is an integral

$$\int \psi_{i,\text{elec space}} \psi_{f,\text{elec space}} \, d\tau_{\text{elec space}} = \int 1s_a(1) 2s_a(1) \, d\tau_{\text{elec space}}$$

where $1s_a$ and $2s_a$ are atomic orbitals on atom a. In both cases the integrand involves descriptions of the electron that have different energies, i.e., in a magnetic field the energy of spin state α is different from that of β, and the electronic energy of $1s$ is different than that of $2s$. A particular example of this kind of integral has been discussed in Project 5, and, although it is beyond the scope of the present treatment, it can be shown that such integrals will always be zero.[1] The functions are said to be *orthogonal.*

[1] A precise statement is that when two functions ψ_i and ψ_j have different eigenvalues (in the above, different energies) of the same operator (here the energy operator), then the integral $\int \psi_i^* \psi_j \, d\tau$ equals zero.

(c) An incomplete integration

In $I_{if} = \int \psi_f^* H_p \psi_i \, d\tau$, the $d\tau$ implies integration over *all* coordinates. But in Sec. III-2 it was suggested that the motion of the nuclei was sluggish compared to that of the electrons. Consequently it would seem possible that an electronic transition could take place before the nuclear coordinates had changed very much. In other words in considering the integration of the transition moment integral for electronic transitions, the motion of the electron could build up enough interaction to cause a transition before the nuclear configuration changes. Hence for electronic transitions *it may not be necessary to carry out the integration over the nuclear coordinates R, θ, and ϕ.* This will be discussed shortly under the guise of the Franck-Condon principle.

IV-4 SELECTION RULES

The material presented in this chapter has been pointed toward the generation of "selection rules"—rules that indicate whether or not a given transition is possible! For convenience the selection rules will be presented according to the type of transition.

(i) Electronic transitions

(a) The transition moment integral

Electronic transitions are considered to occur so rapidly that the nuclear configuration may be taken as fixed. Consider, for the moment, only the z component of the interaction $H_{pz} = \varepsilon^0 e(\Sigma_k z_k + \mu_1 r) \cos \theta$; then the transition moment integral for the electronic transition from the initial state ψ_i to the final state ψ_f is

$$
\begin{aligned}
I_{if}(z \text{ component}) &= \varepsilon^0 e \int \psi_i H_{pz} \psi_f \, d\tau_{\text{el}} \\
&= \varepsilon^0 e \int (\psi_i) \Big(\sum_k z_k + \mu_1 r \Big) \cos \theta (\psi_f) \, d\tau_{\text{el}}
\end{aligned}
$$

where, following the discussion of Sec. IV-3 (ii) (c), the integration is over *only* the electronic coordinates. The z component of the transition moment integral may now be written as a sum of two terms A and B (from the two terms in H_{pz}):

$$
\begin{aligned}
&I_{if}(z \text{ component}) \\
&\quad = \varepsilon^0 e \Big(\underbrace{\int (\psi_i) \sum_k z_k \cos \theta (\psi_f) \, d\tau_{\text{el}}}_{A} + \underbrace{\mu_1 \int (\psi_i) r \cos \theta (\psi_f) \, d\tau_{\text{el}}}_{B} \Big) \\
&\quad = \varepsilon^0 e (A + B)
\end{aligned}
$$

The constant term ε^0 will now be dropped since it does not affect the *possibility* of a transition. In each term both ψ_i and ψ_f are products of an electronic part times a vibrational part, etc., as

$$\psi = \psi_{\text{elec space}}\psi_{\text{vib}}\psi_{\text{rot}}\psi_{\text{elec spin}}\psi_{\text{n spin}}$$

Further, in the interaction terms, z_k refers to the position of the electron k, $\cos\theta$ refers to rotation, and r refers to vibration. Thus in both A and B the electronic parts can be collected, as can the vibrational parts, etc. The integral then becomes a product of integrals:

$$\begin{aligned}
&I_{if}(z \text{ component})\\
&= \int (\psi_{i,\text{elec space}}\psi_{i,\text{vib}}\psi_{i,\text{rot}}\psi_{i,\text{elec spin}}\psi_{i,\text{n spin}}) \sum_k ez_k\\
&\quad \cos\theta(\psi_{f,\text{elec space}}\psi_{f,\text{vib}}\psi_{f,\text{rot}}\psi_{f,\text{elec spin}}\psi_{f,\text{n spin}})\, d\tau_{\text{el}}\\
&\quad + e\mu_1 \int (\psi_{i,\text{elec space}}\psi_{i,\text{vib}}\psi_{i,\text{rot}}\psi_{i,\text{elec spin}}\psi_{i,\text{n spin}}) r\\
&\quad \cos\theta(\psi_{f,\text{elec space}}\psi_{f,\text{vib}}\psi_{f,\text{rot}}\psi_{f,\text{elec spin}}\psi_{f,\text{n spin}})\, d\tau_{\text{el}}\\
&= \underbrace{\left(\int \psi_{i,\text{elec space}} \sum_k ez_k \psi_{f,\text{elec}}\, d\tau_{\text{elec space}}\right)}_{A_1} \cdot \underbrace{\psi_{i,\text{vib}}\psi_{f,\text{vib}}}_{A_2} \cdot \underbrace{\psi_{i,\text{rot}}\cos\theta\psi_{f,\text{rot}}}_{A_3}\\
&\quad \underbrace{\left(\int \psi_{i,\text{elec spin}}\psi_{f,\text{elec spin}}\, d\tau_{\text{elec spin}}\right)}_{A_4} \cdot \underbrace{\psi_{i,\text{n spin}}\psi_{f,\text{n spin}}}_{A_5}\\
&\quad + \underbrace{e\mu_1\left(\int \psi_{i,\text{elec space}}\psi_{f,\text{elec space}}\, d\tau_{\text{elec space}}\right)}_{B_1} \cdot \underbrace{\psi_{i,\text{vib}} r \psi_{f,\text{vib}}}_{B_2} \cdot \underbrace{\psi_{i,\text{rot}}\cos\theta\psi_{f,\text{rot}}}_{B_3} \cdot\\
&\quad \underbrace{\left(\int \psi_{i,\text{elec spin}}\psi_{f,\text{elec spin}}\, d\tau_{\text{elec spin}}\right)}_{B_4} \cdot \underbrace{\psi_{i,\text{n spin}}\psi_{f,\text{n spin}}}_{B_5}\\
&= A_1A_2A_3A_4A_5 + B_1B_2B_3B_4B_5\\
&= A + B
\end{aligned}$$

Clearly since $I_{if}(z)$ is a sum of two terms, for $I_{if}(z) = 0$ *both* the first and second terms must vanish. However, if *either* A or B is nonzero, then so is $I_{if}(z)$, and a transition is possible. (It should be noted that the x and y components of I_{if} would have to be examined as well before any definitive comments on I_{if} could be made.) Further, in determining whether A or B above are zero, it should clear that, since they are both the product of several factors, if any factor is zero, the product will be zero. Thus if $A_5 = 0$, then $A = 0$, or if $B_1 = 0$, then $B = 0$. Each factor must be examined separately!

In an electronic transition the initial and final electronic states are, by definition, different. Thus $B_1 = \int \psi_{i,\text{elec space}}\psi_{f,\text{elec space}}\, d\tau_{\text{elec space}}$ involves the integration over the product of two different eigenfunctions. But this is the same kind of integral that appeared in discussing orthogonality in Sec. IV-3(ii)(*b*), where it was found that this integral was always zero if the two functions had different eigenvalues of the same operator. [A similar example encountered much earlier (in Project 5) was the integral over two atomic orbitals having different energies $\int 2s2p\,d\tau = 0$.] With this in mind it is evident that $B_1 = 0$, and thus $B = 0$. Hence $I_{if}(z) = A + B = A + 0 = A$.

(b) Electron spin considerations

In the term A the factor A_4 is $\int \psi_{i,\text{elec spin}}\,\psi_{f,\text{elec spin}}\,d\tau_{\text{elec spin}}$, an integration over the product of two functions that, if they have different eigenvalues, give zero for the integral, or, if they are the same, give a nonzero integral:

$$A_4 = 0 \qquad \text{if } \psi_{i,\text{elec spin}} \neq \psi_{f,\text{elec spin}}, \text{ say, } A_4 = \int \alpha\beta\,d\tau_{\text{elec spin}} = 0$$
$$A_4 \neq 0 \qquad \text{if } \psi_{i,\text{elec spin}} = \psi_{f,\text{elec spin}}, \text{ say, } A_4 = \int \alpha\alpha\,d\tau_{\text{elec spin}} \neq 0$$

Thus since $I_{if}(z \text{ component}) = A = A_1A_2A_3A_4A_5$, then

$$I_{if}(z \text{ component}) = 0$$

if $A_4 = 0$, and there would be zero probability of a transition. But $A_4 = 0$ only if the electronic spin description changes, so that no electronic transitions can take place with a change in electron spin. *Only if the spin is unchanged will* $A_4 \neq 0$ and there be a possibility for a transition. The rule is: *in an electronic transition the spin function is unchanged;* thus a singlet ($\alpha\beta - \beta\alpha$) to triplet ($\alpha\alpha$, etc.) transition is forbidden here.

PROBLEM IV-8

If one of the electrons in the bonding orbital of HF were to be excited to the σ^* molecular orbital, would the space description of electrons 9 and 10 be $[\sigma(9)\sigma^*(10) + \sigma(10)\sigma^*(9)]$ or $[\sigma(9)\sigma^*(10) - \sigma(10)\sigma^*(9)]$? (*Hint:* What is the spin function of the excited state?)

(c) Space considerations

Even if A_4 is not zero by the restriction of the previous paragraph, we must still inquire as to the value of the remaining factors in A. Consider the factor $A_1 = \Sigma_k \int_{-\infty}^{\infty} \psi_{i,\text{elec space}} e z_k \psi_{f,\text{elec space}}\,d\tau_{\text{elec space}}$. The symmetry arguments of Sec. IV-3(ii) would be useful here, for, if the product $\psi_{i,\text{elec space}}\,z_k\psi_{f,\text{elec space}}$ were odd, then A_1 would be zero giving A zero, and no transition would take place. However, if $\psi_{i,\text{elec space}}\,z_k\psi_{f,\text{elec space}}$ were even, then A_1 would not necessarily be zero; A could be nonzero and a transition could be possible. The factor z will, of course, be odd (for the integration $\int_{-\infty}^{\infty} dz$), so that the remaining terms in the integral

$\psi_{i,\text{elec space}}\,\psi_{f,\text{elec space}}$ must be such that an odd function is generated that, when multiplied by z, results in an even integrand:

$$
\begin{aligned}
A_1 &= \int[(\psi_{i,\text{elec space}})\cdot(\psi_{f,\text{elec space}})]\cdot(z = \text{odd function})\,d\tau_{\text{elec space}} \\
&= \int\{[\psi_{i,\text{elec space}}(\text{odd})]\cdot[\psi_{f,\text{elec space}}(\text{even})]\}\cdot \\
&\qquad\qquad (\text{odd function})\,d\tau_{\text{elec space}} \\
&= \int(\text{odd}\cdot\text{even})\cdot(\text{odd function})\,d\tau_{\text{elec space}} \\
&= \int(\text{odd})\cdot(\text{odd function})\,d\tau_{\text{elec space}} \\
&= \int\text{even function}\,d\tau_{\text{elec space}} \\
&\neq 0
\end{aligned}
$$

The requirement can be summarized by saying that the initial and final electronic states must have different symmetry for the probability of the transition to be nonzero. Thus *electronic transitions are allowed only between states of different symmetry.*

PROBLEM IV-9

Which of the following electronic transitions would be likely to be observed, $\sigma 1s \rightarrow \sigma 2s$, $\sigma 1s \rightarrow \sigma 2p$, $\sigma 1s \rightarrow \sigma^* 2s$, $\sigma 1s \rightarrow \pi 2p$? (*Hint:* Consider both homonuclear and heteronuclear diatomic molecules.)

(*d*) *The Franck-Condon principle*

The foregoing analysis has indicated the conditions under which A_1 and A_4 are nonzero. The remaining factors A_2, A_3, A_5, of A must now be examined. These factors all involve nuclear coordinates, and, since the nuclear configuration is considered fixed, there is no integration over these coordinates. However, it is evident that the larger A_2, A_3, and A_5, the larger will be their product, the larger will be A, and hence, the more probable the transition. Consider, for example, the factor $A_2 = \psi_{i,\text{vib}}\,\psi_{f,\text{vib}}$. If this factor is to be large for a given value of r, then $\psi_{i,\text{vib}}$ and $\psi_{f,\text{vib}}$ should be large in magnitude.

Consider the energy level diagram of Fig. IV-8, in which some of the vibrational functions $\psi_{i,\text{vib}}$ and $\psi_{f,\text{vib}}$ are indicated on their respective electronic curves. If the molecule is initially in its ground vibrational state, the more probable internuclear separations are $R \simeq R_e$. The values of the vibrational functions at this particular internuclear separation are indicated in the figure for the initial vibrational state ($n_i = 0$) and two final vibrational states $n_f = 0$ and $n_f = 1$. A transition from the initial electronic state having an internuclear separation of R_e to a final electronic state having an internuclear separation R_e (the internuclear separation is constant during the transition) would have as the A_2- factor

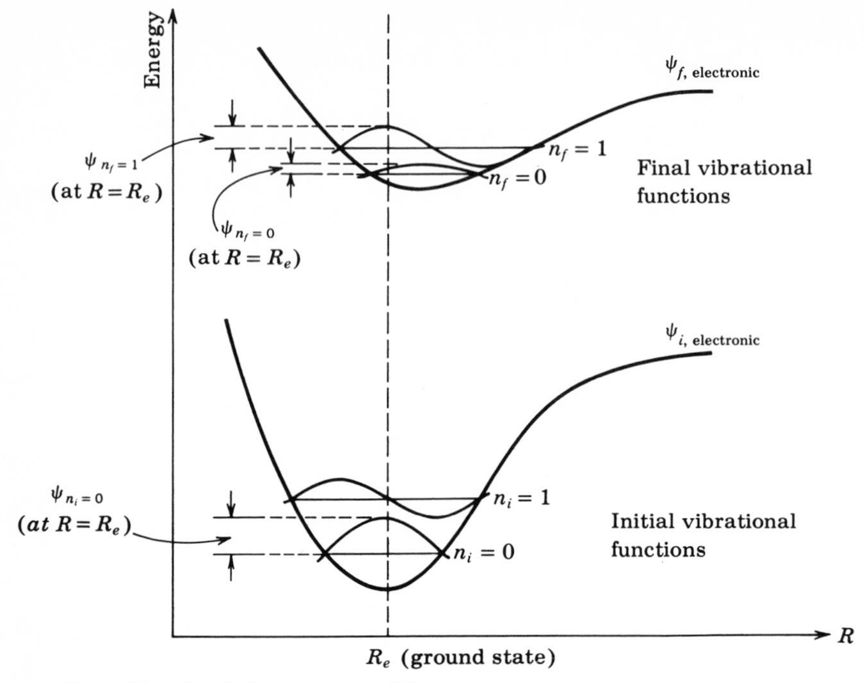

Fig. IV-8 Vibrational-electronic transitions.

in the transition moment integral:

$$A_2 = \psi_{n_i=0,\text{vib}}(\text{at } R = R_e) \cdot \psi_{n_f=0,\text{vib}}(\text{at } R = R_e) \qquad \text{for a transition to } n_{f,\text{vib}} = 0$$

or

$$A_2 = \psi_{n_i=0,\text{vib}}(\text{at } R = R_e) \cdot \psi_{n_f=1,\text{vib}}(\text{at } R = R_e) \qquad \text{for a transition to } n_{f,\text{vib}} = 1$$

But from Fig. IV-8 it is clear that $\psi_{n_f=1,\text{vib}}(\text{at } R = R_e)$ is considerably larger than $\psi_{n_f=0,\text{vib}}(\text{at } R = R_e)$, so that A_2 will be larger when the transition is made to $n_{f,\text{vib}} = 1$. Thus one would predict that an electronic transition, at least for this case, *could be accompanied* by a vibrational transition $\Delta n_{\text{vib}} = 1$. One could carry out a somewhat similar analysis for the term A_3. The procedure is rather more complicated, in that one must consider the relative population of the rotational states. The result is again that rotational as well as vibrational changes may accompany an electronic transition (see, for example, Fig. V-29).

PROBLEM IV-10

Use Fig. IV-8 to predict the vibrational change if the initial state were originally vibrationally excited ($n_i = 1$).

(ii) Rotational-vibrational transitions

(a) The transition moment integral

Where electronic transitions do *not* occur, the nuclear coordinates would have time to take up all their values, and so integration over r, θ, and ϕ must be carried out. Neglecting the spin terms, for which the same restrictions[1] as for the previous section hold, the transition moment integral becomes

$$
\begin{aligned}
I_{if} &= \underbrace{\left(\int \psi_{i,\text{elec space}} \sum_k e z_k \psi_{f,\text{elec space}}\, d\tau_{\text{elec space}}\right)}_{C_1} \underbrace{\left(\int \psi_{i,\text{vib}} \psi_{f,\text{vib}}\, d\tau_{\text{vib}}\right)}_{C_2} \\
&\quad \underbrace{\left(\int \psi_{i,\text{rot}} \cos\theta\, \psi_{f,\text{rot}}\, d\tau_{\text{rot}}\right)}_{C_3} + e\mu_1 \underbrace{\left(\int \psi_{i,\text{elec space}} \psi_{f,\text{elec space}}\, d\tau_{\text{elec space}}\right)}_{D_1} \\
&\quad \underbrace{\left(\int \psi_{i,\text{vib}}\, r\, \psi_{f,\text{vib}}\, d\tau_{\text{vib}}\right)}_{D_2} \underbrace{\left(\int \psi_{i,\text{rot}} \cos\theta\, \psi_{f,\text{rot}}\, d\tau_{\text{rot}}\right)}_{D_3} \\
&= C_1 C_2 C_3 + D_1 D_2 D_3 \\
&= C + D
\end{aligned}
$$

The probability of a transition is again made up of a sum of two terms, each of which is a product of factors, but now *all* factors involve an integration over the appropriate variable.

In $C_1 = \int \psi_{i,\text{elec space}} \Sigma_k e z_k \psi_{f,\text{elec space}}\, d\tau_{\text{elec space}}$, the term $e z_k$ is the z component of the instantaneous electric dipole due to electron k. By definition $\psi_{i,\text{elec space}} = \psi_{f,\text{elec space}}$. Then, since $\psi^2_{i,\text{elec space}}$ is a probability, we see that the integral really generates the average value of the electric dipole as

$$
C_1 = \underbrace{\int \psi^2_{i,\text{elec space}}}_{\text{Probability}} \underbrace{\left(\sum_k e z_k\right)}_{\text{Dipole}} d\tau_{\text{elec space}} = \mu_0
$$

(Strictly speaking, this is μ_{0z}, the z component of the electric dipole of the molecule.) Furthermore, the factor

$$
D_1 = \int \psi_{i,\text{elec space}} \psi_{f,\text{elec space}}\, d\tau_{\text{elec space}} = \int \psi^2_{i,\text{elec space}}\, d\tau_{\text{elec space}} = 1
$$

since $\psi_{i,\text{elec space}} = \psi_{f,\text{elec space}}$ by definition, and all descriptions are normalized.

The result is simply

$$
I_{if}(z \text{ component}) = \mu_0 C_2 C_3 + \mu_1 D_2 D_3
$$

[1] Since nuclear spin is being integrated over, the nuclear spin must also be unchanged.

(b) Pure rotational transitions

The integration of $C_2 = \int \psi_{i,\text{vib}} \psi_{f,\text{vib}}\, d\tau_{\text{vib}}$ will give zero unless $\psi_{i,\text{vib}} = \psi_{f,\text{vib}}$, for this is the familiar integration of a product of two eigenfunctions, which is zero if the eigenfunctions have different eigenvalues. Only if $n_{i,\text{vib}} = n_{f,\text{vib}}$ that is, $\Delta n_{\text{vib}} = 0$, will this integral be nonzero. If

$$\Delta n_{\text{vib}} = 0$$

no vibrational transition can take place, and one is dealing with only pure rotational transitions for which I_{if} (z component) $= \mu_0 1 C_3 + \mu_1 D_2 D_3$. However, if $\Delta n_{\text{vib}} = 0$, the integral

$$D_2 = \int_{-\infty}^{\infty} \psi_{i,\text{vib}} r \psi_{f,\text{vib}}\, d\tau_{\text{vib}} = \int_{-\infty}^{\infty} \psi_{i,\text{vib}}^2 r\, d\tau_{\text{vib}}$$

But $\psi_{i,\text{vib}}^2$ is even and r is odd, so that the integrand is odd and will result in a zero value for the integral. Hence $D_2 = 0$, and the probability of a pure rotational transition is simply

$$I_{if}(z \text{ component}) = \mu_0 C_3 + \mu_1 0 = \mu_0 C_3$$

so that *a pure rotational transition will take place only for molecules that have a nonzero value of the permanent dipole.*

Also $C_3 = \int \psi_{i,\text{rot}} \cos\theta \psi_{f,\text{rot}}\, d\tau_{\text{rot}}$ must be nonzero for there to be any chance of a transition. This integration is rather more difficult to give in terms of familiar symmetry arguments, but, if the so-called recursion formulas are used, the integral can be cast in more familiar terms. These formulas simply relate one rotational description to another, for example, they relate the rotational description $\psi_{3,\text{rot}}$ to its "nearest neighbors" $\psi_{2,\text{rot}}$ and $\psi_{4,\text{rot}}$ as $\psi_{3,\text{rot}} = (1/\cos\theta)(a\psi_{4,\text{rot}} + b\psi_{2,\text{rot}})$, where a and b are constants. In this way the final rotational description $\psi_{f,\text{rot}}$ can be given as $\psi_{f,\text{rot}} = (1/\cos\theta)(a\psi_{f+1,\text{rot}} + b\psi_{f-1,\text{rot}})$, where a and b are constants, and $\psi_{f+1,\text{rot}}$ and $\psi_{f-1,\text{rot}}$ are the rotational descriptions "above and below" $\psi_{f,\text{rot}}$. This statement for $\psi_{f,\text{rot}}$ may be inserted in C_3 as

$$\begin{aligned} C_3 &= \int \psi_{i,\text{rot}} \cos\theta \frac{1}{\cos\theta} (a\psi_{f+1,\text{rot}} + b\psi_{f-1,\text{rot}})\, d\tau_{\text{rot}} \\ &= a \int \psi_{i,\text{rot}} \psi_{f+1,\text{rot}}\, d\tau_{\text{rot}} + b \int \psi_{i,\text{rot}} \psi_{f-1,\text{rot}}\, d\tau_{\text{rot}} \end{aligned}$$

Each of the terms in C_3 is the familiar integration discussed in Sec. IV-3(ii)(*b*), and the integral will be zero unless the ψ's have the same quantum number. Thus in $\int \psi_{i,\text{rot}} \psi_{f+1,\text{rot}}\, d\tau_{\text{rot}}$, $\psi_{i,\text{rot}}$ must be the same as $\psi_{f+1,\text{rot}}$, that is, i must be the same as $f + 1$, otherwise the integral will be zero. Similarly the second term will be zero unless $i = f - 1$. Unless *either* of these conditions hold, C_3 will be zero and there will be no rotational transition. The conditions for rotational transition are then $i = f \pm 1$, or $i - f = \pm 1$, or $\Delta l_{\text{rot}} = \pm 1$, so that the rotational transition can only change to its "nearest neighbor," say, $l = 0 \rightarrow l = 1$, or $l = 1 \rightarrow l = 2$ but not $l = 0 \rightarrow l = 2$. One obtains, finally, the statement that *pure rotational transitions only occur for molecules with a permanent dipole* ($\mu_0 \neq 0$) and that, *for these transitions*, $\Delta l = \pm 1$.

PROBLEM IV-11

Which of the following molecules would be expected to give "pure" rotational spectra, HCl, H_2, Cl_2? (*Hint:* In the evaluation of C above consider whether $\psi_{i,\text{elec space}}$ would be symmetric about $z = 0$.)

(c) Pure vibrational transitions

By definition, in a pure vibrational transition the rotational description is unchanged, and, following the lines of the previous paragraph, it is clear that C_3 will be zero if the rotational description remains unchanged. The probability of a transition is then given by I_{if} (z component) $= \mu_1 D_2 D_3$. But D_3 is the same as C_3 and hence is zero, so that the *probability of a pure vibrational transition is indeed zero for diatomic molecules.*

(d) Mixed vibrational-rotational transitions

Treating the electronic part as in Sec. IV-4(ii) (*a*) gives the transition moment integral as

$$I_{if}(z \text{ component}) = \mu_0 C_2 C_3 + \mu_1 D_2 D_3$$

If a vibrational change is allowed, then $C_2 = \int \psi_{i,\text{vib}} \psi_{f,\text{vib}} \, d\tau_{\text{vib}}$ will be zero since the integrand is a product of two *different* vibrational eigenfunctions. Thus $I_{if}(z \text{ component}) = \mu_1 D_2 D_3$. Considering the factors D_2 and D_3, it is clear, following the arguments of Sec. IV-4(ii) (*b*), that D_3 will be nonzero only for rotational changes to "adjacent states," that is, $\Delta l = \pm 1$. The integral $D_2 = \int \psi_{i,\text{vib}} r \psi_{f,\text{vib}} \, d\tau_{\text{vib}}$ presents the same kind of problems that C_3 raised earlier, and a similar "recursion relation" for $\psi_{f,\text{vib}}$ must be used:

$$\psi_{f,\text{vib}} = \frac{1}{r} (a' \psi_{f+1,\text{vib}} + b' \psi_{f-1,\text{vib}})$$

so that

$$\begin{aligned} D_2 &= \int \psi_{i,\text{vib}} r \frac{1}{r} (a' \psi_{f+1,\text{vib}} + b' \psi_{f-1,\text{vib}}) \, d\tau_{\text{vib}} \\ &= a' \int \psi_{i,\text{vib}} \psi_{f+1,\text{vib}} \, d\tau_{\text{vib}} + b' \int \psi_{i,\text{vib}} \psi_{f-1,\text{vib}} \, d\tau_{\text{vib}} \end{aligned}$$

Again the integrals will be nonzero only if the functions are the same within the integral, that is, $i = f \pm 1$, or $i - f = \pm 1$, or $\Delta n_{\text{vib}} = \pm 1$.

In summary the only *vibrational-rotational transitions that are possible are those for which* $\Delta l_{\text{rot}} = \pm 1$, $\Delta n_{\text{vib}} = \pm 1$ *and for molecules for which* $\mu_1 \neq 0$.

It has been possible to get to these selection rules rather easily for diatomic molecules. However, on obtaining these rules, one must not expect them to apply in all cases, for the models are approximate, e.g., the harmonic-oscillator model is approximate, and one might expect that, due to *an harmonicity*, terms in r^2, r^3 would occur in a corrected form of H_{pz} as

$$H_{pz} = \mathcal{E}^0 e \left(\sum_k z_k + \mu_1 r + \mu_2 r^2 + \cdots \right) \cos\theta$$

and then, of course, there could be a nonzero value for the transition $\Delta n = 2$ (see Prob. IV-12). However, since μ_2 will be small, these transitions would be less likely to occur. Another well-known violation of the selection rules is the "spin-forbidden" transition in mercury where the dominant contribution is a singlet $\leftrightarrow$ triplet transition. Such transitions are not found in our treatment because the spin-orbit terms have been omitted. The selection rules are only as good as the model! The rules are summarized in Table IV-2.

Table IV-2 Selection rules for diatomic molecules

Type of transition	*Electronic*	*Vibrational*	*Rotational*	*Spin*	*Comments*
Pure electronic	Different symmetry	$\Delta n = 0$	$\Delta l = 0$	No change	....
Pure vibrational	No change	$\Delta n = 0$	$\Delta l = 0$	No change	Does not occur with dipole interaction
Pure rotational	No change	$\Delta n = 0$	$\Delta l = \pm 1$	No change	$\mu_0 \neq 0$
Vibrational-rotational	No change	$\Delta n = \pm 1$	$\Delta l = \pm 1$	No change	$\mu_1 \neq 0$
Vibrational-electronic	Different symmetry	$\Delta n = 0, 1, 2, \ldots$	$\Delta l = 0, \pm 1, \pm 2, \ldots$	No change No change	Δn depends on relative position of potential curves

PROBLEM IV-12

If the z component of H_p contains $[\Sigma_k z_k + \mu_1 r + \mu_2 r^2] \cos\theta$, show that a vibrational transition $\Delta n_{\text{vib}} = 2$ is possible. (*Hint:* Consider the integral $\int_{-\infty}^{\infty} \mu_2 \psi_{0,\text{vib}} r^2 \psi_{2,\text{vib}}\, dr$.)

When polyatomic molecules are considered, the integrals are less easily evaluated, and here the use of symmetry becomes much more prominent. Although the same principles apply, the derivation of these selection rules is beyond the scope of this text, and the polyatomic selection rules will be quoted only where needed.

It must be emphasized that only *electric* dipole-induced transitions have been discussed. The magnetic dipole-induced transitions of NMR will have different selection rules. Again these will be quoted where necessary.

V
Analysis of Spectra

V-1 INTRODUCTION

As indicated in the previous chapter, the spectra observed for molecular systems can be quite complicated, and the "sorting out" of the profusion of lines and their assignment to the appropriate transitions is a formidable task. In fact, it is this step that is the major problem of spectroscopy. In the spectroscopic applications given so far, the assignments have frequently been taken as "obvious." They are not really obvious but are the result of a fairly straightforward analysis and the application of the results of the previous chapter. This analysis, skimmed over in the applications of the first three chapters because the tools were not available, may now be undertaken. Once the proper assignment has been completed, the calculations that can be made are relatively straightforward.

The application of the previous chapters might be divided into two levels: the analysis and assignment of the lines in the spectrum, and the calculation of properties of the molecule given the proper spectral assignment. The two steps are, of course, not completely independent since the same model for the system may be used in both.

The sort of problems one is faced with in the first step could be summarized in the two questions:

1. To what type of transition does the line belong, or in other words which quantum numbers are changing?
2. What are the initial and final descriptions of the system; i.e., what are the quantum numbers of the initial and final states?

To answer these questions, we know:

1. The frequency range corresponding to the usual energy change for a given type of transition (e.g., an electronic transition will lie in the visible or ultraviolet).
2. The source of the multitude of lines [e.g., the mixed transitions discussed in Secs. IV-1 and IV-4(ii)].
3. The selection rules that tell which transitions are possible (this is based in part on other nonspectroscopic information, e.g., whether the molecule has a dipole moment).
4. The Franck-Condon principle and statistical mechanics, which indicate the *relative* probability of allowed transitions.

In the second step, significant features of the system can be deduced with use of the model selected for the system. An example, already discussed, was the calculation of the force constant for a molecule. Another example is the determination of the approximate bond length for the unsaturated dyes (see Project 2 in Chap. I, where the particle-in-a-box model could be used for the system). Often one is provided with the frequency for a given transition, and the first step is bypassed; at other times the assignment may be carried out without our being clearly aware of the steps being taken. This is particularly true of elementary applications of spectroscopy. Nevertheless, it is essential to know what is going on, and why, in the simple cases, so that in the complicated situations, where it really matters, the procedure will be more familiar.

V-2 LOW-RESOLUTION SPECTRA

(i) Elementary spectral analysis

Complicated and profuse experimental detail about a chemical system may frequently be a hindrance in obtaining the general features since the detail may, in fact, mask the significant features. An example is the

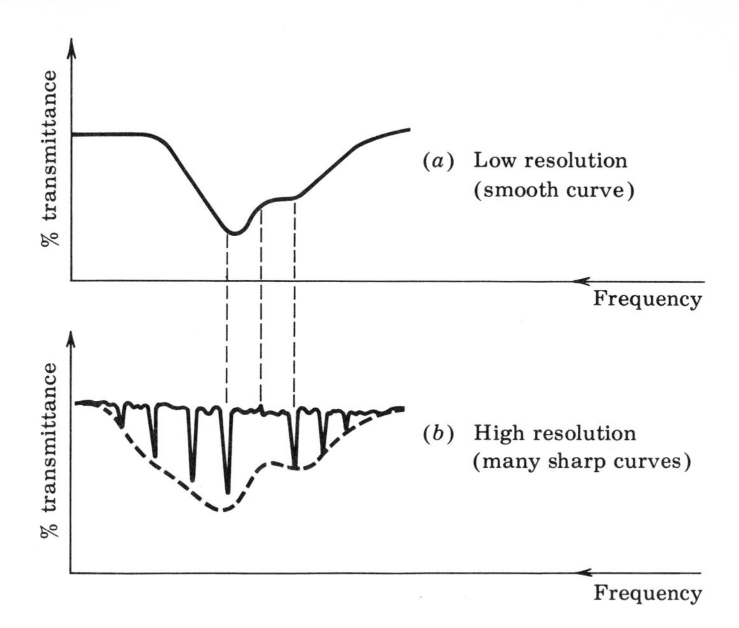

Fig. V-1 Comparison of low- and high-resolution spectra. (*a*) Low resolution (smooth curve); (*b*) high resolution (many sharp curves).

simple test for metal ions of inserting the metal salt solution into a bunsen flame. One sees a color, characteristic of the system, and identification may be made. If we were to photograph the line spectrum of this system, a profusion of lines would be recorded, and the simple general feature of color might be missed. In the same way, but on a somewhat more sophisticated level, worthwhile initial information about a system can be obtained from low-resolution spectra that consist of more or less smooth curves indicating a general area of frequency absorption rather than the detailed lines of high-resolution spectra. Such a spectrum is given in Fig. V-1*a*, which, under high resolution, would yield the spectral detail found in Fig. V-1*b*.

The spectra in the ultraviolet, infrared, and microwave regions will now be examined. Particular emphasis will be given to the steps in the analysis, so that complicated cases will be more readily interpreted.

(ii) Visible and ultraviolet spectroscopy—electronic spectra

The visible and ultraviolet region may be considered as including wavelengths from about 7000 Å to 1000 Å, or encompassing wave numbers from $\bar{\nu} = 14{,}000\ \text{cm}^{-1}$ to $\bar{\nu} = 100{,}000\ \text{cm}^{-1}$. A typical low-resolution spectrum is sketched in Fig. V-2. (This spectrum could be that of one of the dyes of Project 2.) From Table IV-1 it is known that the energy change corresponding to this range is of the magnitude produced by a change in the electronic description; i.e., this is an "electronic spectrum." There may, indeed, be other changes in the system, but since all other changes have a far smaller energy contribution, they will produce lines relatively closely spaced to some central line; i.e., they would be the detail of the spectrum, which, for the moment, will not concern us.

Thus the general feature of the spectrum corresponds to some electronic transition. But this general feature, i.e., the absorption region, stretches over such a considerable frequency range that *some* frequency must be selected to which the electronic change corresponds. Transitions in which there are vibrational changes as well as electronic changes could contribute to this width.[1] For example, in the discussion of the Franck-Condon principle for electronic transitions, we saw that the vibrational quantum number could change as $\Delta n_{\text{vib}} = 0, \pm 1$, etc. The change $\Delta n = -1$ would imply that the initial vibrational state must have been at least $n_{i,\text{vib}} = 1$. But this has a considerably higher energy than $n_{i,\text{vib}} = 0$, so this state will be less likely, and the change $\Delta n = -1$ will be relatively rare. Thus one need consider only electronic vibrational transitions $\Delta n = 0, 1, 2$, etc., for which the energy change would be $\Delta E = \Delta E_{\text{el}} + 0$, $\Delta E = \Delta E_{\text{el}} + \Delta E_{\text{vib}}$, etc. Consequently the lower-energy transition would be more likely to correspond to the pure electronic change. Hence in Fig. V-2 the position b at higher wavelength (i.e., lower frequency–lower energy) would be taken for the $\lambda_{\max}$ corresponding to the electronic change.

Having settled on the fact that this is chiefly an electronic transition, and having settled on the frequency corresponding to this transition, one must now turn to the question of *which* particular electronic transition is

[1] In addition, the range of frequencies admitted by the optical system and the response of the recorder will contribute to the breadth as will (to a much lesser extent) the Heisenberg uncertainty $\Delta E > h/\Delta t 4\pi$.

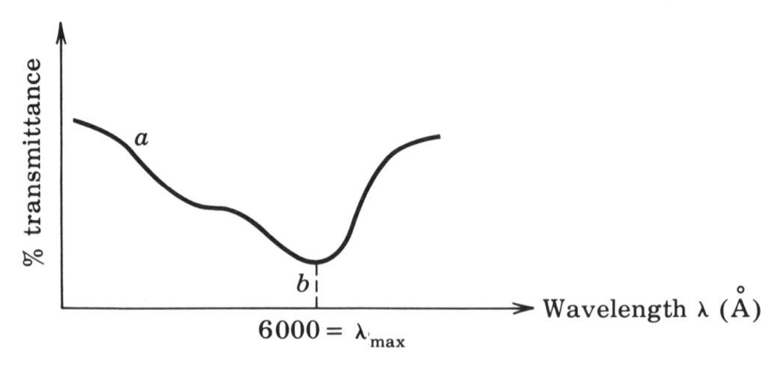

Fig. V-2 An ultraviolet spectrum.

being observed—what are the initial and final electronic descriptions? To answer this, the descriptions of the system must be found in terms of some model. Having found the descriptions of the system, one should use statistical mechanics and selection rules to indicate which of these descriptions correspond to the initial and final states of the observed transition.

An example of the procedure is the analysis of the spectrum produced by the transitions of the delocalized electrons in the molecule-ion

$$\gt N^{+}{=}\overset{|}{C}{-}\underset{|}{C}{=}\overset{|}{C}{-}\underset{|}{C}{=}\overset{|}{C}{-}N\lt$$

(see Project 2). The model is the particle-in-a-box, which, it should be pointed out, may work well for such systems of π electrons but is *not* a general model for electronic systems—rather, the MO approach described earlier is more generally applicable. However, using this "box model," the molecular orbitals describing the individual electrons are taken as $\psi_n = \sin(n\pi x/L)$ with energy

$$E_n = \frac{n^2h^2}{8mL^2}$$

Since there are eight π-electrons in the system illustrated, the description of the electrons would be

$$\Psi_{n_1,n_2,\ldots,n_8} = \psi_{n_1}\psi_{n_2}\cdots\psi_{n_8}$$

with energy

$$E_{n_1,\ldots,n_8} = \sum_{i=1}^{8} \frac{n_i{}^2h^2}{8mL^2}$$

The larger the values of n_i, the more energy the system would have. But statistical mechanics (see Project 4) would indicate that the higher the energy of a state, the less likely is the system to be in that state. The lowest possible energy would result from having two electrons in each of the first four orbitals, giving

$$\Psi_{1,2,3,4} = (\psi_1)^2(\psi_2)^2(\psi_3)^2(\psi_4)^2$$

with energy

$$E_{1,2,3,4} = \frac{h^2}{8mL^2}\,2\sum_{n=1}^{4} n^2 = \frac{h^2}{8mL^2}\left[2\sum_{n=1}^{3} n^2 + 2(4)^2\right]$$

$$= \frac{h^2}{8mL^2}\,[28 + 2(4)^2]$$

The next lowest state would result from having the first six electrons paired in the first three orbitals and the last two electrons in ψ_4 and ψ_5, respectively. Then

$$\Psi_{1,2,3,4,5} = (\psi_1)^2(\psi_2)^2(\psi_3)^2(\psi_4)(\psi_5)$$

and

$$E_{1,2,3,4,5} = \frac{h^2}{8mL^2}\left(2\sum_{n=1}^{3} n^2 + 4^2 + 5^2\right) = \frac{h^2}{8mL^2}(28 + 4^2 + 5^2)$$

A somewhat higher energy would have the first six electrons paired as before, and the last two paired in ψ_5. Then

$$\Psi_{1,2,3,5} = (\psi_1)^2(\psi_2)^2(\psi_3)^2(\psi_5)^2$$

and

$$E_{1,2,3,5} = \frac{h^2}{8mL^2}\left(2\sum_{n=1}^{3} n^2 + 2(5)^2\right) = \frac{h^2}{8mL^2}(28 + 2(5)^2)$$

An even higher-energy description is

$$\Psi_{1,2,3,4,6} = (\psi_1)^2(\psi_2)^2(\psi_3)^2(\psi_4)(\psi_6)$$

with

$$E_{1,2,3,4,6} = \frac{h^2}{8mL^2}(28 + 4^2 + 6^2)$$

These are the four lowest electronic levels, and those most likely to be populated; in fact, the first one, with all electrons paired, is probably by far the most populated level. The first four energies and descriptions could be summarized as

π-electron energy	*π-electron description*
$\frac{h^2}{8mL^2}(28 + 4^2 + 6^2)$	$(\psi_1)^2(\psi_2)^2(\psi_3)^2(\psi_4)(\psi_6)$
$\frac{h^2}{8mL^2}[28 + 2(5)^2]$	$(\psi_1)^2(\psi_2)^2(\psi_3)^2(\psi_5)^2$
$\frac{h^2}{8mL^2}(28 + 4^2 + 5^2)$	$(\psi_1)^2(\psi_2)^2(\psi_3)^2(\psi_4)(\psi_5)$
$\frac{h^2}{8mL^2}[28 + 2(4)^2]$	$(\psi_1)^2(\psi_2)^2(\psi_3)^2(\psi_4)^2$

Since the description of all but the last two electrons is the same throughout, the first six may be ignored, and the description of only the last two electrons need be indicated. This procedure is illustrated in Fig. V-3. The transitions that must be considered as candidates for the

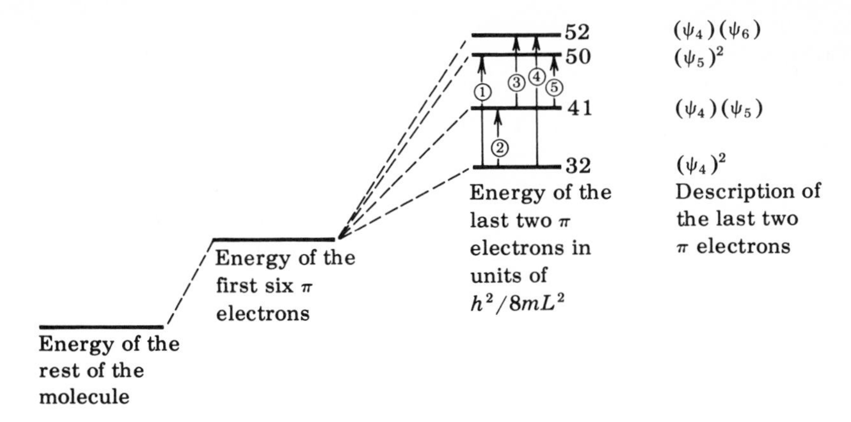

Fig. V-3 The π-electron energy for the transitions.

one observed are indicated by the arrows ①, ②, ③, ④, and ⑤. Transition ① involves the *simultaneous* change of two electrons from ψ_4 to ψ_5; but the probability of such a simultaneous change is very small, and this type of transition can be ignored. The selection rules may now be used to see if any of the other transitions can be ruled out; i.e., for an electronic transition the description of the initial and final states must have different symmetry along at least one of the axes. Transition ② has a final state described by $\psi_4\psi_5$. To determine the symmetry of this product, it may be noted that $x = L/2$ would be the midpoint of the integration for the transition moment integral $I_{45} \sim \int_0^L \psi_4 H_p \psi_5 \, dx$. But as illustrated in Fig. V-4, ψ_4 is antisymmetric (odd) and ψ_5 symmetric (even) about this point. This means that $\psi_4\psi_5$ = odd $\times$ even = odd, so the final state has a different symmetry from the initial state, making transition ② *possible.*

Similarly transitions ③ and ⑤ are possible, for the description of the initial and final states will have different symmetry. However, ④

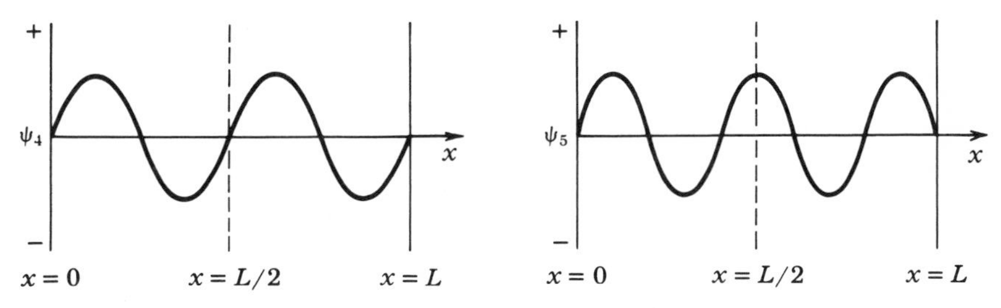

Fig. V-4 Symmetry of the particle-in-a-box wave function.

is not possible, since the initial and final states have the same symmetry. In choosing from among ②, ③, and ⑤ as the transition being observed, one must remember that there will be many more molecules in the ground state, and this, in turn, would suggest a much higher probability of transition ② taking place. Thus the wavelength of $\lambda = 6000$ Å may be taken to correspond to ②, the transition of an electron from ψ_4 to ψ_5.

The second step may now be taken—an attempt to obtain further information about the molecule within the context of the particular model chosen. Although already encountered in Project 2, the procedure may be summarized briefly here. The energy change for ψ_4 to ψ_5, given by the model, is

$$\Delta E = \frac{h^2}{8mL^2}(5^2 - 4^2) = \frac{h^2}{8mL^2}9$$

But, from experiment,

$$E_{\text{photon}} = h\nu = \frac{hc}{\lambda} = \frac{hc}{6000 \times 10^{-8}} \quad \text{so that} \quad \frac{hc}{6000 \times 10^{-8}} = \frac{h^2}{8mL^2}9$$

in which everything is known except L, the length of the box. Solving for L gives $L^2 = 9h6000 \times 10^{-8}/8mc$. The length of the box L is the domain over which the π electrons are delocalized, and it should be proportional to the length of the individual π bonds as $bl_c + 2p$, where b is the number of bonds, l_c is the length of the bond, and p is some constant. Clearly, if p is known (or can be found as in Project 3 from a series of spectra), then the bond length is given by solving L for l_c. Thus, given the proper assignment of the frequency, it is possible for us to derive information of importance to the determination of molecular structure.

(iii) Infrared spectroscopy—vibrational spectra

The low-resolution infrared spectrum for HCl given in Project 3 is reproduced in Fig. V-5. This range of ν corresponds to the energy absorption accompanying a change in the vibrational coordinates, and, even though other coordinates may also change, they will contribute to only the detailed structure of the absorption depression.

Once again the region of absorption extends over a considerable range of frequency, and a value of the frequency that corresponds to the vibrational transition must be selected. In the electronic spectrum a frequency toward the lower end of the absorption range in the depression was taken as the frequency of the electronic transition. In the present case there are *two* depressions, at *a* and *c* in Fig. V-5. Does this mean there are two different vibrational transitions? Or should the midpoint *b* between the two be taken as the vibrational frequency?

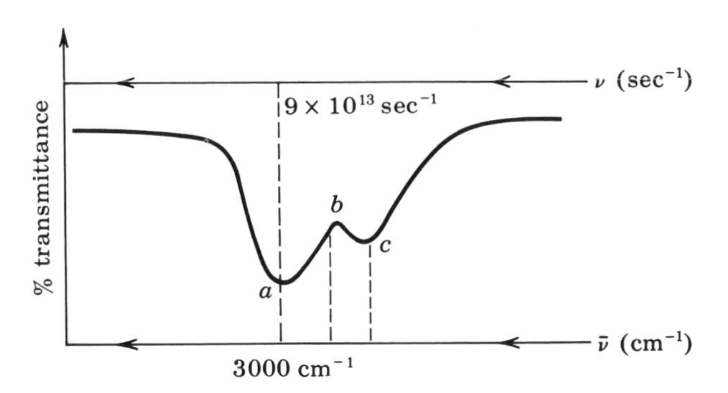

Fig. V-5 Low-resolution infrared spectrum.

The question of which one of the many frequencies in the region of absorption corresponds to that of the transition was less important for the smoother curve in the electronic case. Now, in a more complicated case, the question is not trivial. Nevertheless, the same principles apply. In the earlier case of the electronic transition, the vibrational selection rule was used to suggest that a frequency toward the low-frequency end of the depression was the appropriate one. The selection[1] rule for a diatomic molecule $\Delta J = \pm 1$ would suggest a symmetrical distribution about a midpoint. But what is even more to the point, the selection rule (Table IV-2) indicates that the rotational part must *always* change, so that there will be no possibility of absorption corresponding to a pure vibrational change. For example, a vibrational transition $n = 0 \rightarrow n = 1$ is accompanied by the rotational change $J = 0 \rightarrow J = 1$ for an energy $h\nu_0 + (2h^2/8\pi^2 I)$ or by the transition $J = 1 \rightarrow J = 0$ with the energy change $h\nu_0 - (2h^2/8\pi^2 I)$, etc. Clearly, because energy changes slightly *greater* or slightly *less* than $h\nu_0$ occur, it would be expected that the general absorption region would be divided into two parts by a midpoint where there was *no* absorption. This is exactly the appearance of the spectrum, and the midpoint, or hump, b should be the value of $\bar{\nu}$ or ν corresponding to a pure vibrational change. In the case of HCl the point b gives a value of $\bar{\nu}$ equal to approximately 2886 cm^{-1}.

Having settled on the *type* of transition being observed and the appropriate value of $\bar{\nu}$ for the transition, one must consider the question of *which* particular vibrational transition is being observed, i.e., what are the initial and final vibrational states? The selection rule $\Delta n = \pm 1$ indicates that the system is simply making a transition from one state

[1] Up to this point the letter l has been used for the quantum number for *both* the electronic and molecular *rotations*. It is common practice to use the letter J for the quantum number of the rotation of the molecule and l for the quantum number of the orbital rotation of the electron. This will be done henceforth.

to its neighbor; for example, $\psi_0 \rightarrow \psi_1$ or $\psi_1 \rightarrow \psi_2$ but not $\psi_0 \rightarrow \psi_2$. But is it $\psi_0 \rightarrow \psi_1$ or $\psi_1 \rightarrow \psi_2$?

Since statistical mechanics implies that more molecules should be in the ψ_0 state than in the ψ_1 state, the $\psi_0 \rightarrow \psi_1$ transition will be the more probable. Thus, although transitions $\psi_1 \rightarrow \psi_2$ may also be observed, their absorption will be *much* less intense. The "forbidden" ($\Delta n_{\text{vib}} = 2$) transitions $\psi_0 \rightarrow \psi_2$ that result from anharmonicity, as discussed in Sec. IV-4(ii), are called *overtones* and, of course, are also weak.

Having settled upon the transition type, the value of $\bar{\nu}$, and the initial and final states, one finds it then possible to take the second step and attempt to obtain some fundamental molecular information. The harmonic-oscillator model for the vibration gives the energy for the transition $\psi_0 \rightarrow \psi_1$ as $\Delta E = E_1 - E_0 = (h/2\pi)\sqrt{k/\mu}$. From the spectrum, the energy for the transition is $E_{\text{photon}} = h\nu_{\text{absorption}}$ or

$$\Delta E = hc(\bar{\nu})_{\text{absorption}}$$

On equating the two equations for ΔE, we obtain the equation for k, the force constant, as $k = \mu(2\pi c\bar{\nu})^2$. Once again a quantity, characteristic of the bond in the molecule, has been extracted from the spectrum.

It is worthwhile commenting here that it has been possible to recognize very easily chemically useful information—the bond "stiffness" k—simply because there is only the one bond in the diatomic molecule to which this force constant could correspond. In polyatomic molecules having many bonds and many vibrational frequencies, there is the additional step of sorting out which force constant belongs to which bond. For example, the SO_2 molecule has more than one bond and more than one vibration. It has the three "motions" illustrated in Fig. V-6, where the arrow indicates the direction of motion of the nuclei. For each of these motions there is a characteristic frequency (ν_1^0, ν_2^0, or ν_3^0) related to the force constants and masses in a way that is more complicated than, but similar to, the way the frequency ν^0 in the diatomic case was related to the force constant [$\nu^0 = (1/2\pi)\sqrt{k/\mu}$ for the diatomic case]. There will be a set of energy levels for each of these motions, just as there was for the harmonic motion in the diatomic case. The energy levels are sketched in Fig. V-6, along with a spectrum for the $\Delta n = 1$ transitions.

Generally it is the assignment of a given absorption frequency to its appropriate motion that is the difficult part to do, and the use of selection rules (say, $\Delta n = 1$ above), the calculation of relative energies (e.g., the relative energy of the $n = 0 \rightarrow 1$ transitions can be predicted—in SO_2 they are in the order $\bar{\nu}_2^0 < \bar{\nu}_1^0 < \bar{\nu}_3^0$), and the use of symmetry all become much more important. In even more complicated cases, the analysis can be furthered by isotopic substitution. (Since the reduced mass μ is

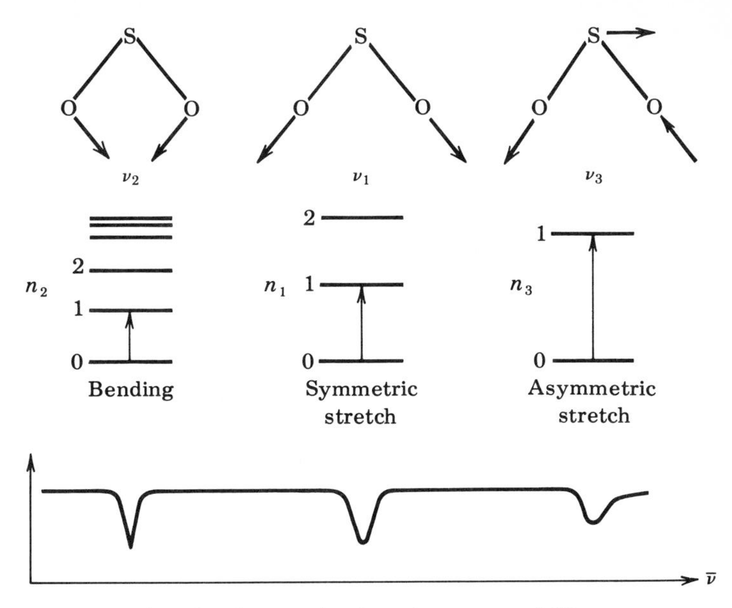

Fig. V-6 Vibrational-energy levels and spectrum of SO_2.

involved in ν_1^0, etc., the way a given absorption frequency shifts in the isotopically substituted spectra can be compared with the shift predicted by theory.)

Once the frequencies have been assigned, the second step—the calculation of force constants and bond angles—can be carried out. Even without the detailed assignment, the vibrational spectrum of SO_2 is useful, since the presence of three vibrational absorptions indicates that the molecule is not linear.

(iv) Far-infrared, or microwave, spectroscopy—rotational spectra

The far-infrared, or "short" microwave, region can be considered as encompassing the frequency range 10 to 100 cm^{-1}. From the discussion in the previous chapter, it is known that the frequency in this range corresponds to the energy change of a rotational transition—i.e., this is a rotational spectrum. A typical spectrum might look like Fig. V-7.

This spectrum is considerably different from those discussed in the ultraviolet and infrared. There are many absorption regions instead of a single principal one, and several of these depressions are of roughly the same depth; i.e., there are several transitions of approximately the same probability. There may, indeed, be detailed structures in each of these regions but they will be ignored for the present; e.g., there might be the magnetic or electric interactions mentioned in Sec. III-3.

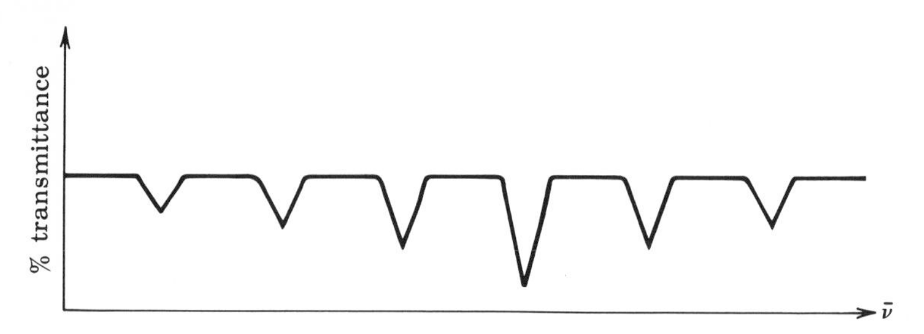

Fig. V-7 Rotational spectrum.

The chief feature seems to be the fact that there are several rotational "lines" of roughly the same intensity and more or less evenly spaced. It might, first of all, be recalled that the allowed rotational transitions satisfy $\Delta J = \pm 1$, i.e., the transitions $J = 0 \rightarrow J = 1$, $J = 1 \rightarrow J = 0$, $J = 1 \rightarrow J = 2$, $J = 2 \rightarrow J = 1$, and so on are allowed but *not* $J = 0 \rightarrow J = 2$. In previous discussions when the answer to the question: *Which* of these allowed transitions corresponds to the one observed? was attempted, it was done on the basis of statistical mechanics (only the lowest energy was significantly populated, and hence only transitions from the lowest energy were probable). In the present case the question is different, for there are many depressions, and one must inquire, first of all: Why so many depressions? The answer, as discussed in Project 4, comes from statistical mechanics, if it is noted that the energy *difference* between rotational levels is relatively small, so that *several* low-lying rotational levels could be significantly populated. Thus the probability of the transition $J = 1 \rightarrow J = 2$ is only slightly different from that for $J = 0 \rightarrow J = 1$. Consequently several absorptions of roughly the same depth would be expected. Actually, because of degeneracy, the population rises slightly from $J = 0$ to $J = 3$ or 4 and then decreases due to dominance of the increasing energy in the exponential weighting factor (see, for example, Probs. 4-8 and 4-9 of Project 4).

Earlier [Sec. III-2(ii)(*d*)] it was found that the difference between rotational energy levels J and $J + 1$ for a constant I was given by the formula $\Delta E = (h^2/8\pi^2 I)2(J + 1)$, where J is the rotational quantum number for the initial state. Consequently the energy change of $J = 0 \rightarrow J = 1$ would be $2h^2/8\pi^2 I$; of $J = 1 \rightarrow J = 2$, $4h^2/8\pi^2 I$; and of $J = 2 \rightarrow J = 3$, $6h^2/8\pi^2 I$. Absorption of energy at frequencies corresponding to the energies $2h^2/8\pi^2 I$, $4h^2/8\pi^2 I$, $6h^2/8\pi^2 I$, etc., would be expected. The difference between these energies is always the same—simply $2h^2/8\pi^2 I$. Hence the depressions in the spectrum would be evenly spaced [the value of $\bar{\nu}$ for the spacing would be $(2h/c)/8\pi^2 I$]. The first step in the analysis has not really been completed, in that each depression has not been assigned to its appropriate transition. Nevertheless, the equivalent has been accomplished, in that the relation of an experimental quantity (the spacing between depressions) to a particular property of the model for the system (the moment of inertia I) has been found.

The second step, the attempt to obtain significant information on the molecule, may now be undertaken. Although it has already been encountered in Project 4, the procedure is summarized briefly here. We know that the separation between depressions is related to a property of the model by $\bar{\nu}$ (separation) $= (2h/c)/8\pi^2 I$. For the rotational spectrum of the HCl molecule, this separation varies between 20.1 and 21.1 cm^{-1}. Taking the average value, 20.6 cm^{-1}, and solving the statement $20.6 = (2h/c)/8\pi^2 I$ for the moment of inertia I gives

$$I = 2.72 \times 10^{-40} \text{ g cm}^2$$

But I is related to the internuclear distance by $I = \mu R^2$, so that an approximate bond distance of 1.30 Å can be found.

In the preceding discussion we were able to obtain without difficulty a significant molecular parameter R simply because there was only one moment of inertia in the molecule. In polyatomic molecules there would be the possibility of three moments of inertia I_x, I_y, and I_z about the three axes. Consequently the relation of the rotational spectrum to the appropriate molecular parameters can present a problem, but, by the same token, one can obtain more information about the molecule; for example, bond angles as well as internuclear distances can be found.

One of the possible arrangements of the nuclei in a polyatomic molecule results in the so-called symmetric-top molecule, of which methyl chloride is an example. Here two of the three moments of inertia are the same, and the energy levels[1] are

$$E_{\text{rot}} = \frac{h^2}{8\pi^2 I_b} J(J+1) + \frac{h^2}{8\pi^2}\left(\frac{1}{I_a} - \frac{1}{I_b}\right) M^2$$

where I_a and I_b are the two moments of inertia. Selection rules can be found for each situation (e.g., here $\Delta M = 0$, $\Delta J = \pm 1$). As with polyatomic vibrations the spectrum is complex but may be analyzed, albeit with more difficulty than in the diatomic case, and, given the appropriate frequencies, step two can be carried out to yield the bond distances and bond angles.

(v) Proton NMR spectroscopy

A number of examples of proton NMR spectra were given in Sec. III-3(ii) and in Project 7. Since there are only two possible states for any par-

[1] L. Pauling and E. B. Wilson, "Introduction to Quantum Mechanics," McGraw-Hill, 1935.

ticular proton (α or β), the question: Which transition is the one observed? is trivial; the initial and final states of the transition may have only $m_s = \pm\frac{1}{2}$, so that $\Delta m_s = \pm 1$. (It should be noted that this selection rule assumes that simultaneous transitions $\alpha\alpha \rightarrow \beta\beta$ do not occur.)

Although the selection rule is relatively simple, the assignment of the NMR peaks to the appropriate proton may be difficult. In many cases the assignment can be carried out by a consideration of the relative peak heights (or peak areas)—indeed, this method has been used to determine the structure of molecules (see Project 7, Prob. 7-4). In other cases substitution of deuterium for a particular proton, followed by comparison of the spectra of the substituted and unsubstituted molecules, may help in carrying out the assignment. Finally the use of a model to calculate the expected chemical shift may allow the assignment to be made (see Project 8).

(vi) Project 8. Calculation of the chemical shift for a series of molecules[1]

(a) *Introduction*

The NMR chemical shift τ depends on the electron density in the region of the nucleus. Consequently as a first approximation, changes in the τ value for a proton can be taken as due to a change in electron density. For example, the change in τ_{H_A} for the proton H_A in

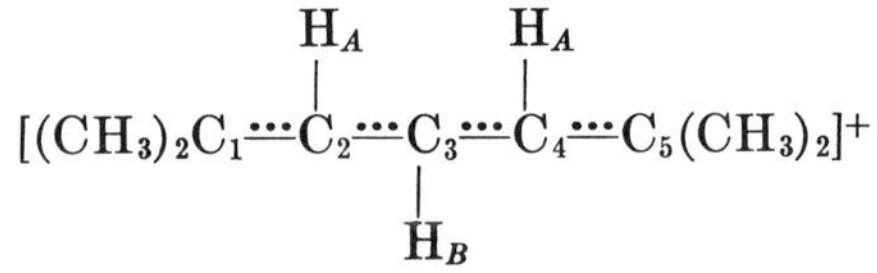

```
            H_A        H_A
            |          |
[(CH3)2C1···C2···C3···C4···C5(CH3)2]+
                 |
                 H_B
```

to τ'_{H_A} for the proton at the same position in

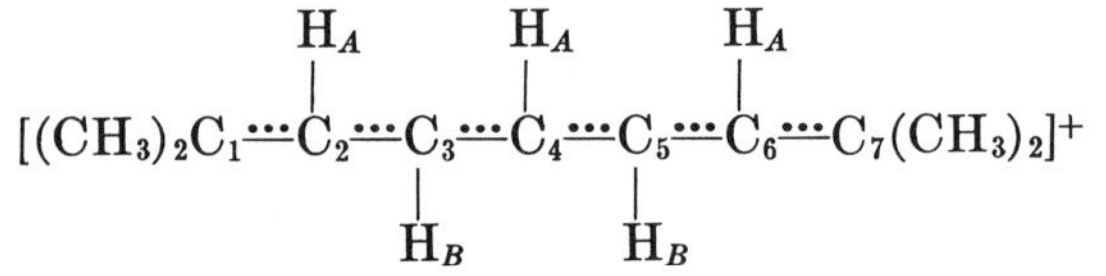

```
            H_A        H_A        H_A
            |          |          |
[(CH3)2C1···C2···C3···C4···C5···C6···C7(CH3)2]+
                 |          |
                 H_B        H_B
```

is an indication of a change in the electron density in the neighborhood of this proton. It would not be expected that an increase in chain length would alter the electron distribution in the σ bond between the proton and the chain carbon. However, as we saw in Project 2, the delocalized π electrons are much more susceptible to an increase in chain length. Hence it would be reasonable to attribute the changes in τ to a change in the π-electron density in the region of the carbon C_2 to which the

[1] This project is based on the articles by the author in *J. Am. Chem. Soc.*, **90**:4208 (1968) and *J. Chem. Ed.*, **46**:355 (1969).

proton H_A is attached, that is,

$$\tau_{H_A} = k_1 \rho_{C_2} + k_2 \tag{V-1}$$

Similarly the π-electron density "on" carbon C_3 would be expected to influence the chemical shift of the proton H_B. In this way the τ value of the protons attached to the chain carbons could be associated with a π-electron density in a region half a bond length on either side of the appropriate carbon. Although the methyl protons[1] are two σ bonds removed from the terminal carbon C_1, their τ value could be related to the π-electron density associated with C_1.

The results of Project 2 would suggest that particle-in-a-box functions are adequate representations for the π electrons for these systems. Consequently the π-electron density to be associated with a given proton would be a sum of the electron density for each center from the electrons in each molecular orbital. Hence we would add the electron densities $\rho = 2/L \int_{x_1}^{x_2} [\sin (n\pi x/L)]^2 \, dx$ (due to the electron in orbital n) as

$$\rho = 2 \sum_{n}^{\text{occ}} \left(\frac{2}{L} \int_{x_1}^{x_2} \sin^2 \frac{n\pi x}{L} \, dx \right) \tag{V-2}$$

where the factor of 2 is a result of the double occupancy of the orbitals; Σ_n^{occ} is a summation over the *occupied* π molecular orbitals, for example, occ $= 2$ if two molecular orbitals are filled; and x_2 and x_1 are points half a bond length on either side of the carbon to which the proton is attached. For the methyl protons the limits would be the origin of the box (that would depend on the penetration) and a point midway between carbons C_1 and C_2.

(b) The length of the box

The box length L could be obtained by simply summing the individual bond lengths and adding a semiempirical value for the penetration p to give L as

$$L = (n_C - 1) l_C + 2p$$

where n_C is the number of chain carbons, and $l_C = 1.4 \times 10^{-8}$cm. If the series of molecules is given by the general formula

$$(CH_3)_2C \cdots C(H) \cdots (CH \cdots CH)_{m-2} \cdots C(CH_3)_2 \qquad m = 2, 3, \ldots$$

then

$$L = 2(m - 1) l_C + 2p \tag{V-3}$$

[1] The proton referred to here is the nucleus of a hydrogen in the CH_3 group.

PROBLEM 8-1

Using λ_{max} for $m = 4$ (from Table V–1) and Eq. (V-3) for L, calculate a value for p. Use this value of p to predict the λ_{max} for $m = 2, 5$ and compare to the experimentally measured λ_{max} given in Table V-1.

Table V-1 λ_{max} **for polyenylic ions, mμ (10^{-7} cm)**

Ion m	2	3	4	5	6	7
Experimental λ_{max}	305	396	473	550	626	702

The procedure of Prob. 8-1 does not give satisfactory values of λ_{max}. However, it should be remembered that the adjacent carbon-carbon bonds are at an angle of 120° to one another, and, if the chain is in the all-trans configuration of Fig. V-8, the box length would more realistically be given as the distance along the x axis rather than as the zigzag distance along the chain. Hence

$$L = l_C(n_C - 1) \cos 30° + 2p$$
$$= 2(m - 1)l_C \cos 30° + 2p \qquad \text{(V-4)}$$

PROBLEM 8-2

Repeat Prob. 8-1 with the box length given by Eq. (V-4).

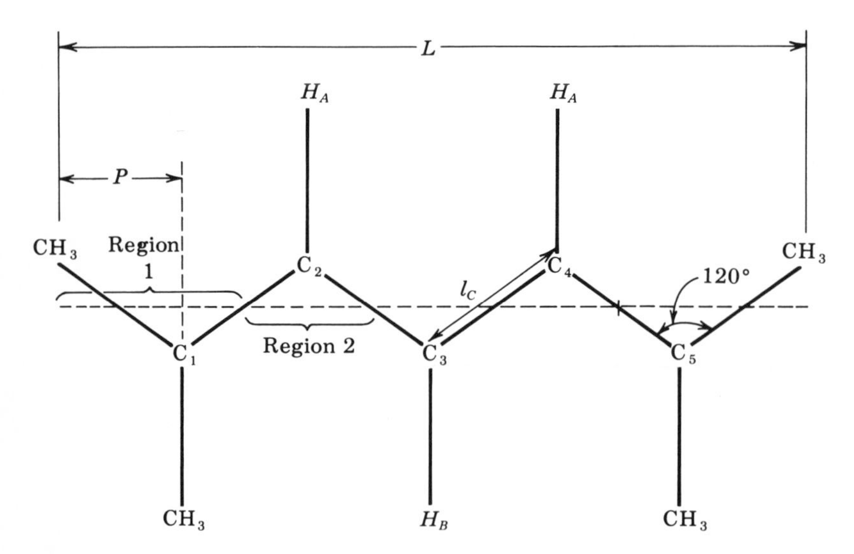

Fig. V-8 The bent-chain model.

Since the results of Prob. 8-2 suggest that the bent-chain model is an adequate representation for the π electrons of these ions, the calculation of the π-electron density can be undertaken.

(c) *Electron density*

Values of the electron density given by Eq. (V-2) using the L of Eq. (V-4) are displayed in Table V-2 for the various members of the series.

Table V-2 Electron densities "on" various centers of the polyenylic ions

	Center					
Ion m	1	2	3	4	5	6
2	0.558	0.884				
3	0.762	☐	0.668			
4	☐	0.915	0.755	0.928		
5	0.929	☐	0.809	0.939	0.801	
6	0.972	0.927	0.846	0.944	0.836	0.949
7	1.00	0.932	0.872	0.948	0.861	0.955
8	1.02	0.935	0.892	0.951	0.881	0.958
9	1.04	0.938	0.907	0.954	0.896	0.961
10	1.06	0.940	0.919	0.956	0.909	0.963

PROBLEM 8-3

Calculate the missing quantities in Table V-2. (*Hint:* In determining the appropriate x_1 and x_2 for a particular carbon, remember that the origin of x is p units to the left of C_1.)

The electron densities given in Table V-2 appear to be of three types: the electron density ρ_{Mc} associated with the terminal chain carbon (center 1); the electron density ρ_A that is approximately the same for centers 2, 4, 6, etc.; and the electron density ρ_B associated with centers 3, 5, 7, etc.

PROBLEM 8-4

In view of the electron densities displayed in Table V-2, how many different τ values would one expect to obtain for a *low-resolution* NMR spectrum of the ion with $m = 6$?

The proportionality constant k_1 in Eq. (V-1) can be taken[1] as 11.5 for the protons attached to the chain carbons. For the more-distant

[1] Values quoted in the literature range from 10.6 to 13 or higher; see, for example, T. S. Sorensen, *J. Am. Chem. Soc.*, **87**:5080 (1965).

methyl protons, a value of $k_1 = 2.80$ may be used. Equation (V-1) then becomes

$$\tau_H = 11.5\rho_{C_{chain}} + k_2 \qquad \text{for the chain protons}$$

and

$$\tau_{H_{Me}} = 2.80\rho_{C_1} + k_3 \qquad \text{for the methyl protons}$$

The remaining constant in each equation may be evaluated if an experimental value of τ and the appropriate calculated value of ρ are used.

Table V-3 Chemical shift values for the polenylic ions

Proton chemical shift	*Ion m* 3	4	5	6
τ_{Me}	7.1	7.58	7.73	7.86
$\tau_{A,chain}$	2.45	2.95	3.10	3.40
$\tau_{B,chain}$		1.42	1.80	2.13

PROBLEM 8-5

Given that the τ_{Me} for the ion $m = 4$ is 7.58, find k_3.

PROBLEM 8-6

Given that the τ's for the chain protons in the ion $m = 4$ are $\tau = 2.95$ and $\tau = 1.42$, find k_2.

PROBLEM 8-7

Using the values of k_2 and k_3 obtained in Probs. 8-5 and 8-6 and the electron densities from Table V-2, calculate the τ values for the two types of chain protons and the methyl protons for the ions $m = 2, 3, 5$. Compare to the experimentally measured τ values given in Table V-3.

V-3 HIGH-RESOLUTION SPECTRA

(i) Detailed analysis of spectra

In the previous sections the general features of a number of different types of spectra have been used to obtain information about the molecular system. This rather approximate picture will now be refined by an investigation of the detailed structure of spectra. This detail can be due to field-independent contributions or to fine structure introduced by the interaction of the system with an external field. The detail of vibrational bands resulting from "mixed transitions" (see Sec. IV-1) and the spin-spin fine structure of NMR spectra are examples of field-independent detail.

(ii) NMR and ESR spin-spin spectra

(a) NMR spectra

If the sample of pure ethanol, for which the low-resolution spectrum was given in Fig. III-24, is run under conditions that allow the detail of the spectrum to be distinguished, the result is Fig. V-9*b*. For example, where, under low resolution, we had just one methyl peak, we now have several peaks under high resolution. Further, the splitting "$J_{NN'}$" of the peaks is independent of the external field and must be attributed to an internal interaction. The interaction can be explained if it is remembered that the energy of a proton of the CH_3 group could be influenced by the presence of nearby magnetic nuclei. For example, the magnetic arrangement of the two nearby CH_2 protons could be $\alpha\alpha$, $\beta\beta$, or $\alpha\beta$. The energy of a proton on CH_3 could then be due to the chemical-shift term ($\frac{1}{2}BH_0[1 - \sigma]$) (see Fig. III-23) *plus* the contribution from any one of the above three terms. We would expect the effect of the $\alpha\beta$ configuration to be zero and $\alpha\alpha$ and $\beta\beta$ to have equal and opposite effects; thus the chemical-shift energy levels would be modified, as in Fig. V-10*b*. It should be noted that there are still only two possible descriptions of a given proton (α or β). However, since the *field* at this proton can take several different values (depending on the neighboring protons), the energy of the proton can be one of several different values.

The energy for a β spin of the CH_3 proton is lowest when the two protons of CH_2 are $\alpha\alpha$, and, for an α spin of the CH_3 proton, the energy is lowest when the two protons of CH_2 are $\beta\beta$. Since the selection rule is $\Delta m_s = \pm 1$, the spin of one of the methyl protons changes, but the spins of the methylene protons remain unchanged during this transition.

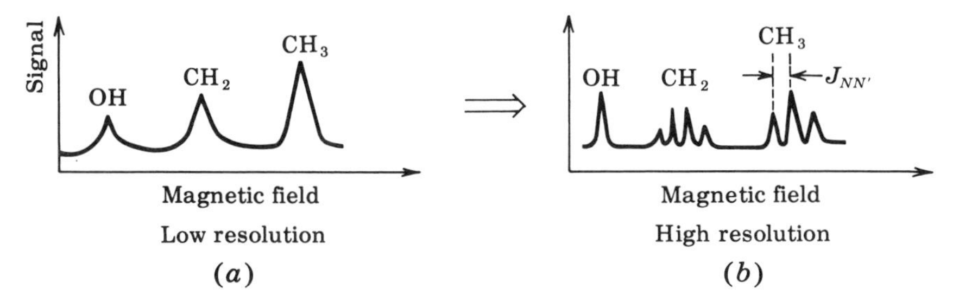

Fig. V-9 NMR spectra of ethanol.

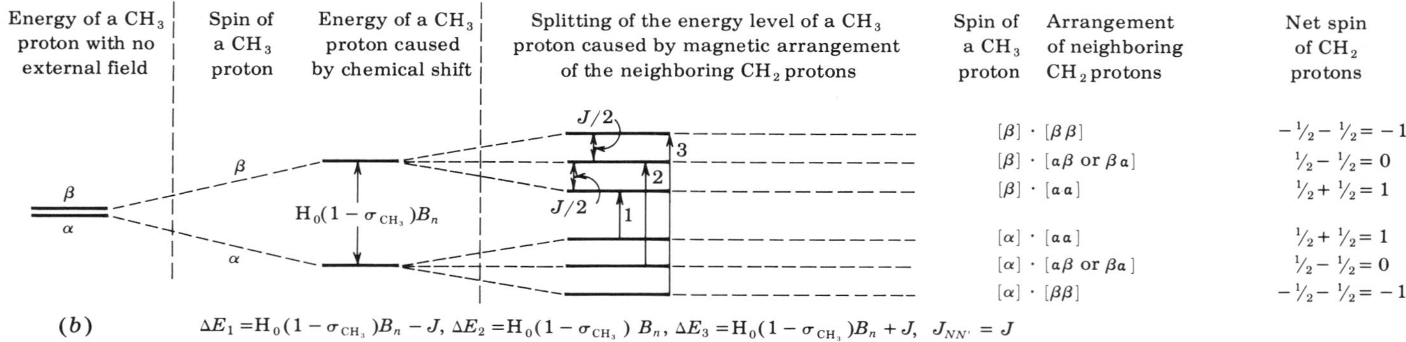

(*a*) $\Delta E_1 = H_0(1-\sigma_{CH_2})B_n - \frac{3}{2}J$, $\Delta E_2 = H_0(1-\sigma_{CH_2})B_n - J/2$, $\Delta E_3 = H_0(1-\sigma_{CH_2})B_n + J/2$, $\Delta E_4 = H_0(1-\sigma)B_n + \frac{3}{2}J$, $J_{NN'} = J$

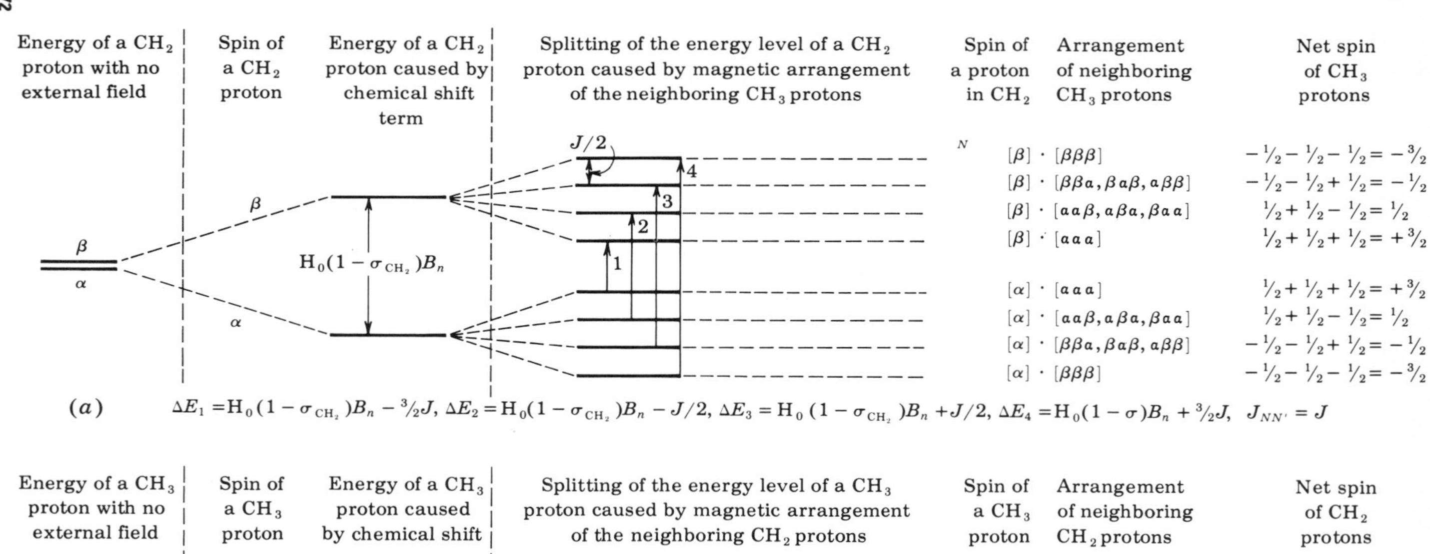

(*b*) $\Delta E_1 = H_0(1-\sigma_{CH_3})B_n - J$, $\Delta E_2 = H_0(1-\sigma_{CH_3})B_n$, $\Delta E_3 = H_0(1-\sigma_{CH_3})B_n + J$, $J_{NN'} = J$

Fig. V-10 NMR spin-spin splitting. (*a*) Splitting of the CH_2 peak by CH_3 protons; (*b*) splitting of the CH_3 peak by CH_2 protons.

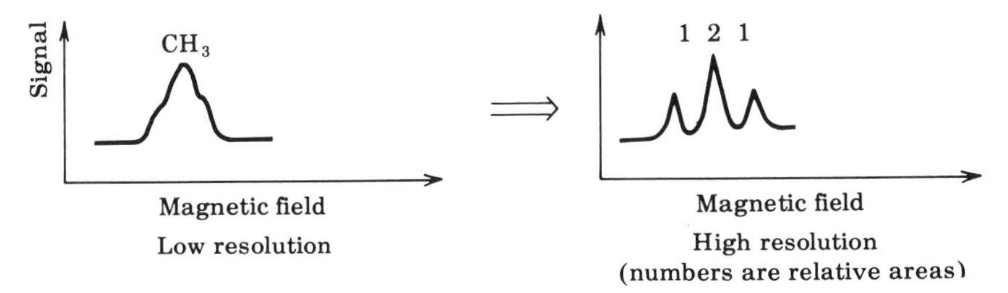

Fig. V-11 The methyl "peak."

Hence there are only the three possible transitions indicated in Fig. V-10*b* and likewise three absorptions. Transition ② in Fig. V-10*b* corresponds to the energy level difference due to only chemical shift. To either side of this transition there is an absorption whose splitting is a measure of the effect (or "coupling") of the CH_2 protons on a CH_3 proton. Furthermore, since there are two "ways" in which the spins of the neighboring CH_2 protons can be paired, namely, $\alpha\beta$ or $\beta\alpha$, it is twice as probable that the CH_3 proton will be affected by this configuration. Hence transition ② of Fig. V-10*b* will be twice as likely, and so one would expect the methyl "peak" under high resolution to show three "peaks," as in Fig. V-11, with heights in a ratio 1:2:1. In a similar way the energy level of a CH_2 proton would depend on the spin arrangement of the CH_3 protons. The four possible arrangements of the CH_3 protons and their effects are indicated in Fig. V-10*a*. There are now four possible transitions, and, since either $\alpha\alpha\beta$ or $\beta\alpha\alpha$ can be formed three times as many ways as either $\alpha\alpha\alpha$ or $\beta\beta\beta$, the methylene proton would experience their interactions three times as often. Transitions ② and ③ would be three times as probable as transitions ① and ④. The methylene peak under high resolution would show four peaks, as in Fig. V-12. In fact, one would expect that *each* of these latter peaks would be split into two peaks due to the influence of the two possible spin states of the proton of the OH group. Such is the case in *pure* ethanol. In an acidified solution, the OH proton of the

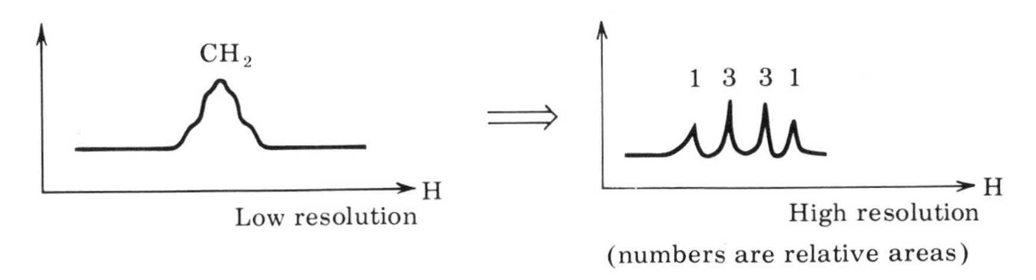

Fig. V-12 The methylene peak.

alcohol exchanges rapidly with a proton from the solvent, and the result is an average zero spin effect leaving the methylene peaks as in Fig. V-12.

Since the spin-spin "coupling" depends on the proximity of the respective types of protons, high-resolution NMR spectra can be used to give not only the number of each kind of proton but also their relative arrangement.

PROBLEM V-1

Predict the high-resolution NMR spectra of isopropyl and *n*-propyl alcohol, assuming no splitting due to the OH proton.

(*b*) *ESR spectra*

In the same way that the spin of a nucleus affects the energy of another nucleus, so would we expect that the spin of the nucleus could interact with the spin of an unpaired electron. This interaction, the energy levels, and resulting spectrum is the subject of electron spin resonance (ESR), sometimes called electron-proton resonance (EPR).

Consider a single electron in the presence of two protons. We might expect the interaction of the electron spin with the nuclear spin to be proportional to the electron density ρ_i in the region of the nucleus as: interaction energy $= A_i = \rho_i Q$, where Q is the proportionality constant. If the electron density is evenly distributed on both nuclei a and b (that is, $\rho_a = 0.5$, $\rho_b = 0.5$), then the interaction of the electron will be $A = 0.5Q$ for both nuclei. The energy level diagram for this situation is given in Fig. V-13. It might be pointed out that the signal in ESR spectroscopy is usually measured as a derivative,[1] and, as with most magnetic resonance measurements, the frequency is fixed and the field is varied to achieve resonance.

Frequently the unpaired electron is distributed over several nuclei. For example, in the *p*-benzosemiquinone radical-ion, the unpaired electron is distributed over the carbon and oxygen nuclei but some of the spin density, i.e., the unpaired electron density, does "leak" out onto the protons. The amount of spin density that resides on the proton is, in

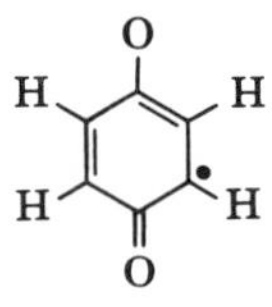

p-benzosemiquinone radical-ion

fact, proportional to the amount of spin density on the carbon to which the proton is attached. In the case of *p*-benzosemiquinone the spin density is the same on all four protons. When the argument of the

[1] The derivative of [peak] is [derivative curve]

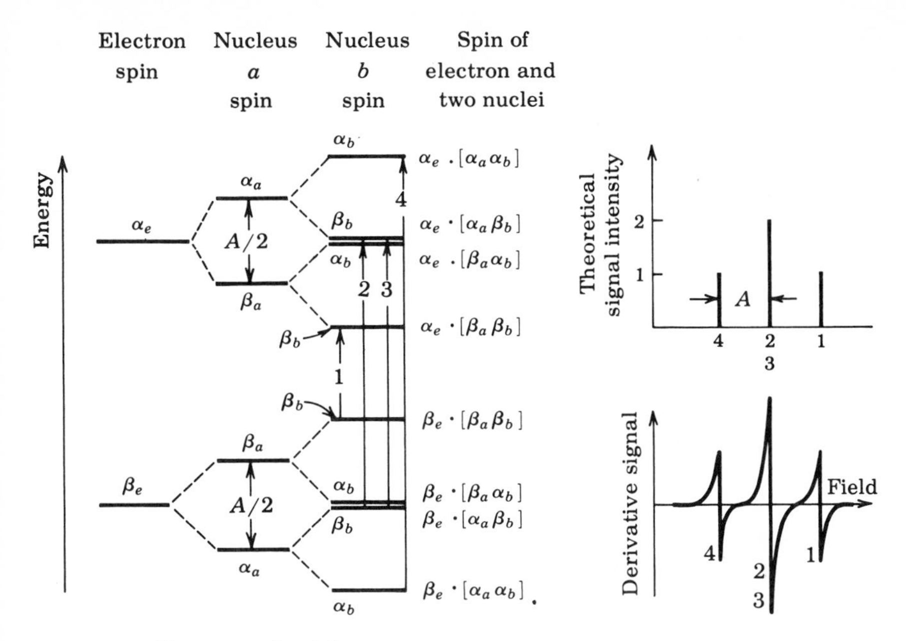

Fig. V-13 ESR energy level diagram and spectrum.

previous paragraph is applied here (see Project 9), the spectrum of the *p*-benzosemiquinone radical-ion would be expected to have five lines, as illustrated in Fig. V-14.

(iii) Project 9. High-resolution spin-spin spectroscopy

(*a*) *Equivalent protons*

The foregoing analysis has indicated the general principles of high-resolution NMR and ESR spectroscopy. The procedure, although tedious when there are many equivalent nuclei to consider, is relatively straight-

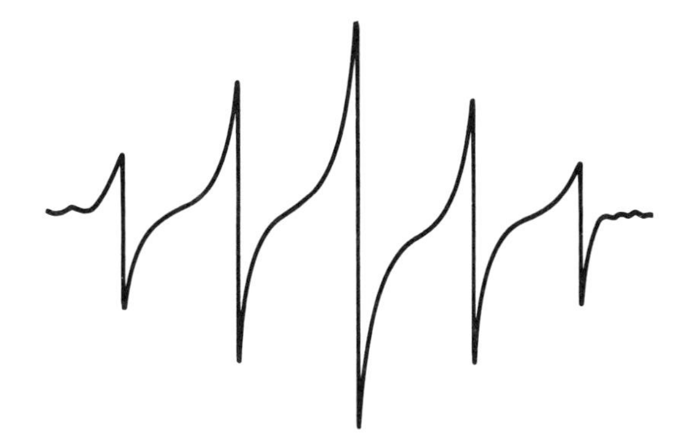

Fig. V-14 ESR spectrum of *p*-benzosemiquinone radical ion.

forward. Indeed, the pattern of intensities can be obtained from the entries in the Pascal triangle in Table V-4. For example, if there are 4

Table V-4 The Pascal triangle

Number of equivalent nuclei	*Peaks and relative intensities*	*Example*	*Proton NMR spectrum*
0	1	$C_6H_5—OC\underline{H}_3$	
1	1 1	$>C=CH—C\underline{H}O$	
2	1 2 1	$CH_2—C\underline{H}_3$	
3	1 3 3 1	$C\underline{H}_2—CH_3$	
4	1 4 6 4 1	$—CH_2—C\underline{H}_2—CH_2—$	
5	1 5 10 10 5 1		
6	1 6 15 20 15 6 1		
	etc.	etc.	etc.

equivalent nuclei interacting with a nucleus, we would expect an NMR signal of five lines having intensities in the ratio 1:4:6:4:1. Similarly if four equivalent protons interact with an unpaired electron, as in the *p*-benzosemiquinone radical, we would expect an ESR signal of five lines having intensities in the ratio of 1:4:6:4:1. In both cases the lines are evenly spaced, and the spacing is proportional to the nuclear-nuclear spin-spin coupling $J_{NN'}$ in the NMR case, or to the nuclear-electron spin-spin interaction A in the ESR case.

PROBLEM 9-1

Draw an energy level–NMR-transition diagram (similar to Fig. V-10) for the splitting of a CH_3 proton by the aldehyde proton in

$$\begin{array}{l} CH_3C{=}O \\ \quad\;\; | \\ \quad\;\; H \end{array}$$

PROBLEM 9-2

Draw an energy level–NMR-transition diagram like Fig. V-10 for the splitting of the aldehyde proton by the methyl protons in

$$\begin{array}{l} CH_3C{=}O \\ \quad\;\; | \\ \quad\;\; H \end{array}$$

Show that the intensity pattern would be the same as that predicted by the Pascal triangle.

PROBLEM 9-3

Use the Pascal triangle to predict the intensity pattern for the NMR spin-spin splitting in

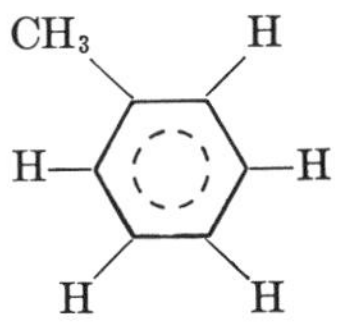

CH_3 H

H— ⬡ —H $(CH_3)_3CH$

H H

PROBLEM 9-4

Draw an energy level–ESR-transition diagram like Fig. V-13 for the splitting of the unpaired electron by four equivalent protons in the *p*-benzosemiquinone radical-ion. Show that the intensity pattern of the ESR signal would be that predicted by the Pascal triangle. Compare to the spectrum of Fig. V-14.

PROBLEM 9-5

Use the Pascal triangle to predict the intensity pattern of the ESR signal for the benzene anion where the spin density of the unpaired electron is the same for all protons.

(*b*) *Nonequivalent protons*

In the foregoing we have investigated the splitting of a line due to interaction with a *set* of protons that are *all equivalent*. Frequently the nuclei are not all equivalent. For example, the interaction between the methylene protons and a methyl proton in

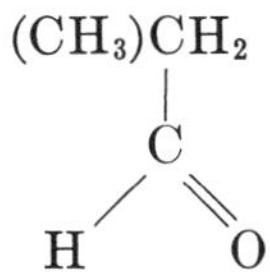

$(CH_3)CH_2$
|
C
/ ⫽
H O

is different from the interaction between the methylene protons and the aldehyde proton in the same molecule. Similarly the unpaired electron in the naphthalene ion is not distributed uniformly on all carbon centers, and, as a result, the interaction is different for different protons in this ion. Consequently we should investigate the effect on NMR and ESR spin-spin spectra when there are different interactions.

Figure V-15 contains the energy level–ESR-transition diagram for the case of an electron in the presence of two nuclei. In the left-hand side of the figure we have nuclei whose interactions with an electron are represented as a_1 and a_2. The resulting spectrum is a pair of doublets. In the right-hand side we have an electron split by two equivalent nuclei. In this case the inner lines of the previous case have merged to form the

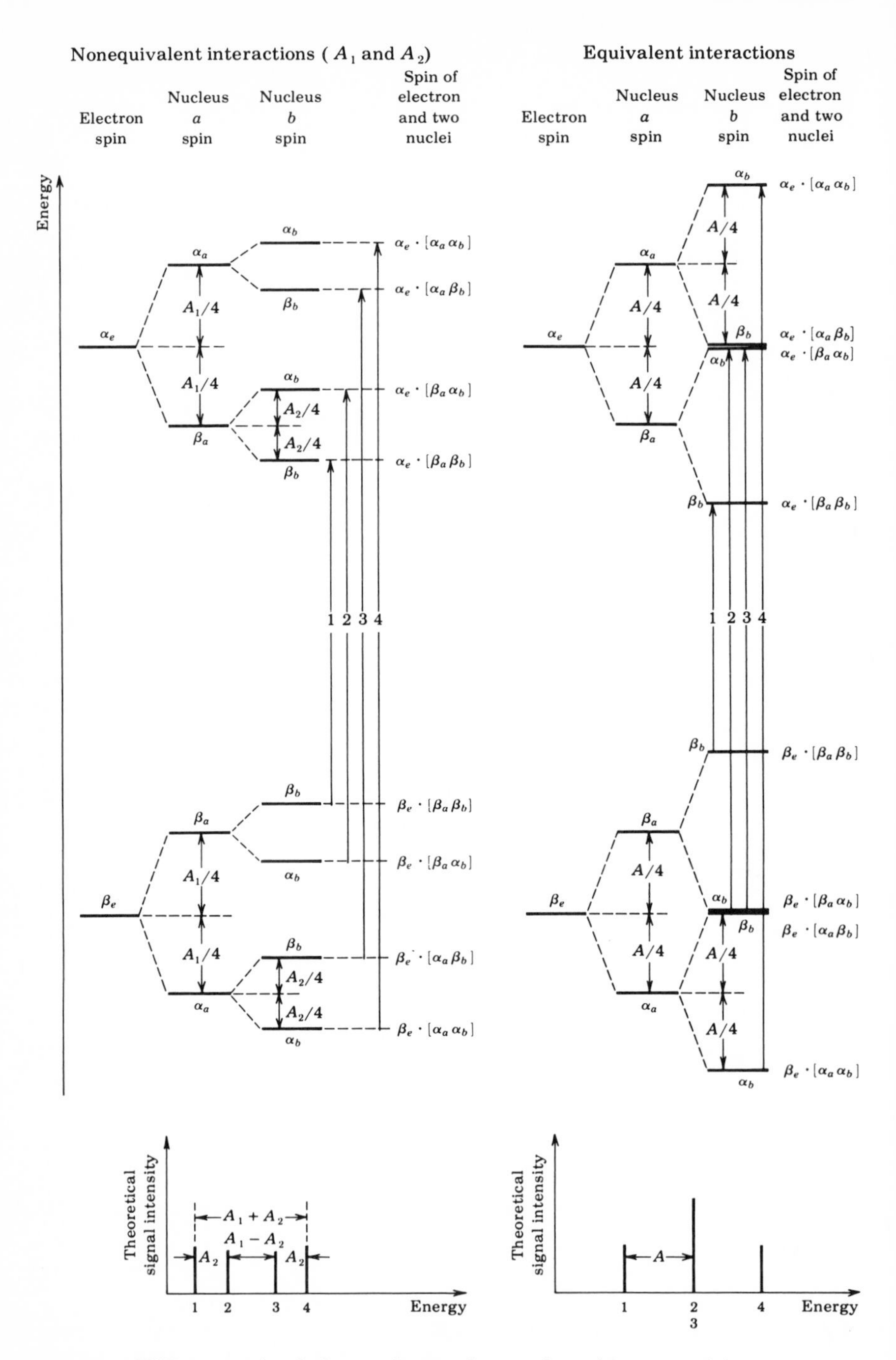

Fig. V-15 ESR energy levels for an electron interacting with two nuclei.

expected triplet. Figure V-16 depicts the somewhat more complicated case of an electron split by three nuclei, two of which are equivalent. The resulting spectrum is essentially a doublet (transitions ①′ and ②′ in the left-hand column of the diagram) in which each line of the doublet is split into a triplet by the interaction with the remaining two equivalent nuclei.

PROBLEM 9-6

Draw an energy level–ESR-transition diagram for the case of an unpaired electron split by four nuclei, where two nuclei have an interaction energy A_1 and two nuclei have an interaction energy A_2 ($A_1 = 5A_2$). Describe the resulting spectrum in terms of its basic structure (for example, the basic structure of the example in the previous paragraph was a doublet, each line of which was split into a triplet).

PROBLEM 9-7

Sketch the high-resolution NMR spectrum for the methyl protons in

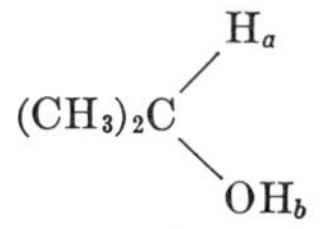

H_a
$(CH_3)_2C$
OH_b

assuming that the OH proton does interact (i.e., this proton does not exchange with the solvent). Note that the OH proton is one more bond removed from the methyl protons than the proton H_a, and so the coupling $J_{(CH_3)\leftrightarrow(OH)}$ should be smaller.

In naphthalene the spin density of the unpaired electron is distributed such that the electron spin interactions with the protons can be grouped into two types *a* or *b*, as illustrated; i.e., there are two groups of four equivalent protons.

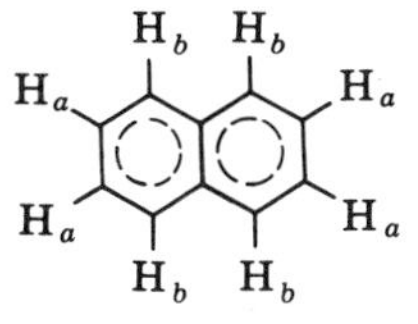

H_b H_b
H_a H_a
H_a H_a
H_b H_b

PROBLEM 9-8

What would be the basic structure of the ESR spectrum of the naphthalene ion? Sketch the spectrum in detail.

(*c*) *Calculated splittings*

Throughout this section we have referred to the "interaction" of the spins without explicitly discussing the interaction. Indeed, an exact

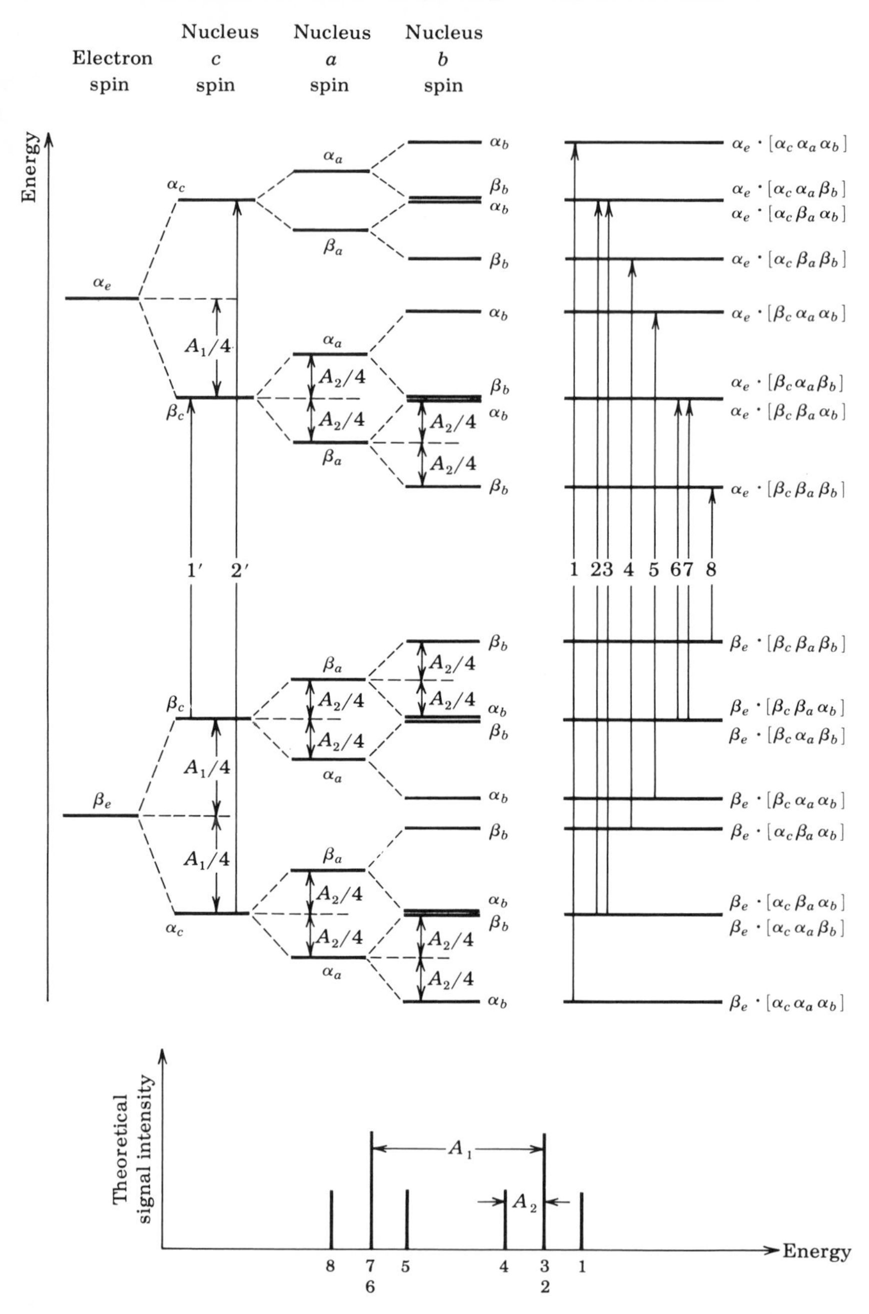

Fig. V-16 ESR energy levels with three nuclei.

treatment is prohibitively complex. However, in the case of the electron spin–nuclear spin interaction, the unpaired electron density in the region of the nucleus is an adequate measure of the interaction. In particular the electron spin density on the carbon to which a proton is attached appears to correlate[1] well with the interaction energy as: (energy of electron spin–proton spin) = Q (spin density on carbon to which the proton is attached), that is,

$$A_i = Q\rho_i \tag{V-5}$$

The interaction of nuclear spins with nuclear spins appears to involve[2] the "bond order" between the nuclei concerned as $J_{NN'} = kp_{NN'}$ and does not appear to have as wide an applicability as does Eq. (V-5).

In Project 8 the description of the electrons in the polyenylic ions was obtained from the particle-in-a-box-model solutions. These same solutions might be used to predict the ESR spectra. In particular we might form the radical

$$[(CH_3)_2C_1 \cdots C_2(H) \cdots C_3(H) \cdots C_4(H) \cdots C_5(CH_3)_2]^{++}$$

which would have three electrons in the π-electron system. The unpaired electron would be described by the function ψ_n for $n = 2$. The unpaired electron density associated with centers 2 and 3 could be found from $\rho_i = \int_{ai}^{bi} \psi_2{}^2\, dx$. The limits are the same as in Project 8. The ESR spectra could then be predicted in terms of two equivalent protons H_a (attached to C_2 and C_4, respectively) and a second type of proton H_b (attached to C_3).

PROBLEM 9-9

Calculate the spin density on centers C_2 and C_3 for the ion

$$[(CH_3)_2C_1 \cdots C_2(H) \cdots C_3(H) \cdots C_4(H) \cdots C_5(CH_3)_2]^{++}$$

Give the ratio of interactions $A_a\!:\!A_b$ assuming Q [in Eq. (V-5)] is the same for both protons. Sketch the ESR spectrum.

The ESR spectrum obtained experimentally for this ion suggests that the methyl protons also interact with the unpaired spin density.

[1] H. M. McConnell, *J. Chem. Phys.*, **24**:764 (1956).
[2] H. M. McConnell, *J. Chem. Phys.*, **24**:460 (1956).

PROBLEM 9-10

Calculate the spin density on the terminal carbons of the radical-ion in Prob. 9-9. Assuming Q is *approximately* the same as Q for the chain protons, sketch the ESR spectrum.

(iv) Vibrational-rotational bands

(a) General analysis

This type of spectra is due to transitions in which both vibrational and rotational descriptions change. A typical well-resolved spectrum is that illustrated in Fig. V-17 for the $n = 0 \rightarrow n = 1$ vibrational change in HCl.

Such a spectrum can be conveniently divided into three regions:[1] a region to the left with several absorptions, called the *P branch;* a central portion, or "gap," with, in this case, no absorptions, called the *Q gap;* and a region to the right with several absorptions, called the *R branch.* As indicated in Sec. V-2(iii), a position in the approximate center of the gap corresponds to the frequency of a pure vibrational transition.

If, for the moment, it is assumed that the moment of inertia is the same in the vibrational energy levels $n = 0$ and $n = 1$, the energy change for transitions $n = 0 \rightarrow n = 1$, $J_i = J \rightarrow J_f = J + 1$ can be written[2]

$$\Delta E_R = (E_{1,\text{vib}} - E_{0,\text{vib}}) + (E_{J+1,\text{rot}} - E_{J,\text{rot}})$$
$$= hc\bar{\nu}_{01} + \frac{h^2}{8\pi^2 I} 2(J+1) \qquad \text{(V-6}a\text{)}$$

For transitions $n = 0 \rightarrow n = 1$, $J_i = J \rightarrow J_f = J - 1$, the energy change is

$$\Delta E_P = (E_{1,\text{vib}} - E_{0,\text{vib}}) + (E_{J-1,\text{rot}} - E_{J,\text{rot}})$$
$$= hc\bar{\nu}_{01} - \frac{h^2}{8\pi^2 I} 2(J) \qquad \text{(V-6}b\text{)}$$

[1] Compare to the three regions a, b, and c of the low-resolution spectrum of the same transition given in Fig. V-5.

[2] The subscript i will be used throughout to indicate the initial state; that is, J_i indicates the rotational quantum number of the initial state. Similarly f refers to the final state.

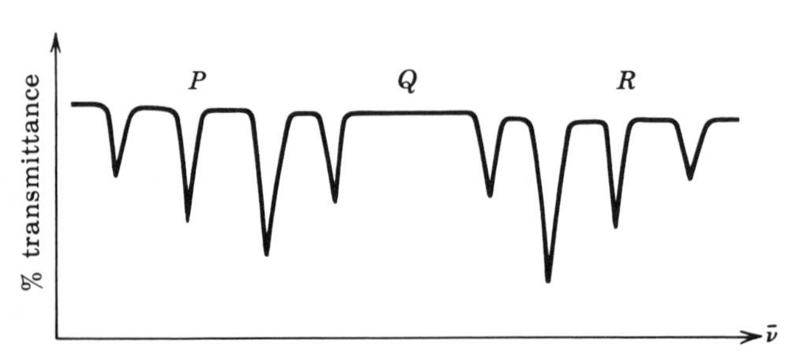

Fig. V-17 Vibrational-rotational bands.

Equation (V-6*b*) produces the *P* branch (absorptions with $\bar{\nu}$ *less* than $\bar{\nu}_{01}$); Eq. (V-6*a*), the *R* branch (absorptions with $\bar{\nu}$ greater than $\bar{\nu}_{01}$). The first line to the right of the gap, *i.e.*, the first line in the *R* branch, will, of course, correspond to a transition from the lowest possible value of J, i.e., a transition $J = 0$ to $J = 1$, and will have an energy

$$\Delta E = hc\bar{\nu}_{01} + (2h^2/8\pi^2 I)$$

The second line will be for $J = 1$ to $J = 2$ and will have an energy $\Delta E = hc\bar{\nu}_{01} + (4h^2/8\pi^2 I)$. Similarly the first absorption to the left of the gap will correspond to a transition *from* the lowest possible value of J. Since J is decreasing by one, the lowest initial value of J will be $J = 1$, and so the first line corresponds to a transition $J = 1$ to $J = 0$, with an energy

$$\Delta E = hc\bar{\nu}_{01} - \frac{2h^2}{8\pi^2 I}$$

In this way all the absorptions in the *P* and *R* branches can be assigned to their appropriate transitions. The assignment is illustrated in Fig. V-18.

The separation (in units of $\bar{\nu}$) between the innermost lines of the *P* and *R* branches is $(4h/c)/8\pi^2 I$, whereas between successive lines in either branch it would be $(2h/c)/8\pi^2 I$. Since this separation can be measured from the spectrum, it is possible to calculate the value of I (note the assumption that I is constant, so that if the separation does vary, it would be necessary to take the average separation). From the value of I so obtained, a good estimate of the internuclear separation could be extracted. In addition a slightly more accurate value for $\bar{\nu}_{01}$ can be obtained, since the midpoint between the innermost lines of the *P* and *R* branches can be measured with more accuracy than can the lowest point of the low-resolution vibrational curve.

All the above molecular information could be obtained from the spectra discussed in the previous section—although, perhaps, not so accurately. Certainly before the improvement of microwave, or far-infrared, techniques, the foregoing use of vibrational-rotational spectra was the principal source of such rotational information.

The picture of the molecule provided by the above measurements can be refined. An accurate measurement of the separation between the lines in a given branch indicates that the separation is not constant, as the previous discussion predicted. This is because, among other things, the moment of inertia is not the same in the two vibrational levels, and, further, the moment of inertia is not the same in all the rotational levels. The former is a result of anharmonicity of the vibration. The latter

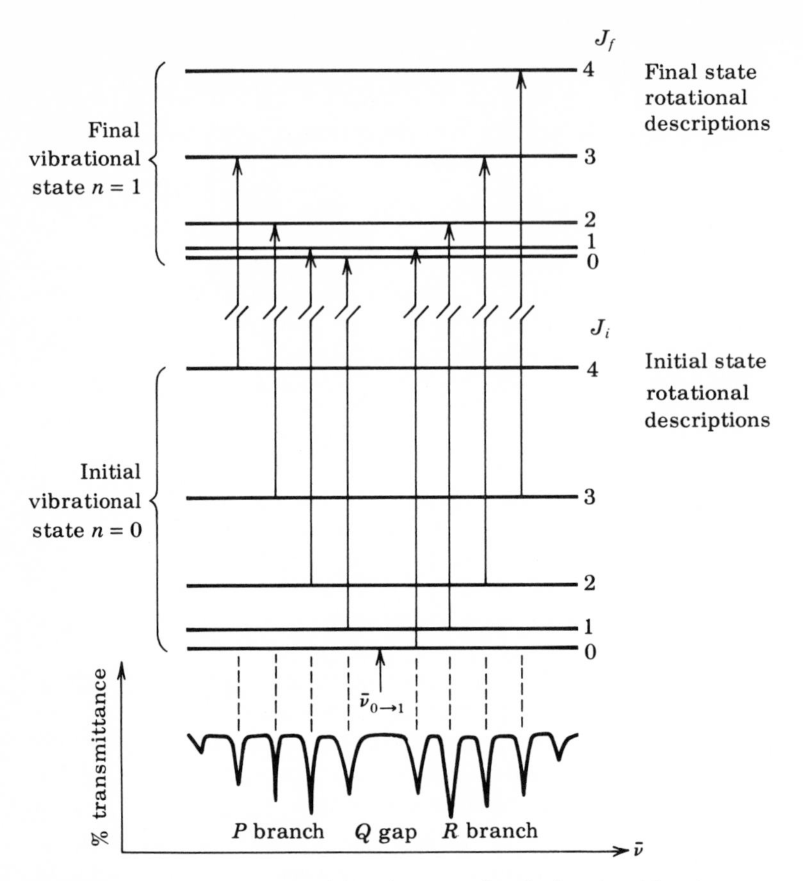

Fig. V-18 Assignment of transitions in a rotational-vibrational band.

is a result of the centrifugal distortion of the internuclear distance (and thus a change in I) as the system assumes higher rotational levels.

To account for the change in I for different vibrational levels, the energy change of the transition $n = 0 \rightarrow n = 1$, $\Delta J = +1$ should be written

$$\Delta E_R = hc\bar{\nu}_{01} + \frac{h^2}{8\pi^2}\left[\frac{(J+1)(J+2)}{I_1} - \frac{J(J+1)}{I_0}\right] \qquad J_i = J \tag{V-7}$$

where I_0 and I_1 are the moments of inertia in the first and second vibrational levels. Similarly for $n = 0 \rightarrow n = 1$, $\Delta J = -1$, one should write

$$\Delta E_P = hc\bar{\nu}_{01} + \frac{h^2}{8\pi^2}\left[\frac{(J-1)J}{I_1} - \frac{J(J+1)}{I_0}\right] \qquad J_i = J \tag{V-8}$$

If the energy of a transition in the P branch is subtracted from the energy of a transition in the R branch *arising* from the same J value, the result is

$$\Delta E_R - \Delta E_P = \frac{h^2}{8\pi^2}\left[\frac{(J+1)(J+2)}{I_1} - \frac{J(J+1)}{I_0} - \frac{J(J-1)}{I_1} + \frac{J(J+1)}{I_0}\right]$$
$$= \frac{4h^2}{8\pi^2 I_1}(J+\tfrac{1}{2}) \qquad \text{(V-9)}$$

$(1/hc)(\Delta E_R - \Delta E_P)$ can be measured from the spectrum and, in turn, the above equation solved for I_1 (for a given J).

By comparing lines for transitions *terminating* in the same J, an expression for the moment of inertia I_0 can also be obtained. Thus two values of I, one for the vibrational level $n = 1$ and the other for $n = 0$, can be found. However, since the state $n = 0$ to which I_0 refers still contains vibrational energy, I_0 does *not* refer to the moment of inertia at the bottom of the potential curve—rather, it would be necessary to extrapolate from I_1 to I_0 to obtain $I_{\min}$, as in Fig. V-19. From this procedure a very accurate value of the internuclear separation, independent of any vibrational contribution, can be obtained.

The value for $\bar{\nu}_{01}$ obtained up to now by taking the value of $\bar{\nu}_{01}$ at the center of the Q gap can be improved. The energy of the first line to the right of the gap is

$$\Delta E_R = hc\bar{\nu}_{01} + \frac{h^2}{8\pi^2}\left[\frac{(0+1)(0+2)}{I_1} - \frac{0(0+1)}{I_0}\right]$$
$$= hc\bar{\nu}_{01} + \frac{h^2}{8\pi^2}\left(\frac{2}{I_1}\right) \qquad \text{(V-10)}$$

Solving for $\bar{\nu}_{01}$ gives $\bar{\nu}_{01} = (\bar{\nu}$ of the first line in $R) - [(h/c)/8\pi^2](2/I_1)$, and, since I_1 is known, $\bar{\nu}_{01}$ can be found. The value of $\bar{\nu}_{01}$ so obtained

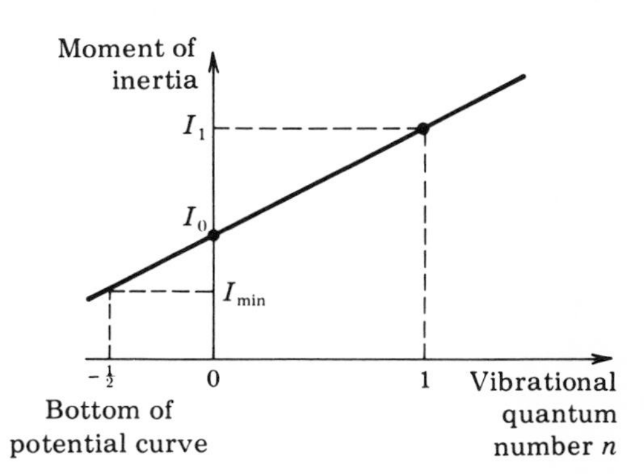

Fig. V-19 Extrapolation of the moment of inertia.

will not be exactly the midpoint of the gap, since now the inequality of I_1 and I_0 has been recognized, and the first line to the left is

$$\Delta E_P = hc\bar{\nu}_{01} - \frac{h^2}{8\pi^2}\left(\frac{2}{I_0}\right)$$

This is illustrated in Fig. V-20.

The treatment of the previous few paragraphs has recognized the approximate nature of the harmonic oscillator and the rigid-rotor models, and the details of the spectra have been used to provide more correct information on the molecule. The inadequacy of the models could be recognized at a much earlier position in the treatment. For example, the results of the simplest approximation may be used to suggest an improved form for the energy. Since the simplest approximation for molecular rotation (i.e., the rigid-rotor description of rotation) indicates that the energy depends upon $J(J + 1)$, an improved form for the energy would be a power series in $J(J + 1)$ as

$$E_{\text{rot}} = \frac{h^2}{8\pi^2 I} J(J + 1) + Dhc[J(J + 1)]^2 \qquad \text{(V-11)}$$

where the first term is simply that of the rigid rotor, and the second term is introduced to account for stretching due to the centrifugal force generated by high rotational energies. Similarly the vibrational energy level given by the harmonic oscillator may be corrected by the "anharmonicity term" as $E_{\text{vib}} = (n + \frac{1}{2})h\nu_0 - (n + \frac{1}{2})^2 h\nu_0\chi_e$, where χ_e is the constant introduced to account for the asymmetry of the potential energy (and thus account for the nonharmonic nature, or "anharmonicity," of the system). As will be seen in Project 10, the constant χ_e can be evaluated with the use of appropriate experimental data—for χ_e one needs the value of $\bar{\nu}$ for transitions between more than one vibrational level, that is, $\bar{\nu}_{01}$ and $\bar{\nu}_{02}$.

Alternatively the correction can be introduced at an even earlier stage in the development. For example, the Hooke's law potential of

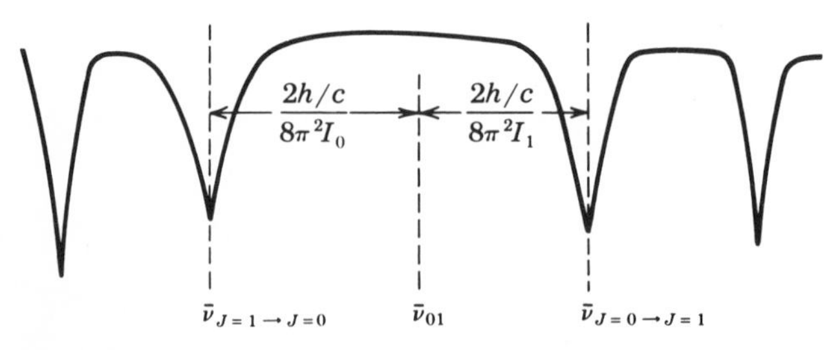

Fig. V-20 The "pure vibrational" transition.

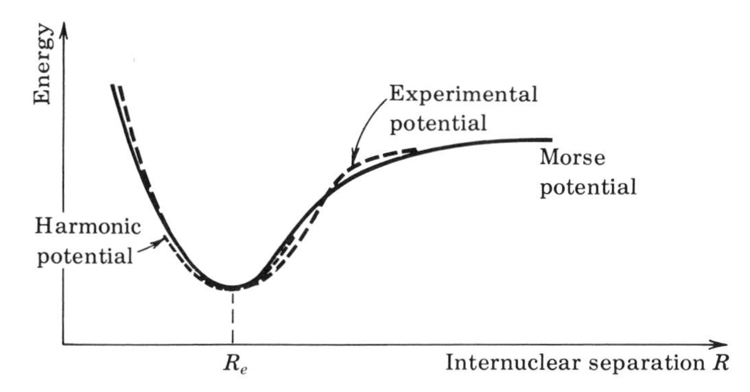

Fig. V-21 The Morse potential.

the harmonic oscillator can be replaced by a Morse potential (Fig. V-21)

$$V(r) = D_e(1 - e^{-Br^2})$$

and the SE for this potential can be solved for the energy levels and eigenfunctions. Other, less simple, functions have also been proposed, but all are attempting essentially the same thing, correcting for the inadequacy of the original model and the original separation of the hamiltonian.

(v) Project 10. Vibrational-rotational spectrum of HCl

The usefulness of a high-resolution vibrational-rotational spectrum is best illustrated by carrying out the calculations[1] for a spectrum such as that given in Fig. V-22. It might be pointed out that this is the same sample that produced the spectra presented earlier in Figs. II-5 and V-5, except now it has been run on a more sensitive spectrometer that reveals the detail. The units of the spectrum are cm^{-1}. It might also be noted that, in Fig. V-22, the higher values of $\bar{\nu}$ are to the left, so that the left-hand branch is the R branch.

PROBLEM 10-1

Convert the $\bar{\nu}$ value of the two most intense absorptions in each branch to frequency ν and wavelength λ.

PROBLEM 10-2

To each of the first five lines in the P and R branches in the spectrum of Fig. V-22, assign the appropriate initial and final values of n and J.

[1] See also F. E. Stafford, C. W. Holt and G. L. Paulson, *J. Chem. Ed.* **40**:245 (1963).

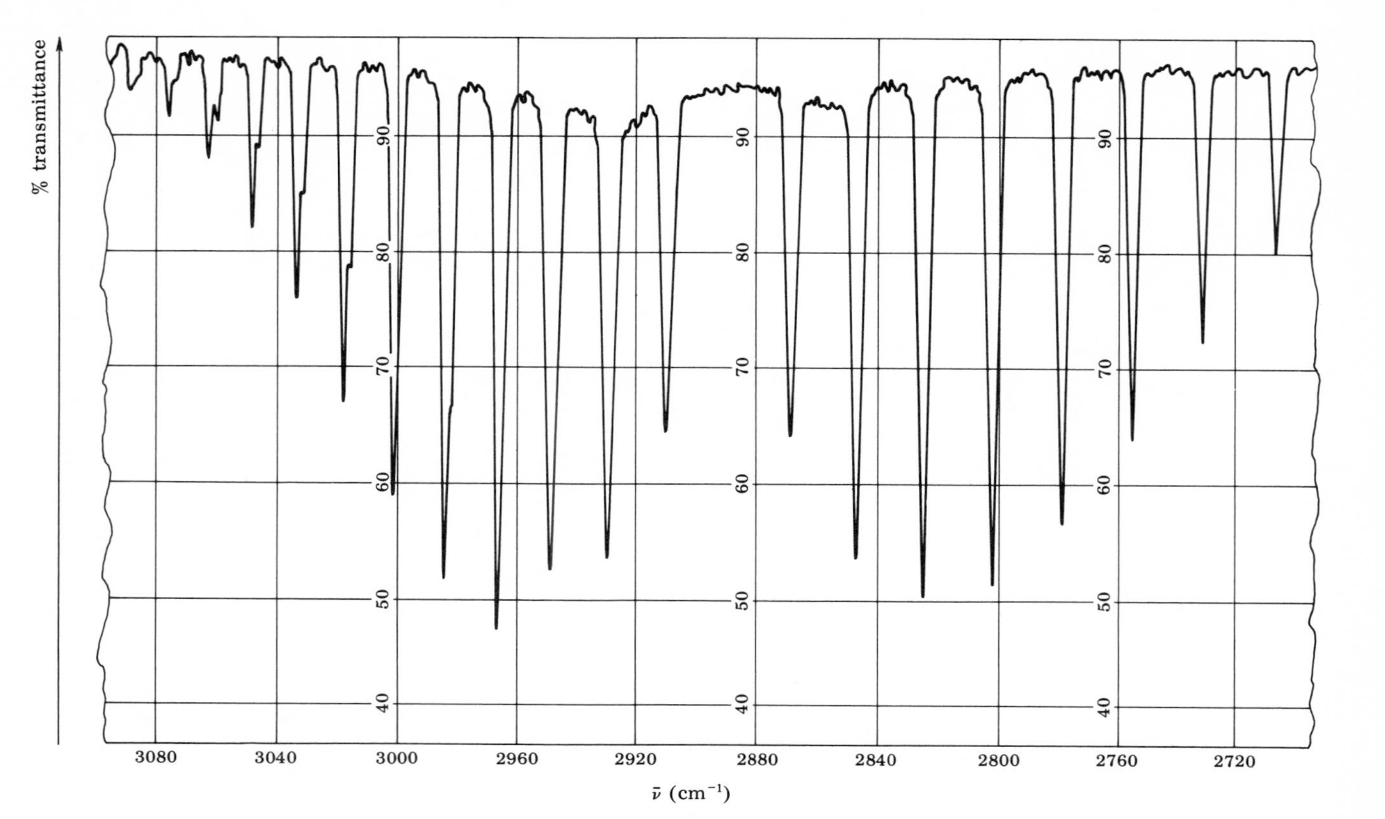

Fig. V-22 High-resolution HCl spectrum (on a Beckman IR-7). (*Courtesy Dr. H. Wieser.*)

PROBLEM 10-3

Make a sketch like Fig. V-18 with appropriate n and J labeling for the first five transitions in each branch.

PROBLEM 10-4

By using Eqs. (V-6*a*) and (V-6*b*):

(i) Show that the separation between successive lines in the P branch is $(2h/c)/8\pi^2 I$.

(ii) Show that the separation between the innermost lines of the P and R branches (the gap Q) is $(4h/c)/8\pi^2 I$.

Since the separations referred to in Prob. 10-4 can be measured from the spectrum, it is possible to calculate the value of I (note that I is assumed constant in the argument so far, so that, if the separation does vary, its average value would be required). From the value of I so obtained, a good estimate of the internuclear separation can be extracted.

PROBLEM 10-5

Measure the separation between the innermost line of the P branch and the innermost line of the R branch and calculate a value for:

(i) The moment of inertia.

(ii) The internuclear separation.

These values are still only approximate. Why?

A slightly more accurate value for $\bar{\nu}_{01}$ than obtained earlier can be obtained now, since the midpoint between the innermost line of the P and R branches can be given more precisely than one can measure the lowest point or "midpoint" of the smooth curve in the low-resolution vibrational spectra (recall Project 3).

PROBLEM 10-6

Using the center of the gap as the value of $\bar{\nu}_{01}$ corresponding to the pure vibrational transition:

(i) Calculate the force constant k.

(ii) Compare k to that found for HCl in Project 3.

The picture of HCl presented by the preceding calculations can be refined, as indicated in Sec. V-3(iv), by recognizing that the moments of inertia in the two vibrational levels are different. Equation (V-9) has already been derived and indicates a method for finding I_1.

In a similar way the absorptions in the P and R branches corresponding to transitions that *terminate* with the *same* J value (i.e., with J_f the same) give

$$\Delta E_R - \Delta E_P = \frac{+4h^2}{8\pi^2 I_0}(J + \tfrac{1}{2}) \qquad J_f = J \tag{V-12}$$

PROBLEM 10-7

Using Eqs. (V-6) and the definitions of the P- and R-branch transitions, prove Eq. (V-12).

PROBLEM 10-8

From Fig. V-22 and Eqs. V-9 and V-12

(i) Determine I_1 for $J_i = 1, 2$, and an average value of I_1.
(ii) Determine I_0 for $J_f = 1, 2$, and an average of I_0.
(iii) Suggest a reason for I_0 and I_1 being different for different J values.

There are then two values of I: one for the vibrational level $n = 1$, and the other for $n = 0$. But I_0 does *not* refer to the moment of inertia for the bottom of the potential curve. One would need to extrapolate from I_1 to I_0 to obtain I_{min}, as illustrated in Fig. V-19.

PROBLEM 10-9

Carry out the plot of Fig. V-19 to obtain I_{min}, and from I_{min} obtain the value of R_e.

PROBLEM 10-10

Following the method of Fig. V-20, calculate an improved value of $\bar{\nu}_{01}$ and, from it, an improved value of the force constant.

As indicated in the preceding section, the energy provided by the simple harmonic-oscillator description of vibration can be improved by writing the energy as a power series. Since, in the simplest approximation (the harmonic oscillator), the energy is proportional to $(n + \frac{1}{2})$, this is used as the basic term in the series as

$$E_{n,\text{vib}} = C_1(n + \tfrac{1}{2}) + C_2(n + \tfrac{1}{2})^2 + \cdots$$

If only the first two terms are retained, then the energy difference between the first two vibrational energy levels would be

$$\begin{aligned}\Delta E_{\text{vib}}(0 \rightarrow 1) = E_{1,\text{vib}} - E_{0,\text{vib}} &= [C_1(1 + \tfrac{1}{2}) + C_2(1 + \tfrac{1}{2})^2] \\ &\qquad - [C_1(\tfrac{1}{2}) + C_2(\tfrac{1}{2})^2] \\ &= C_1 + C_2[(\tfrac{3}{2})^2 - (\tfrac{1}{2})^2] \\ &= C_1 + 2C_2\end{aligned}$$

and[1]

$$\begin{aligned}\Delta E_{\text{vib}}(0 \to 2) &= E_{2,\text{vib}} - E_{0,\text{vib}} \\ &= [C_1(2 + \tfrac{1}{2}) + C_2(2 + \tfrac{1}{2})^2] - [C_1(\tfrac{1}{2}) + C_2(\tfrac{1}{2})^2] \\ &= 2C_1 + C_2[(\tfrac{5}{2})^2 - (\tfrac{1}{2})^2] \\ &= 2C_1 + 6C_2\end{aligned}$$

There are two equations and two unknowns, and solving for C_2 gives

$$\Delta E_{\text{vib}}(0 \to 2) - 2\Delta E_{\text{vib}}(0 \to 1) = (2C_1 + 6C_2) - (2C_1 + 4C_2) = 2C_2$$

or

$$\bar{\nu}_{02} - 2\bar{\nu}_{01} = \frac{2C_2}{hc}$$

The power series in E_{vib} can be written in terms of ω_e (formerly $h\nu_0\chi_e$)

$$E_{n,\text{vib}} = \omega_e(n + \tfrac{1}{2}) - \omega_e\chi_e(n + \tfrac{1}{2})^2 + \cdots \qquad \text{(V-13)}$$

in which case $\omega_e = C_1$ and $\omega_e\chi_e = -C_2$, so that $\chi_e = -C_2/C_1$. The anharmonicity may then be quoted in terms of χ_e.

PROBLEM 10-11

Given that $\bar{\nu}_{02} = 5668\ \text{cm}^{-1}$, use Eq. V-13 and the experimental value of $\bar{\nu}_{01}$ to find χ_e.

The spacing between *adjacent* vibrational levels is given in the power series by:

$$\begin{aligned}\Delta E_n &= E_{n+1,\text{vib}} - E_{n,\text{vib}} = [C_1(n + \tfrac{3}{2}) + C_2(n + \tfrac{3}{2})^2] \\ &\qquad - [C_1(n + \tfrac{1}{2}) + C_2(n + \tfrac{1}{2})^2] \\ &= C_1[(n + \tfrac{3}{2}) - (n + \tfrac{1}{2})] + C_2[(n + \tfrac{3}{2})^2 - (n + \tfrac{1}{2})^2] \\ &= C_1 + 2C_2(n + 1)\end{aligned}$$

From the sketch of the vibrational levels in Fig. V-23, it is clear that the dissociation energy D_0 is simply the *sum* of the *separations* between adjacent vibrational levels. Thus D_0 is the *sum* of all the spacings $[\Delta E = C_1 + 2C_2(n + 1)]$ from the first spacing $(\Delta E = C_1 + 2C_2)$ up to a spacing for $n = \infty$, which, from Fig. V-23, has $\Delta E = 0$, that is,

$$\begin{aligned}D_0 &= \Delta E(n = 0 \to n = 1) + \Delta E(n = 1 \to n = 2) \\ &\qquad + \cdots + \Delta E(n = \infty - 1 \to n = \infty) \\ &= (C_1 + 2C_2) + (C_1 + 4C_2) + (C_1 + 6C_2) + \cdots + [0]\end{aligned}$$

This summation may be obtained graphically as the area under the curve obtained by plotting ΔE vs. n. (The curve is approximated by a linear

[1] This so-called forbidden transition is much less intense but, as a result of anharmonicity, is allowed [see Sec. IV-4(ii) for a discussion].

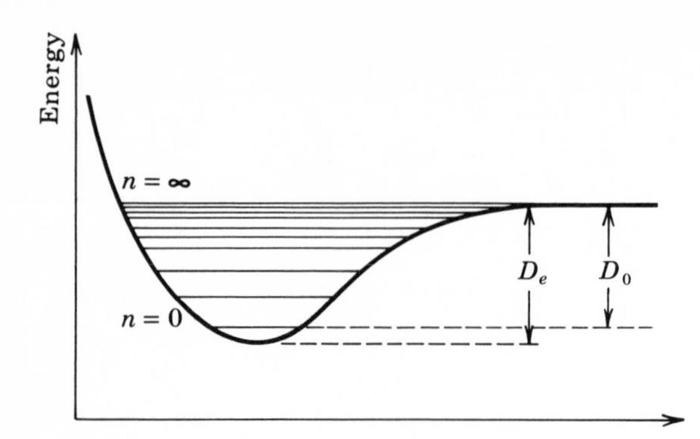

Fig. V-23 Vibrational energy levels.

extrapolation of the first few points. See Fig. V-24.) The height of the triangle is ΔE for $n = 0$, that is, $\Delta E = C_1 + 2C_2$. The base is the value n_D for which $\Delta E = 0$, that is, $\Delta E = 0$ for the transition

$$[n = (n_D - 1)] \rightarrow [n = n_D]$$

Hence $\Delta E = 0 = C_1 + 2C_2(n_D - 1 + 1)$, giving $n_D = -C_1/2C_2$. The area is then $\frac{1}{2}(C_1 + 2C_2)(-C_1/2C_2) = D_0$ *or*

$$D_0 = \frac{-C_1{}^2}{4C_2} - \frac{C_1}{2} = \frac{\omega_e}{4\chi_e} - \frac{\omega_e}{2} = \frac{\omega_e}{4}\left(\frac{1}{\chi_e} - 2\right)$$

PROBLEM 10-12

Find the dissociation energy for HCl.

Close examination of some of the vibrational-rotational lines reveals that the absorptions have shoulders or are made up of two absorptions, as in Fig. V-25. Since the rotational energy levels depend on the moment of inertia that, in turn, depends on the reduced mass $m_H m_{Cl}/(m_H + m_{Cl})$,

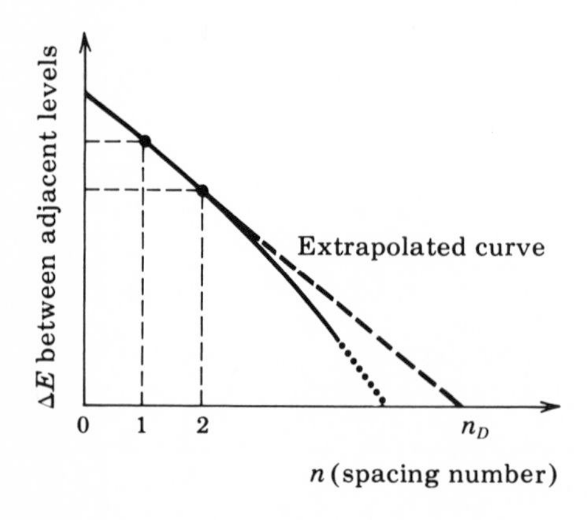

Fig. V-24 Energy between levels as a function of the spacing number.

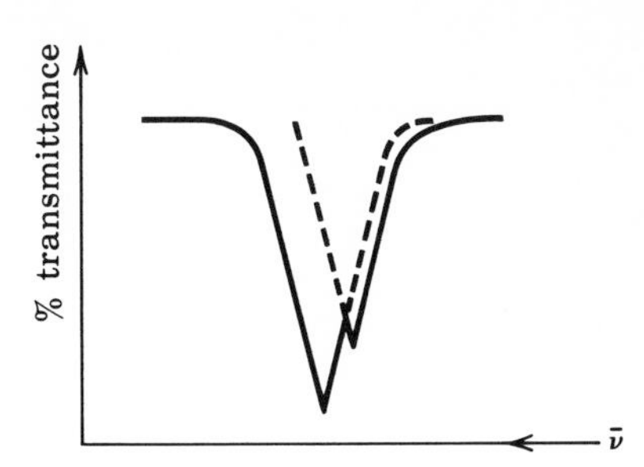

Fig. V-25 Isotope peaks.

it is clear that these two peaks could be due to the two different chlorine isotopes.

PROBLEM 10-13

Calculate the separation in $\bar{\nu}$ one would anticipate due to the effect of the isotopes on the moment of inertia of HCl (use the internuclear separation determined in Prob. 10-5). Do the calculation for the $J_i = 9 \rightarrow J_f = 10$ transition, and compare the answer to the observed splitting in Fig. V-22.

PROBLEM 10-14

Use the relative areas of the absorptions in the $J_i = 7 \rightarrow J_f = 8$ transition to calculate the isotope ratio of Cl^{35} and Cl^{37}. Compare the answer to the known ratio.

(vi) Electronic band spectra

(a) *Introduction*

The analysis of transitions in Sec. IV-4 indicated that electronic and vibrational changes could take place simultaneously—indeed, rotational transitions could occur at the same time. Thus the region of absorption of CO indicated in the low-resolution spectrum of Fig. V-26 could, under high resolution, yield the details of the vibrational and rotational transitions.

The usual method of obtaining high-resolution electronic absorption spectra is to take a "spectrogram" of the transmitted light after it has

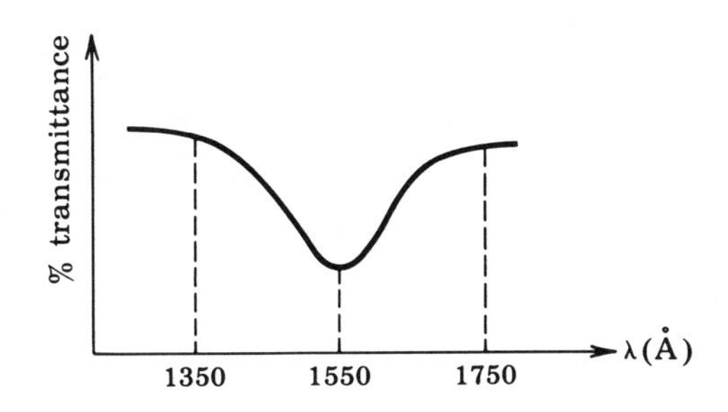

Fig. V-26 Low-resolution absorption spectrum of CO for the $n \rightarrow \pi^*$ electronic transition.

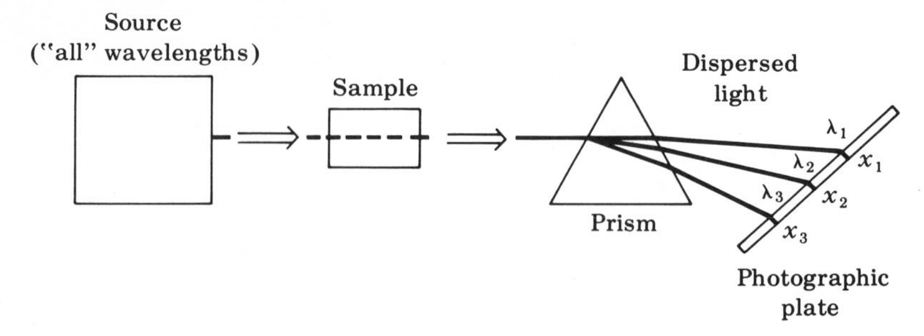

Fig. V-27 Absorption spectrograph.

been "spread out" by a prism. The procedure[1] is illustrated in Fig. V-27. The light of wavelength λ_1 then strikes the photographic plate at a certain point x_1, while light of wavelength λ_2 strikes at point x_2, etc. The intensity of light striking the plate at a given point depends, consequently, on whether or not that particular wavelength was absorbed by the sample. The developed photographic plate for CO is depicted in Fig. V-28,[2] with the quantum numbers of the initial and final vibration states indicated.

Certainly the broad region of absorption of Fig. V-26 can be seen in Fig. V-28 to be a number of separate "lines," i.e., a *number of* rather *narrow regions* of absorption. The principal absorptions (the series of heavy lines) are the result of the same electronic transition (here $n \rightarrow \pi^*$, see Fig. II-21) taking place at the same time as the various vibrational transitions $0 \rightarrow 1$, $0 \rightarrow 2$, etc. The series of lighter lines (less intense absorptions) are, for the $n \rightarrow \pi^*$ electronic transition, accompanied by the

[1] High-resolution electronic spectra are frequently measured as emission spectra, where the sample molecules, for example, C_2, CO, are excited to higher states by spark discharges, etc., and the frequencies of the light emitted as the molecule drops to lower levels are studied. Although easier to obtain, these emission spectra are much more complicated than the absorption spectra.

[2] After Fig. 14 in: G. Herzberg, "Spectra of Diatomic Molecules," 2d ed., Van Nostrand, 1950.

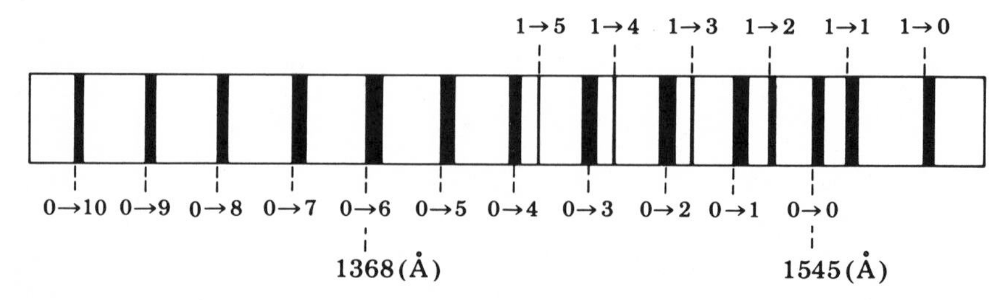

Fig. V-28 Absorption spectrogram of CO for the $n \rightarrow \pi^*$ electronic transition.

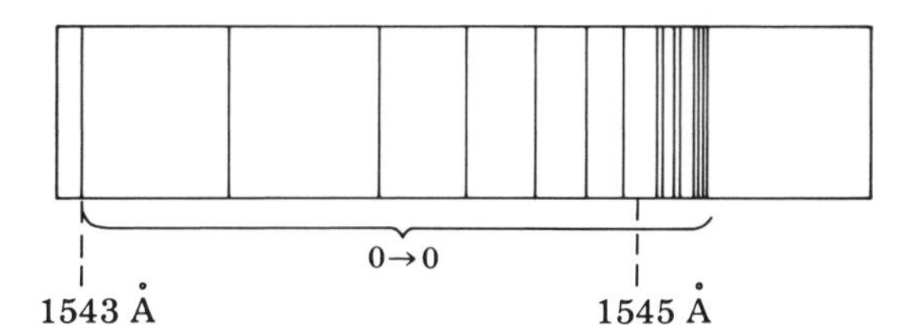

Fig. V-29 Rotational fine structure.

1 ⟶ 2, 1 ⟶ 3, etc., vibrational changes.[1] In fact, when one of these rather heavy lines, such as the "line" 0 ⟶ 0 of Fig. V-28, is examined under very high resolution, the result is a number of closely spaced lines, as indicated in Fig. V-29. These are the result of the *rotational* changes accompanying the vibrational-electronic (vibronic) changes.

(b) *General analysis*

The analysis of a vibronic spectrum can be carried out in much the same way as was done for the high-resolution vibrational-rotational spectra of the previous section. The procedure is illustrated in Fig. V-30. The energy of any of the transitions depicted in Fig. V-30 is simply

$$\begin{aligned}\Delta E &= E_{\text{final}} - E_{\text{initial}} \\ &= (E_{f,\text{el}} + E_{f,\text{vib}} + E_{f,\text{rot}}) - (E_{i,\text{el}} + E_{i,\text{vib}} + E_{i,\text{rot}}) \\ &= \Delta E_{\text{el}} + \left[\frac{h}{2\pi}(n_{f,\text{vib}} + \tfrac{1}{2})\sqrt{\frac{k_f}{\mu}} \right. \\ &\qquad \left. - \frac{h}{2\pi}(n_{i,\text{vib}} + \tfrac{1}{2})\sqrt{\frac{k_i}{\mu}}\right] + \Delta E_{\text{rot}} \qquad \text{(V-14)}\end{aligned}$$

In Eq. (V-14) k_i and k_f are the force constants in the initial and final electronic states. If, for the moment, the rotational changes are ignored and the force constants are taken to be the same in the initial and final vibrational states of each electronic state, then

$$\Delta E = \Delta E_{\text{el}} + \frac{h}{2\pi}(n_{f,\text{vib}} - n_{i,\text{vib}})\sqrt{\frac{k}{\mu}}$$

For the series of lines originating at $n_{i,\text{vib}} = 0$, this gives

$$\Delta E = \Delta E_{\text{el}} + (h/2\pi)(n_{f,\text{vib}})\sqrt{k/\mu}$$

[1] At ordinary temperatures only the first two vibrational levels of the ground electronic level are occupied, so only the series originating at $n = 0$ and the weaker series from $n = 1$ are observed.

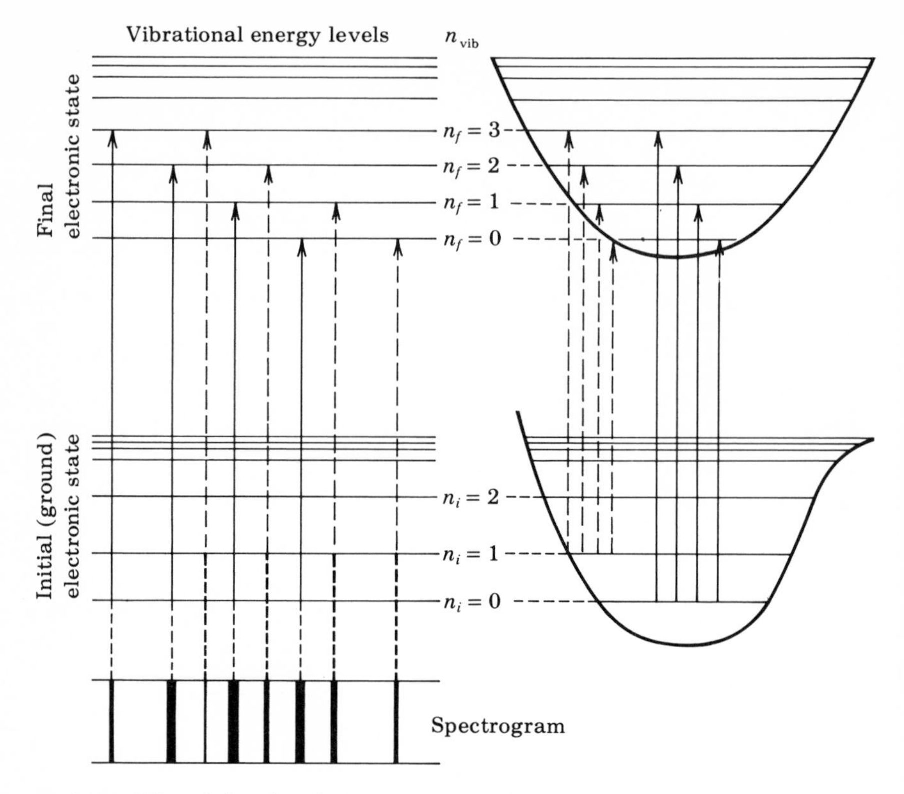

Fig. V-30 Vibronic band analysis.

Thus the spacing between absorptions, as $n_{f,\text{vib}}$ changes by one, should be approximately equal. This means the spacing is given by

$$\begin{aligned}\Delta E(0 \rightarrow 2) - \Delta E(0 \rightarrow 1) &= \Delta E_{\text{el}} + \frac{h}{2\pi} 2 \sqrt{\frac{k}{\mu}} - \Delta E_{\text{el}} - \frac{h}{2\pi} \sqrt{\frac{k}{\mu}} \\ &= \frac{h}{2\pi} \sqrt{\frac{k}{\mu}}\end{aligned}$$

The average spacing in the spectrum should yield an approximate value for the force constant.

The force constant is, of course, unlikely to be the same in the initial and final electronic states—indeed, it will not even be the same in the first two vibrational levels of the initial electronic states. Consequently a more refined analysis is in order. For example, Eq. (V-14) and the average displacement of the $0 \rightarrow 1$ and the $1 \rightarrow 2$ transitions gives a measure of the difference of the force constants k_i and k_f. The next step in the refinement would be to write the vibrational levels, as in Project 10, where a power series was used:

$$\Delta E_{\text{vib}} = (n + \tfrac{1}{2}) \frac{h}{2\pi} \sqrt{\frac{k}{\mu}} - (n + \tfrac{1}{2})^2 \chi_e \frac{h}{2\pi} \sqrt{\frac{k}{\mu}}$$

Both k and χ_e could be obtained.

(vii) Project 11. Vibronic spectra

In the previous projects rather explicit direction was given as to what could be obtained from a given spectrum. With this experience and the general analysis of the previous section as background, less direction should now be required. For convenience Table V-5 provides the line frequencies, rather than the spectrogram, of the vibronic absorptions of CO.

PROBLEM 11-1

Find out as much as possible about the CO molecule from the data of Table V-5.

Table V-5 "Deslandres" table of the transitions (cm^{-1}), of a vibronic band of the CO molecule, at 1350–1750 Å‡

	$n_{i,\text{vib}}$	
$n_{f,\text{vib}}$	0	1
0	(64,703)	62,601.8
1	66,231.3	64,087.6
2	67,674.8	65,533.1
3	69,087.8	66,944.3
4	70,469.5	68,323.4
5	71,807.2	69,666.1
6	(73,093)	70,973.2
7		72,248.3
8		(73,453)

‡ After G. Herzberg, "Spectra of Diatomic Molecules," 2d ed., Van Nostrand, 1950.

appendix I

The Classical Wave Equation

The simplest kind of wave is the harmonic wave that results when the restoring force is directly proportional to the displacement, as in the following:

$$\text{Force} = F = -ky_1 \qquad \text{(AI-1)}$$

where y_1 is the displacement, and k is a constant. The negative sign indicates that the restoring force opposes the displacing force. According to Newton's law of motion, F = mass $\times$ acceleration = ma. The "acceleration" of a is given by $(d^2/dt^2)y_1$, so that

$$F = m\frac{d^2}{dt^2}y_1 \qquad \text{(AI-2)}$$

Combining Eqs. (AI-1) and (AI-2) gives

$$m\frac{d^2}{dt^2}y_1 = -ky_1 \qquad \text{(AI-3)}$$

as the wave equation for a particular position in the medium, where y_1 is a function of time $y_1 = f(t_1)$ and must satisfy this equation.

Certainly not all functions will satisfy this equation. However, the functions

$$y_1 = A \sin wt \qquad \text{and} \qquad y_1 = B \cos wt$$

do satisfy Eq. (AI-3). These functions are illustrated in Fig. AI-1. From these figures one notes that, after a certain time τ, the y value returns to a former value. In other words the *displacement* is *cyclical.* That is, $y_1(t) = y_1(t + \tau)$ or, using the above function for y_1, we can write $y_1 = A \sin wt = A \sin w(t + \tau)$, where[1] $w = 2\pi/\tau$. The number of such cycles per second, the frequency ν, is equal to $1/\tau$, so that $w = 2\pi\nu$ and y_1 can be written as

$$y_1 = A \sin 2\pi\nu t$$

This gives the displacement of the medium with time at one point x_1 in the medium. The next step is to find the equation that governs the function $y = f(x,t)$ describing the motion of the wave as a whole.

The function $y_i = A \sin 2\pi\nu t_i$ describes the displacement in time at a given position x_i, and the time t_i is a "local time" for that point. Since this form gives $y_i = 0$ for $t_i = 0$, then this means that the "local time" starts at the instant the point x_i receives the disturbance. Thus a point at a distance x from the origin, that is, $x_i = x$, will receive the disturbance at a time (x/v) seconds after it has left the origin. Hence the local time t_1 for x_1 starts when $t = x/v$, that is, $t_1 = (x/v) - t$. In such a fashion, all local times can be related to t and the completely general expression for any point x is obtained as $y = f(x,t) = A \sin 2\pi\nu[(x/v) - t]$. But the velocity v of the wave is the distance traveled per second and will be equal to the number of oscillations completed in one second times the "length

[1] From trigonometry $\sin \theta = \sin(\theta + 2\pi)$, so that $\sin wt = \sin(wt + 2\pi)$. Using this expression for $\sin wt$, and the previous one obtained from the diagram, gives $\sin(wt + 2\pi) = \sin w(t + \tau)$. This gives $wt + 2\pi = w(t + \tau)$ or $w = 2\pi/\tau$.

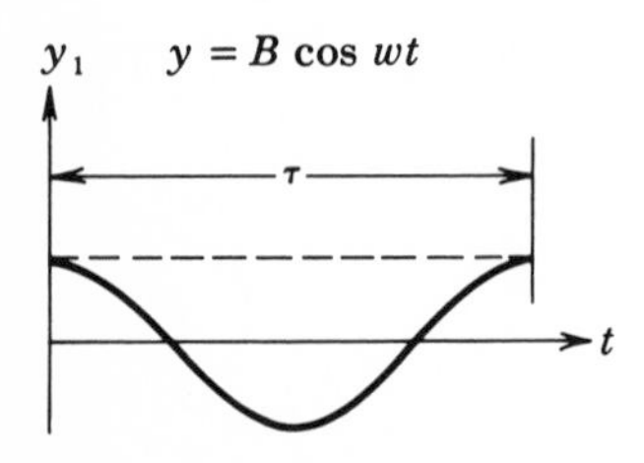

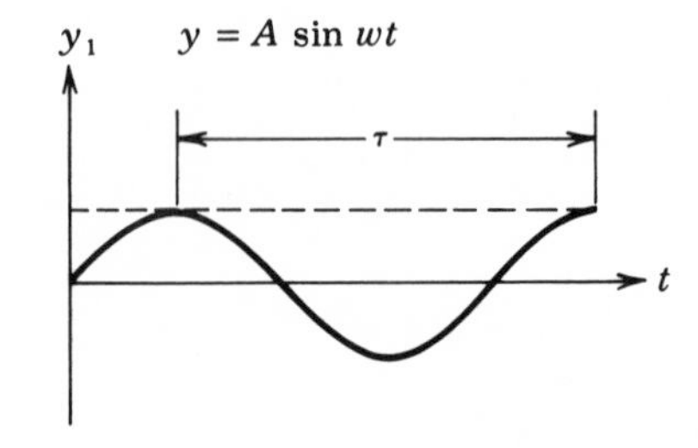

Fig. AI-1 Sine and cosine functions.

in space of the oscillation" (the wavelength λ). Thus $v = \nu\lambda$, and so the function y can be rewritten as

$$y = A \sin 2\pi[(x/\lambda) - \nu t] \qquad \text{(AI-4)}$$

The second derivative with respect to time of Eq. (AI-4) is

$$\frac{d^2}{dt^2} y = -4\pi^2\nu^2 y \qquad \text{(AI-5)}$$

And the second derivative[1] with respect to x of Eq. (AI-4) is

$$\frac{d^2}{dx^2} y = -\frac{4\pi^2 y}{\lambda^2} \qquad \text{(AI-6)}$$

Combining Eqs. (AI-5) and (AI-6) gives an equation that the description of the wave as a whole must satisfy:

$$\frac{d^2y}{dx^2} = \frac{1}{v^2}\frac{d^2y}{dt^2} \qquad \text{(AI-7)}$$

The function y so defined will give the description of the wave in time t and in space x. Writing $y(x,t)$ as a product of a description of the space behavior $\psi(x)$ and a description of the time behavior $g(t)$, where $g(t) = A \sin 2\pi\nu t$, gives

$$y(x,t) = \psi(x)\, A \sin 2\pi\nu t \qquad \text{(AI-8)}$$

To find the equation that $\psi(x)$ must satisfy, substitute Eq. (AI-8) into the wave equation (AI-7). We obtain for the right-hand side

$$\frac{1}{v^2}\frac{d^2}{dt^2}\psi(x)\, A \sin 2\pi\nu t = -\left(\frac{A4\pi^2\nu^2}{v^2}\right)\psi(x) \sin 2\pi\nu t$$

and for the left-hand side $(d^2/dx^2)\psi(x)\, A \sin 2\pi\nu t = A \sin 2\pi\nu t(d^2/dx^2)\psi(x)$. Equating the two and canceling the common terms gives

$$\left(\frac{d^2}{dx^2}\right)\psi(x) = -\left(\frac{2\pi\nu}{v}\right)^2 \psi(x)$$

or, in terms of the wavelength, the equation that $\psi(x)$ must satisfy is

$$\frac{d^2}{dx^2}\psi(x) = -\left(\frac{2\pi}{\lambda}\right)^2\psi(x) \qquad \text{(AI-9)}$$

[1] $(d^2y/dx^2) = (d^2/dx^2)A \sin 2\pi[(x/\lambda) - \nu t] = +A(2\pi/\lambda)(d/dx) \cos 2\pi[(x/\lambda) - \nu t]$
$= -A(2\pi/\lambda)^2 \sin 2\pi[(x/\lambda) - \nu t] = -(4\pi^2/\lambda^2)y.$

appendix II
The Rigid Rotor

(a) THE CLASSICAL DESCRIPTION

In Fig. AII-1 the center-of-mass position $x_{CM}y_{CM}z_{CM}$ is defined by the requirement that $m_1R_1 = m_2R_2$. The coordinates of the two masses relative to $x_{CM}y_{CM}z_{CM}$ may now be established. In Fig. AII-2 the scale of Fig. AII-1 is expanded, and it is assumed that the internuclear axis forms angles θ and ϕ with planes parallel to the cartesian planes x, y, and z. From the figure the distance OB is $R_2 \cos (90 - \theta) = R_2 \sin \theta$. Hence the distance O to x_2 is $(R_2 \sin \theta) \cos \phi$, and the value of x_2 is given by $x_2 = x_{CM} + R_2 \sin \theta \cos \phi$. Similarly the distance OB projected onto the y axis is $(R_2 \sin \theta) \cos (90 - \phi) = R_2 \sin \theta \sin \phi$. This gives $y_2 = y_{CM} + R_2 \sin \theta \sin \phi$. The value of $z_2 = z_{CM} + R_2 \cos \theta$. Similarly the coordinates of m_1 are

$$
\begin{aligned}
x_1 &= x_{CM} - R_1 \sin \theta \cos \phi \\
y_1 &= y_{CM} - R_1 \sin \theta \sin \phi \\
z_1 &= z_{CM} - R_1 \cos \theta
\end{aligned}
$$

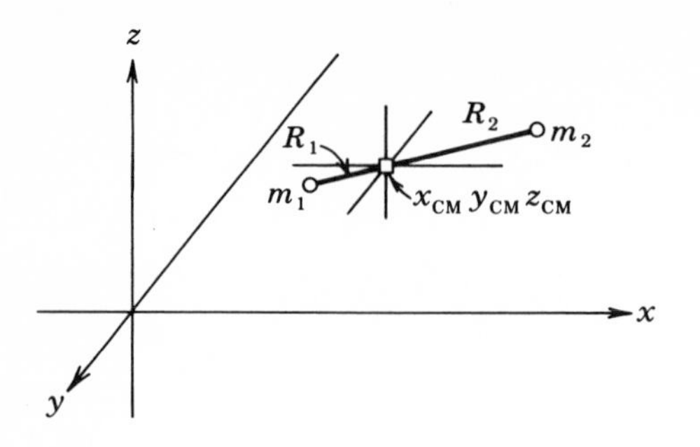

Fig. AII-1 The rigid rotor.

The kinetic energy of the rotor is given by

$$\begin{aligned}\text{KE} &= \text{KE}(m_1) + \text{KE}(m_2) \\ &= \tfrac{1}{2}m_1\left[\left(\frac{dx_1}{dt}\right)^2 + \left(\frac{dy_1}{dt}\right)^2 + \left(\frac{dz_1}{dt}\right)^2\right] \\ &\qquad + \tfrac{1}{2}m_2\left[\left(\frac{dx_2}{dt}\right)^2 + \left(\frac{dy_2}{dt}\right)^2 + \left(\frac{dz_2}{dt}\right)^2\right]\end{aligned}$$

To express this in terms of $x_{CM}y_{CM}z_{CM}$, R_1, R_2, θ, and ϕ, we need to take the derivatives of the preceding equations for x_1, y_1, z_1, x_2, y_2, and z_2. For example,

$$\begin{aligned}\frac{dx_1}{dt} &= \frac{d}{dt}(x_{CM} - R_1 \sin\theta\cos\phi) \\ &= \frac{dx_{CM}}{dt} - R_1\left(-\sin\theta\sin\phi\,\frac{d\phi}{dt} + \cos\theta\cos\phi\,\frac{d\theta}{dt}\right)\end{aligned}$$

This gives

$$\begin{aligned}\left(\frac{dx_1}{dt}\right)^2 &= \left(\frac{dx_{CM}}{dt}\right)^2 - 2\left(\frac{dx_{CM}}{dt}\right)R_1\left(-\sin\theta\sin\phi\,\frac{d\phi}{dt} + \cos\theta\cos\phi\,\frac{d\theta}{dt}\right) \\ &\quad + R_1^2\left[\sin^2\theta\sin^2\phi\left(\frac{d\phi}{dt}\right)^2 + \cos^2\theta\cos^2\phi\left(\frac{d\theta}{dt}\right)^2\right. \\ &\qquad\left. - 2\sin\theta\sin\phi\cos\theta\cos\phi\left(\frac{d\theta}{dt}\right)\left(\frac{d\phi}{dt}\right)\right]\end{aligned}$$

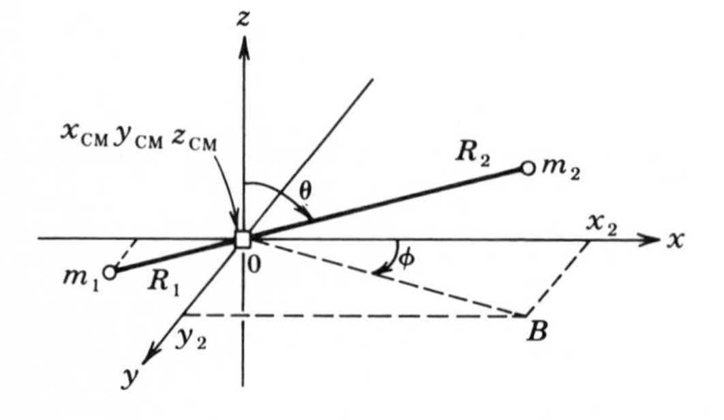

Fig. AII-2 Rigid-rotor internal coordinates.

Similarly

$$\frac{dx_2}{dt} = \frac{dx_{CM}}{dt} + R_2\left(-\sin\theta\sin\phi\frac{d\phi}{dt} + \cos\theta\cos\phi\frac{d\theta}{dt}\right)$$

gives

$$\left(\frac{dx_2}{dt}\right)^2 = \left(\frac{dx_{CM}}{dt}\right)^2 + 2\left(\frac{dx_{CM}}{dt}\right)R_2\left(-\sin\theta\sin\phi\frac{d\phi}{dt} + \cos\theta\cos\phi\frac{d\theta}{dt}\right)$$
$$+ R_2^2\left[\sin^2\theta\sin^2\phi\left(\frac{d\phi}{dt}\right)^2 + \cos^2\theta\cos^2\phi\left(\frac{d\theta}{dt}\right)^2 - 2\sin\theta\sin\phi\cos\theta\cos\phi\left(\frac{d\theta}{dt}\right)\left(\frac{d\phi}{dt}\right)\right]$$

In the kinetic energy, the term

$$KE_x = \tfrac{1}{2}m_1\left(\frac{dx_1}{dt}\right)^2 + \tfrac{1}{2}m_2\left(\frac{dx_2}{dt}\right)^2$$

can now be replaced by

$$KE_x = \tfrac{1}{2}m_1\left(\frac{dx_{CM}}{dt}\right)^2 + \tfrac{1}{2}m_1\left(\frac{-2dx_{CM}}{dt}\right)R_1\left[-\sin\theta\sin\phi\left(\frac{d\phi}{dt}\right) + \cos\theta\cos\phi\left(\frac{d\theta}{dt}\right)\right] + \tfrac{1}{2}m_1R_1^2\left\{\left[\sin^2\theta\sin^2\phi\left(\frac{d\phi}{dt}\right)^2\right] + \left[\cos^2\theta\cos^2\phi\left(\frac{d\theta}{dt}\right)^2\right] - \left[2\sin\theta\sin\phi\cos\theta\cos\phi\left(\frac{d\theta}{dt}\right)\left(\frac{d\phi}{dt}\right)\right]\right\}$$
$$+ \tfrac{1}{2}m_2\left(\frac{dx_{CM}}{dt}\right)^2 + \tfrac{1}{2}m_2\left(\frac{2dx_{CM}}{dt}\right)R_2\left[-\sin\theta\sin\phi\left(\frac{d\phi}{dt}\right) + \cos\theta\cos\phi\left(\frac{d\theta}{dt}\right)\right] + \tfrac{1}{2}m_2R_2^2\left\{\left[\sin^2\theta\sin^2\phi\left(\frac{d\phi}{dt}\right)^2\right] + \left[\cos^2\theta\cos^2\phi\left(\frac{d\theta}{dt}\right)^2\right] - \left[2\sin\theta\sin\phi\cos\theta\cos\phi\left(\frac{d\theta}{dt}\right)\left(\frac{d\phi}{dt}\right)\right]\right\}$$
$$= \tfrac{1}{2}(m_1 + m_2)\left(\frac{dx_{CM}}{dt}\right)^2 + \left(\frac{dx_{CM}}{dt}\right)\left[-\sin\theta\sin\phi\left(\frac{d\phi}{dt}\right) + \cos\theta\cos\phi\left(\frac{d\theta}{dt}\right)\right](-m_1R_1 + m_2R_2)$$
$$+ \tfrac{1}{2}\left\{\left[\sin^2\theta\sin^2\phi\left(\frac{d\phi}{dt}\right)^2\right] + \left[\cos^2\theta\cos^2\phi\left(\frac{d\theta}{dt}\right)^2\right] - \left[2\sin\theta\sin\phi\cos\theta\cos\phi\left(\frac{d\theta}{dt}\right)\left(\frac{d\phi}{dt}\right)\right]\right\}(m_1R_1^2 + m_2R_2^2)$$

Now since $m_1R_1 = m_2R_2$, we can get rid of the cross term, and, setting $m_1 + m_2 = M$, this equation reduces to

$$\text{KE}_x = \tfrac{1}{2}M\left(\frac{dx_{\text{CM}}}{dt}\right)^2 + \tfrac{1}{2}\left[\sin^2\theta\sin^2\phi\left(\frac{d\phi}{dt}\right)^2 + \cos^2\theta\cos^2\phi\left(\frac{d\theta}{dt}\right)^2 - 2\sin\theta\sin\phi\cos\theta\cos\phi\left(\frac{d\theta}{dt}\right)\left(\frac{d\phi}{dt}\right)\right](m_1R_1^2 + m_2R_2^2) \quad \text{(AII-1)}$$

The y component of the kinetic energy of the system is

$$\begin{aligned}\text{KE}_y &= \tfrac{1}{2}m_1\left(\frac{dy_1}{dt}\right)^2 + \tfrac{1}{2}m_2\left(\frac{dy_2}{dt}\right)^2 \\ &= \tfrac{1}{2}M\left(\frac{dy_{\text{CM}}}{dt}\right)^2 + \tfrac{1}{2}\left[\cos^2\theta\sin^2\phi\left(\frac{d\theta}{dt}\right)^2 + \sin^2\theta\cos^2\phi\left(\frac{d\phi}{dt}\right)^2 \right. \\ &\quad \left. + 2\sin\theta\sin\phi\cos\theta\cos\phi\left(\frac{d\theta}{dt}\right)\left(\frac{d\phi}{dt}\right)\right](m_1R_1^2 + m_2R_2^2)\end{aligned} \quad \text{(AII-2)}$$

where, again, the cross term has disappeared. The terms in the z direction are simply

$$\begin{aligned}\text{KE}_z &= \tfrac{1}{2}m_1\left(\frac{dz_1}{dt}\right)^2 + \tfrac{1}{2}m_2\left(\frac{dz_2}{dt}\right)^2 \\ &= \tfrac{1}{2}M\left(\frac{dz_{\text{CM}}}{dt}\right)^2 + \tfrac{1}{2}\left[\sin^2\theta\left(\frac{d\theta}{dt}\right)^2\right](m_1R_1^2 + m_2R_2^2)\end{aligned} \quad \text{(AII-3)}$$

Summing the terms for the kinetic energy in the x, y, and z directions, Eqs. (AII-1), (AII-2), and (AII-3), respectively, give

$$\begin{aligned}\text{KE} &= \tfrac{1}{2}M\left[\left(\frac{dx_{\text{CM}}}{dt}\right)^2 + \left(\frac{dy_{\text{CM}}}{dt}\right)^2 + \left(\frac{dz_{\text{CM}}}{dt}\right)^2\right] \\ &\quad + \tfrac{1}{2}(m_1R_1^2 + m_2R_2^2)\left[\underbrace{\sin^2\theta\sin^2\phi\left(\frac{d\phi}{dt}\right)^2}_{①}\right. \\ &\quad + \underbrace{\cos^2\phi\cos^2\theta\left(\frac{d\theta}{dt}\right)^2}_{②} \underbrace{- 2\sin\theta\sin\phi\cos\theta\cos\phi\left(\frac{d\theta}{dt}\right)\left(\frac{d\phi}{dt}\right)}_{③} \\ &\quad + \underbrace{\cos^2\theta\sin^2\phi\left(\frac{d\theta}{dt}\right)^2}_{④} + \underbrace{\sin^2\theta\cos^2\phi\left(\frac{d\phi}{dt}\right)^2}_{⑤} \\ &\quad \left. + \underbrace{2\sin\theta\sin\phi\cos\theta\cos\phi\left(\frac{d\theta}{dt}\right)\left(\frac{d\phi}{dt}\right)}_{⑥} + \underbrace{\sin^2\theta\left(\frac{d\theta}{dt}\right)^2}_{⑦}\right]\end{aligned} \quad \text{(AII-4)}$$

Certainly terms ③ and ⑥ in the bracket would cancel. Furthermore terms ① and ⑤ could be combined to give

$$\sin^2\theta\,(\sin^2\phi + \cos^2\phi)\left(\frac{d\phi}{dt}\right)^2 = \sin^2\theta\left(\frac{d\phi}{dt}\right)^2$$

Similarly terms ② and ④ give

$$\cos^2\theta\,(\cos^2\phi + \sin^2\phi)\left(\frac{d\theta}{dt}\right)^2 = \cos^2\theta\left(\frac{d\theta}{dt}\right)^2$$

This result could be combined with term ⑦ as

$$(\sin^2\theta + \cos^2\theta)\left(\frac{d\theta}{dt}\right)^2 = \left(\frac{d\theta}{dt}\right)^2$$

As a result Eq. (AII-4) is reduced to

$$\begin{aligned}\text{KE} &= \tfrac{1}{2}M\left[\left(\frac{dx_{\text{CM}}}{dt}\right)^2 + \left(\frac{dy_{\text{CM}}}{dt}\right)^2 + \left(\frac{dz_{\text{CM}}}{dt}\right)^2\right] \\ &\quad + \tfrac{1}{2}(m_1R_1^2 + m_2R_2^2)\left[\sin^2\theta\left(\frac{d\phi}{dt}\right)^2 + \left(\frac{d\theta}{dt}\right)^2\right] \qquad \text{(AII-5)}\end{aligned}$$

Clearly this choice of coordinates allows the kinetic energy to be separated into two parts. The first depends on only the center-of-mass coordinates and the second on the "internal" coordinates R_1, R_2, θ, and ϕ, that is, KE = KE(center-of-mass) + KE(internal). The kinetic energy term in the internal coordinates can be rewritten if it is recalled that

$$m_1R_1 = m_2R_2$$

or

$$R_1 = \frac{m_2R_2}{m_1}$$

which may be substituted into

$$R_1 + R_2 = R$$

to give

$$\frac{m_2}{m_1}R_2 + R_2 = R \qquad \text{or} \qquad R_2 = \frac{m_1}{m_1 + m_2}R$$

Similarly $R_1 = [m_2/(m_1 + m_2)]R$. Thus the term $\frac{1}{2}(m_1R_1^2 + m_2R_2^2)$ in Eq. (AII-5) can be written as

$$\begin{aligned}\frac{1}{2}\left[\frac{m_1m_2^2R^2}{(m_1 + m_2)^2} + \frac{m_2m_1^2R^2}{(m_1 + m_2)^2}\right] &= \tfrac{1}{2}m_1m_2R^2\left[\frac{m_1 + m_2}{(m_1 + m_2)^2}\right] \\ &= \frac{1}{2}\,\frac{m_1m_2}{m_1 + m_2}\,R^2 = \tfrac{1}{2}\mu R^2\end{aligned}$$

Hence the kinetic energy term in R_1,R_2, θ, and ϕ in Eq. (AII-5) can be written as

$$\tfrac{1}{2}\mu R^2 \left[\left(\frac{d\theta}{dt}\right)^2 + \sin^2\theta\left(\frac{d\phi}{dt}\right)^2\right]$$

where μ is a "reduced mass" at a distance R from the center of mass. Equation (AII-5) can now be rewritten as

$$\mathrm{KE} = \tfrac{1}{2}M\left[\left(\frac{dX}{dt}\right)^2 + \left(\frac{dY}{dt}\right)^2 + \left(\frac{dZ}{dt}\right)^2\right] + \tfrac{1}{2}\mu R^2\left[\sin^2\theta\left(\frac{d\phi}{dt}\right)^2 + \left(\frac{d\theta}{dt}\right)^2\right] \tag{AII-6}$$

where the center-of-mass coordinates X, Y, Z replace respectively x_{CM}, y_{CM}, and z_{CM}. It is clear from Eq. (AII-6) that the internal, or rotational, description of a mass μ, moving at a distance R from the origin, is completely separated from the center-of-mass description.

(b) THE SOLUTION OF THE QUANTUM-MECHANICAL PROBLEM

Since the energy is separated into two terms, we can write the hamiltonian as a sum of two parts, one for the center-of-mass coordinates and one for the internal coordinates. The SE can then be separated (recall the treatment of the harmonic oscillator) into two equations:

$$H_{\mathrm{CM}}(XYZ)\chi(XYZ) = E_{\mathrm{CM}}\chi(XYZ) \tag{AII-7}$$

$$H_{\mathrm{rot}}(R\theta\phi)\psi(R\theta\phi) = E_{\mathrm{rot}}\psi(R\theta\phi) \tag{AII-8}$$

These two equations are the equivalent for the rigid rotor of Eqs. (II-12) and (II-13) for the harmonic oscillator. Once again it is only the internal —in this case rotational—description that is of interest. As we have seen, the recipe for obtaining the hamiltonian operator for a mass μ in the cartesian coordinates x, y, z is just $-(h^2/8\pi^2\mu)(\partial^2/\partial x^2 + \partial^2/\partial y^2 + \partial^2/\partial z^2)$. Unfortunately the second derivative terms become rather more complicated[1] when expressed in spherical polar coordinates, and so the kinetic energy *operator* in R, θ, ϕ must be written[2] as

$$-\frac{h^2}{8\pi^2\mu}\left[\frac{1}{R^2}\frac{\partial}{\partial R}R^2\frac{\partial}{\partial R} + \frac{1}{R^2}\frac{1}{\sin\theta}\left(\frac{\partial}{\partial\theta}\sin\theta\frac{\partial}{\partial\theta}\right) + \frac{1}{R^2}\frac{1}{\sin^2\theta}\frac{\partial^2}{\partial\phi^2}\right]$$

The value of R for a *rigid* rotor must be constant, so that the terms in

[1] Just as the volume element $dx\,dy\,dz$ in cartesian coordinates becomes more complicated in spherical polar coordinates $R\theta\phi$—see Project 5.

[2] See section 16 and appendix IV in: L. Pauling and E. B. Wilson, "Introduction to Quantum Mechanics," McGraw-Hill, 1935.

$\partial/\partial R$ are not required. Hence Eq. (AII-8), the SE for the internal coordinates, is simply[1]

$$-\frac{h^2}{8\pi^2\mu R^2}\left[\left(\frac{1}{\sin\theta}\frac{\partial}{\partial\theta}\sin\theta\frac{\partial}{\partial\theta}\right)+\frac{1}{\sin^2\theta}\frac{\partial^2}{\partial\phi^2}\right]\psi_R(\theta\phi) = E_{\text{rot}}\psi_R(\theta\phi)$$

Because the first term in the hamiltonian operator depends on only θ, whereas the second, $(1/\sin^2\theta)(\partial^2/\partial\phi^2)$, depends on both θ and ϕ, we cannot separate the hamiltonian any further. However, if we multiply both sides of the equation by $\sin^2\theta$, the resulting equation

$$-\frac{h^2}{8\pi^2\mu R^2}\left[\sin\theta\left(\frac{\partial}{\partial\theta}\sin\theta\frac{\partial}{\partial\theta}\right)+\frac{\partial^2}{\partial\phi^2}\right]\psi_R(\theta\phi) = E_{\text{rot}}\sin^2\theta\psi_R(\theta\phi) \tag{AII-9}$$

can be separated by carrying out the same steps as those that led to Eqs. (II-1) and (II-2). Letting $\psi_R(\theta\phi) = T(\theta)S(\phi)$ and multiplying by $1/T(\theta)S(\phi)$, we obtain, for Eq. (AII-9),

$$-\frac{h^2}{8\pi^2\mu R^2}\frac{1}{T(\theta)S(\phi)}\left[\sin\theta\left(\frac{\partial}{\partial\theta}\sin\theta\frac{\partial}{\partial\theta}\right)+\frac{\partial^2}{\partial\phi^2}\right]T(\theta)S(\phi) = E_{\text{rot}}\sin{}^2\theta$$

Since $\partial/\partial\theta$ treats $S(\phi)$ as a constant, and $\partial/\partial\phi$ treats $T(\theta)$ as a constant, we can bring $S(\phi)$ to the left of the derivative in θ and $T(\theta)$ to the left of the derivative in ϕ to give

$$-\frac{h^2}{8\pi^2\mu R^2}\left[\frac{\sin\theta}{T(\theta)}\left(\frac{\partial}{\partial\theta}\sin\theta\frac{\partial}{\partial\theta}\right)T(\theta)\right]-E_{\text{rot}}\sin^2\theta = \frac{h^2}{8\pi^2\mu R^2}\frac{1}{S(\phi)}\frac{\partial^2 S(\phi)}{\partial\phi^2}$$

Multiplying by $-(8\pi^2\mu R^2/h^2)$ gives

$$\frac{\sin\theta}{T(\theta)}\left(\frac{\partial}{\partial\theta}\sin\theta\frac{\partial}{\partial\theta}\right)T(\theta)+\frac{8\pi^2\mu R^2}{h^2}E_{\text{rot}}\sin^2\theta = -\frac{1}{S(\phi)}\frac{\partial^2}{\partial\phi^2}S(\phi)$$

The left-hand side of this equation contains θ and the right-hand side ϕ. Since θ and ϕ are independent variables, we must set each side equal to a constant, as

$$-\frac{1}{S(\phi)}\frac{\partial^2}{\partial\phi^2}S(\phi) = m^2$$

$$\frac{\sin\theta}{T(\theta)}\left(\frac{\partial}{\partial\theta}\sin\theta\frac{\partial}{\partial\theta}\right)T(\theta)+\frac{8\pi^2\mu R^2}{h^2}E_{\text{rot}}\sin^2\theta = m^2$$

[1] We retain R as a subscript to emphasize that the description is for a rotor with a particular value of R.

Cross-multiplying and rearranging gives

$$\frac{\partial^2}{\partial \phi^2} S(\phi) = -m^2 S(\phi) \qquad \text{(AII-10)}$$

and

$$-\frac{h^2}{8\pi^2 \mu R^2}\left[\frac{1}{\sin\theta}\left(\frac{\partial}{\partial\theta}\sin\theta\frac{\partial}{\partial\theta}\right) - \frac{m^2}{\sin^2\theta}\right] T(\theta) = E_{\text{rot}} T(\theta) \qquad \text{(AII-11)}$$

An obvious solution to Eq. (AII-10) is

$$S(\phi) = e^{\pm im\phi}$$

When ϕ is increased by 2π, the same point in space is reached, and it would be expected that $S(\phi)$ would be the same as $S(\phi + 2\pi)$. If this restriction is applied as a boundary condition, then

$$e^{\pm im\phi} = e^{\pm im(\phi+2\pi)}$$

which gives $1 = e^{\pm im2\pi}$. But $e^{ix} = 1$ only if[1] $x = \pm n2\pi$, where n is an integer. This means that m can take only values 0, ± 1, ± 2, etc. Again the boundary conditions introduce quantum numbers! We label the allowed function by the quantum number m as $S_m(\phi)$.

The general solution of the differential equation in θ [Eq. (AII-11)] is rather more difficult to obtain; but, just as for the harmonic oscillator, it is easy to find the first few solutions. For example, the simplest solution would be $T(\theta) = K$, a constant. Then the derivative $\partial/\partial\theta$ would be zero, giving the left-hand side of Eq. (AII-11) as

$$-\frac{h^2}{8\pi^2 \mu R^2}\left[\frac{1}{\sin\theta}\left(\frac{\partial}{\partial\theta}\sin\theta\frac{\partial K}{\partial\theta}\right) - \frac{m^2 K}{\sin^2\theta}\right] = -\frac{h^2}{8\pi^2 \mu R^2}\left(0 - \frac{m^2 K}{\sin^2\theta}\right)$$

Equation (AII-11) would then be simply

$$\frac{h^2}{8\pi^2 \mu R^2}\left(\frac{m^2 K}{\sin^2\theta}\right) = E_{\text{rot}} K$$

which must be true for *all* values of θ. Since E is assumed to have only one value for any given state, the right-hand side must certainly be a constant. But the left-hand side could be a constant only if m^2 were zero. Hence if $T(\theta)$ equals a constant, m must be zero, and the energy must be zero.

In the harmonic oscillator we were led to a trial solution by looking at the differential equation for large values of the argument. In the present case since the differential equation (AII-11) involves the angle θ as a trigonometric function it is reasonable to try solutions of the form

[1] $e^{ix} = \cos x + i \sin x$. If $e^{ix} = 1$, then both $\cos x = 1$ and $\sin x = 0$ must hold. This occurs only if $x = n2\pi$, where n is an integer.

$\sin\theta$ or $\cos\theta$. If we now attempt the solution $T(\theta) = \cos\theta$, the left-hand side of the differential equation (AII-11) is

$$-\frac{h^2}{8\pi^2\mu R^2}\left[\frac{1}{\sin\theta}\left(\frac{\partial}{\partial\theta}\sin\theta\frac{\partial}{\partial\theta}\cos\theta\right) - \frac{m^2}{\sin^2\theta}\cos\theta\right]$$

$$= -\frac{h^2}{8\pi^2\mu R^2}\left[\frac{1}{\sin\theta}(-2\sin\theta\cos\theta) - \frac{m^2\cos\theta}{\sin^2\theta}\right]$$

$$= -\frac{h^2}{8\pi^2\mu R^2}\left(-2 - \frac{m^2}{\sin^2\theta}\right)\cos\theta$$

Thus for $T(\theta) = \cos\theta$, Eq. (AII-11) reduces to

$$-\frac{h^2}{8\pi^2\mu R^2}\left(-2 - \frac{m^2}{\sin^2\theta}\right)\cos\theta = E_{\text{rot}}\cos\theta$$

Canceling $\cos\theta$ on both sides gives

$$-\frac{h^2}{8\pi^2\mu R^2}\left(-2 - \frac{m^2}{\sin^2\theta}\right) = E_{\text{rot}}$$

Since this must be true for *all* values of θ, m must be zero. If $m = 0$, then $E = h^2 2/8\pi^2\mu R^2$. Once again the particular solution $T(\theta)$ restricts the value of m.

If we attempt yet another solution, $T(\theta) = \sin\theta$, the left-hand side of Eq. (AII-11) becomes

$$-\frac{h^2}{8\pi^2\mu R^2}\left[\frac{1}{\sin\theta}\left(\frac{\partial}{\partial\theta}\sin\theta\frac{\partial}{\partial\theta}\sin\theta\right) - \frac{m^2}{\sin^2\theta}\sin\theta\right]$$

$$= -\frac{h^2}{8\pi^2\mu R^2}\left[\frac{1}{\sin\theta}\left(\frac{\partial}{\partial\theta}\sin\theta\cos\theta\right) - \frac{m^2}{\sin^2\theta}\sin\theta\right]$$

$$= -\frac{h^2}{8\pi^2\mu R^2}\left[\frac{1}{\sin\theta}(-\sin^2\theta + \cos^2\theta) - \frac{m^2}{\sin^2\theta}\sin\theta\right]$$

$$= -\frac{h^2}{8\pi^2\mu R^2}\left[\frac{1}{\sin^2\theta}(\cos^2\theta - \sin^2\theta) - \frac{m^2}{\sin^2\theta}\right]\sin\theta$$

Inserting $\cos^2\theta = 1 - \sin^2\theta$ in this equation gives

$$-\frac{h^2}{8\pi^2\mu R^2}\left[\frac{1}{\sin^2\theta}(1 - \sin^2\theta - \sin^2\theta) - \frac{m^2}{\sin^2\theta}\right]\sin\theta$$

$$= -\frac{h^2}{8\pi^2\mu R^2}\left(\frac{1 - m^2}{\sin^2\theta} - 2\right)\sin\theta$$

Thus for $T(\theta) = \sin\theta$, Eq. (AII-11) reduces to

$$-\frac{h^2}{8\pi^2\mu R^2}\left(\frac{1 - m^2}{\sin^2\theta} - 2\right)\sin\theta = E_{\text{rot}}\sin\theta$$

Canceling $\sin\theta$ on both sides gives

$$-\frac{h^2}{8\pi^2\mu R^2}\left(\frac{1 - m^2}{\sin^2\theta} - 2\right) = E_{\text{rot}}$$

Since this must be true for all values of θ, $1 - m^2$ must equal zero. Once again the particular $T(\theta)$ solution has restricted the value of m. If $m = \pm 1$, the energy is just $E_{rot} = 2h^2/8\pi^2\mu R^2$.

These results might be summarized in the following manner:

$T(\theta)$	*Energy*	m
Constant	0	0
$\cos\theta$	$2\dfrac{h^2}{8\pi^2\mu R^2}$	0
$\sin\theta$	$2\dfrac{h^2}{8\pi^2\mu R^2}$	-1
$\sin\theta$	$2\dfrac{h^2}{8\pi^2\mu R^2}$	1

Certainly the value of m does not appear to be related to the energy [since E can be zero or E can be $2(h^2/8\pi^2\mu R^2)$ for the same value of m, that is, $m = 0$]. However, it does appear that if we write

$$E_{rot} = l(l+1)\left(\frac{h^2}{8\pi^2\mu R^2}\right)$$

and assign $l = 0$ for the first solution and $l = 1$ for the next three solutions, we would not only obtain the correct energy but we could also state the restrictions on m by saying that m could be any integer from $-l$ to $+l$. Since $T(\theta)$ defines an energy state in terms of l (which in turn restricts m), we label $T(\theta)$ as $T_{lm}(\theta)$ and E_{rot} as $E_{l,rot}$.

The foregoing analysis certainly cannot be taken as indicating that these are the only solutions to the rigid-rotor problem. Indeed, they are not; but, if a general solution were carried out,[1] these four solutions would be obtained, and they would be the four lowest-energy solutions. Before leaving this problem it might also be remarked that the interdependence of the quantum number l with m is a result of the fact that the SE was *not* separable but, rather, that the SE had to be transformed into a new equation (by multiplying by $\sin^2\theta$) that was separable.

[1] See, for example, H. Eyring, J. Walter, and G. Kimball, "Quantum Chemistry," Wiley, 1944.

appendix III
The Hydrogen Atom

The complete solution of the Schroedinger equation for the hydrogen atom is beyond the scope of the material in this book. Nevertheless, the problem can be analyzed in some detail and the first few solutions examined. The two-body problem in terms of the coordinates $x_n y_n z_n x_e y_e z_e$ can be transformed, using a method similar in concept to that for the rigid rotor, into a problem in terms of the center-of-mass coordinates XYZ and a problem in terms of the internal coordinates $r\theta\phi$. The latter coordinates have the position of the center of mass as the origin, and, since the mass of the nucleus is so much larger (of the order of 2×10^3) than the mass of the electron we may, for most purposes, take the nucleus as the center of mass. The internal coordinates $r\theta\phi$ may then be taken as describing the "position" of the electron relative to the nucleus.

The hamiltonian for the electron is then just

$$-\frac{h^2}{8\pi^2 m_e}\left[\frac{1}{r^2}\left(\frac{\partial}{\partial r} r^2 \frac{\partial}{\partial r}\right) + \frac{1}{r^2 \sin\theta}\left(\frac{\partial}{\partial \theta}\sin\theta\frac{\partial}{\partial \theta}\right) + \frac{1}{r^2\sin^2\theta}\frac{\partial^2}{\partial\phi^2}\right] - \frac{e^2}{r}$$

where once again (compare Appendix II) the term in brackets replaces $(\partial^2/\partial x^2 + \partial^2/\partial y^2 + \partial^2/\partial z^2)$ when the kinetic energy operator is expressed in spherical polar coordinates. The SE is simply $H_e\psi(r\theta\phi) = E_e\psi(r\theta\phi)$ or, writing H_e out explicitly,

$$\left\{-\frac{h^2}{8\pi^2 m_e}\left[\frac{1}{r^2}\left(\frac{\partial}{\partial r} r^2 \frac{\partial}{\partial r}\right) + \frac{1}{r^2 \sin\theta}\left(\frac{\partial}{\partial\theta}\sin\theta\frac{\partial}{\partial\theta}\right) + \frac{1}{r^2\sin^2\theta}\frac{\partial^2}{\partial\phi^2}\right] - \frac{e^2}{r}\right\}\psi(r\theta\phi) = E_e\psi(r\theta\phi)$$

This rather formidable looking equation can be separated into simpler equations as follows. Multiplying by r^2 gives

$$\left\{-\frac{h^2}{8\pi^2 m_e}\left[\left(\frac{\partial}{\partial r} r^2 \frac{\partial}{\partial r}\right) + \frac{1}{\sin\theta}\left(\frac{\partial}{\partial\theta}\sin\theta\frac{\partial}{\partial\theta}\right) + \frac{1}{\sin^2\theta}\frac{\partial^2}{\partial\phi^2}\right] - e^2 r\right\}\psi(r\theta\phi) = Er^2\psi(r\theta\phi)$$

As in all previous cases we let the solution be a product of functions as $\psi(r\theta\phi) = R(r)T(\theta)S(\phi)$. Multiplying by $1/R(r)T(\theta)S(\phi)$ and bringing those functions $R(r)$, $T(\theta)$, or $S(\phi)$ that are not affected by a differential operator to the left gives

$$-\frac{h^2}{8\pi^2 m_e}\frac{1}{R(r)T(\theta)S(\phi)}\left[T(\theta)S(\phi)\frac{\partial}{\partial r} r^2 \frac{\partial}{\partial r} R(r) + \frac{R(r)S(\phi)}{\sin\theta}\frac{\partial}{\partial\theta}\sin\theta\frac{\partial}{\partial\theta}T(\theta) + \frac{R(r)T(\theta)}{\sin^2\theta}\frac{\partial^2}{\partial\phi^2}S(\phi)\right] - e^2 r = Er^2$$

Canceling terms in numerator and denominator gives

$$-\frac{h^2}{8\pi^2 m_e}\left[\frac{1}{R(r)}\frac{\partial}{\partial r} r^2 \frac{\partial}{\partial r} R(r) + \frac{1}{T(\theta)\sin\theta}\frac{\partial}{\partial\theta}\sin\theta\frac{\partial}{\partial\theta}T(\theta) + \frac{1}{\sin^2\theta}\frac{1}{S(\phi)}\frac{\partial^2}{\partial\phi^2}S(\phi)\right] - e^2 r = Er^2$$

Multiplying by $-8\pi^2 m_e/h^2$ and putting all terms in r on the left and all others on the right gives

$$\frac{1}{R(r)}\frac{\partial}{\partial r} r^2 \frac{\partial}{\partial r} R(r) + \frac{8\pi^2 m_e}{h^2}(e^2 r + Er^2) = -\left[\frac{1}{T(\theta)\sin\theta}\frac{\partial}{\partial\theta}\sin\theta\frac{\partial}{\partial\theta}T(\theta) + \frac{1}{(\sin^2\theta)S(\phi)}\frac{\partial^2}{\partial\phi^2}S(\phi)\right]$$

The left-hand side depends on only r, and the right-hand side depends on only the angular variables θ and ϕ. Since r is completely independent of θ or ϕ, both sides of this equation must be equal to the same constant.

Thus

$$\frac{1}{R(r)}\frac{\partial}{\partial r}r^2\frac{\partial}{\partial r}R(r) + \frac{8\pi^2 m_e}{h^2}(e^2 r + Er^2) = C \qquad \text{(AIII-1)}$$

$$-\left[\frac{1}{T(\theta)\sin\theta}\frac{\partial}{\partial\theta}\sin\theta\frac{\partial}{\partial\theta}T(\theta) + \frac{1}{(\sin^2\theta)S(\phi)}\frac{\partial^2}{\partial\phi^2}S(\phi)\right] = C \qquad \text{(AIII-2)}$$

Multiplying Eq. (AIII-1) by $R(r)/r^2$ and Eq. (AIII-2) by $T(\theta)S(\phi)$ gives

$$\left[\frac{1}{r^2}\frac{\partial}{\partial r}r^2\frac{\partial}{\partial r} + \frac{8\pi^2 m_e}{h^2}\left(\frac{e^2}{r} + E\right)\right]R(r) = C\frac{R(r)}{r^2} \qquad \text{(AIII-3)}$$

$$-\left[\frac{1}{\sin\theta}\frac{\partial}{\partial\theta}\sin\theta\frac{\partial}{\partial\theta} + \frac{1}{\sin^2\theta}\frac{\partial^2}{\partial\phi^2}\right]T(\theta)S(\phi) = CT(\theta)S(\phi) \qquad \text{(AIII-4)}$$

Equation (AIII-4) is, however, identical in form to that encountered in the rigid rotor, where $C = l(l+1)$. The solutions of Eq. (AIII-4) are, indeed, the same as those for the rigid rotor, and so the angular description of the electron in an atom is characterized by the same functions as for the rotor. Multiplying Eq. (AIII-3) by $-(h^2/8\pi^2 m_e)$, inserting the value for C, and rearranging gives

$$\left\{-\frac{h^2}{8\pi^2 m_e}\left[\left(\frac{1}{r^2}\frac{\partial}{\partial r}r^2\frac{\partial}{\partial r}\right) - \frac{l(l+1)}{r^2}\right] - \frac{e^2}{r}\right\}R(r) = ER(r) \qquad \text{(AIII-5)}$$

The general solution of Eq. (AIII-5) is difficult to obtain but the first few solutions may be attempted. When r is large, the SE(AIII-5) reduces to a form that suggests $R(r) = \exp(-br)$ as a solution [recall the method of obtaining a trial solution of the harmonic oscillator in Sec. II-2(i)]. Using this as our trial solution, we substitute into Eq. (AIII-5) and obtain

$$\frac{-h^2}{8\pi^2 m_e}\left[\frac{1}{r^2}\frac{\partial}{\partial r}r^2\frac{\partial}{\partial r}\exp(-br) - \frac{l(l+1)}{r^2}\exp(-br)\right] - \left(\frac{e^2}{r}\right)\exp(-br) = E\exp(-br)$$

$$\frac{-h^2}{8\pi^2 m_e}\left[\frac{1}{r^2}\frac{\partial}{\partial r}(-br^2\exp(-br)) - \frac{l(l+1)}{r^2}\exp(-br)\right] - \frac{e^2}{r}\exp(-br) = E\exp(-br)$$

$$\frac{-h^2}{8\pi^2 m_e}\left[\frac{1}{r^2}(r^2b^2e^{-br} - 2br\exp(-br)) - \frac{l(l+1)}{r^2}\exp(-br)\right] - \frac{e^2}{r}\exp(-br) = E\exp(-br)$$

Canceling $\exp(-br)$ on both sides and collecting terms gives

$$\frac{1}{r^2}\left[\frac{h^2}{8\pi^2 m_e}l(l+1)\right] + \frac{1}{r}\left[\frac{h^2}{4\pi^2 m_e}b - e^2\right] - \frac{h^2}{8\pi^2 m_e}b^2 = E \qquad \text{(AIII-6)}$$

If $R(r) = \exp(-br)$ is to be a solution of the SE, then Eq. (AIII-6) must hold for *all* values of r. We can ensure this if we require that the coefficients of any term in r be zero (then we have terms such as $(1/r^2)0$ and $(1/r)0$, and the result is the same, i.e., zero, for all nonzero values of r). If $l = 0$, then the coefficient of the $1/r^2$ term is zero. However, the coefficient of the $1/r$ term will be zero only if

$$\frac{h^2}{4\pi^2 m_e} b - e^2 = 0 \qquad \text{(AIII-7)}$$

Solving Eq. (AIII-7) for b, we find that if $b = 4\pi^2 m_e e^2/h^2$ and $l = 0$, then $R(r) = \exp(-br)$ is a solution of the SE(AIII-5).

Returning to Eq. (AIII-6) and recognizing that only one term remains on the left (the others have been set to zero by the results of the preceding discussion), we have $-(h^2/8\pi^2 m_e)b^2 = E$. Inserting the value required of b gives $E = -(2\pi^2 m_e e^4/h^2)$. But this is just the energy of the lowest state according to Bohr theory! The same procedure can be carried out for a number of other functions, and the first few solutions can be obtained. The energy formula for the various solutions can be represented by $E_n = -(2\pi^2 m_e e^4/h^2 n^2)$, where $n = 1, 2, 3$, etc.

As indicated by the foregoing analysis, the solution $R(r)$ imposes restrictions on l, that is, $l = 0$ for the case $n = 1$, $R(r) = \exp(-br)$. When the other solutions $R(r)$ are obtained, it is found that l is restricted by $l = 0, 1, 2, \ldots, n - 1$. But l, in turn, restricts m as $m = 0, \pm 1, \pm 2, \cdots \pm l$.

In summary we obtain the solutions $\psi(r\theta\phi) = R_{nlm}(r)T_{lm}(\theta)S_m(\phi)$, some of which are given in Table II-7.

appendix IV

The Chemical Bond

On the basis that an adequate description of the electron in the molecule-ion H_2^+ is somewhere between the extremes

$$H_a^+ \cdots H_b \qquad \text{and} \qquad H_a \cdots H_b^+$$

the molecular orbital

$$\psi(H_2^+) = \psi_{MO} = c_1\phi_a + c_2\phi_b = c_1 1s_a + c_2 1s_b \qquad \text{(AIV-1)}$$

has been proposed. The values of c_1 and c_2 are to be found such that the energy given by

$$E = \frac{\int \psi_{MO} H \psi_{MO}\, d\tau}{\int \psi_{MO}\psi_{MO}\, d\tau} \qquad \text{(AIV-2)}$$

is a minimum (here H is the hamiltonian for H_2^+). Although eventually $\int \psi_{MO}\psi_{MO}\, d\tau$ in the denominator will be required to be one, at the moment this may not be true since c_1 and c_2 are to be varied, and, hence, for the present the MO is determined solely by the criteria of the lowest energy.

When Eq. (AIV-1) is inserted into Eq. (AIV-2), the expression for which a minimum must be found is

$$E = \frac{\int (c_1\phi_a + c_2\phi_b)H(c_1\phi_a + c_2\phi_b)\,d\tau}{\int (c_1\phi_a + c_2\phi_b)(c_1\phi_a + c_2\phi_b)\,d\tau}$$

On multiplying out the terms in the numerator and denominator,

$$E = \frac{c_1^2\int \phi_a H \phi_a\,d\tau + c_1c_2\int \phi_a H \phi_b\,d\tau + c_1c_2\int \phi_b H \phi_a\,d\tau + c_2^2\int \phi_b H \phi_b\,d\tau}{c_1^2\int \phi_a^2\,d\tau + c_2^2\int \phi_b^2\,d\tau + 2c_1c_2\int \phi_a\phi_b\,d\tau} \qquad \text{(AIV-3)}$$

Now $\int \phi_a^2\,d\tau = 1$ and $\int \phi_b^2\,d\tau = 1$, since these are normalized hydrogenic functions, and, for convenience, the following notation is introduced,

$$H_{aa} = \int \phi_a H \phi_a\,d\tau \qquad H_{bb} = \int \phi_b H \phi_b\,d\tau \qquad H_{ab} = \int \phi_a H \phi_b\,d\tau$$
$$H_{ba} = \int \phi_b H \phi_a\,d\tau \qquad S_{ab} = \int \phi_a \phi_b\,d\tau$$

Equation (AIV-3) can be rewritten as

$$E = \frac{c_1^2 H_{aa} + c_1c_2(H_{ab} + H_{ba}) + c_2^2 H_{bb}}{c_1^2 + c_2^2 + 2c_1c_2S_{ab}} \qquad \text{(AIV-4)}$$

The values for c_1 and c_2 can now be found by either the variational method of setting $\partial E/\partial c_1 = 0$ and $\partial E/\partial c_2 = 0$ (the condition for an extremum) and solving for c_1 and c_2, or the simple symmetry argument of Sec. II-3(iv). The result in any case is $c_1 = \pm c_2$. On inserting $c_1 = c_2$ or $c_1 = -c_2$ into Eq. (AIV-4), the two energies are

$$E_B = \frac{H_{aa} + (H_{ab} + H_{ba}) + H_{bb}}{2(1 + S_{ab})} \qquad c_1 = c_2 \qquad \text{(AIV-5)}$$

$$E_A = \frac{H_{aa} - (H_{ab} + H_{ba}) + H_{bb}}{2(1 - S_{ab})} \qquad c_1 = -c_2 \qquad \text{(AIV-6)}$$

These symbols, H_{aa}, H_{ab}, etc., are at present hard to relate in a meaningful way to familiar energy terms. However, if the hamiltonian is written out explicitly in, for example, $H_{aa} = \int \phi_a H \phi_a\,d\tau$, a more useful form can be obtained. The operator[1] expression H for the interactions in H_2^+ is

$$\begin{aligned} H &= \text{KE}(1) + \text{(attraction of the electron to nucleus } a) \\ &\quad + \text{(attraction of the electron to nucleus } b) \\ &\quad + \text{(repulsion between nuclei)} \\ &= -\frac{h^2}{8\pi^2 m}\nabla^2 - \frac{e^2}{r_a} - \frac{e^2}{r_b} + \frac{e^2}{R} \end{aligned} \qquad \text{(AIV-7)}$$

where r_a and r_b are the distances of the electron to nuclei a and b, respectively, and R is the distance between nuclei.

[1] ∇^2 will be the shorthand used for the second derivative operator in the kinetic energy term. For example, in cartesian coordinates, $\nabla^2 = \partial^2/\partial x^2 + \partial^2/\partial y^2 + \partial^2/\partial z^2$.

Hence,

$$H_{aa} = \int \phi_a \left(-\frac{h^2}{8\pi^2 m} \nabla^2 - \frac{e^2}{r_a} - \frac{e^2}{r_b} + \frac{e^2}{R} \right) \phi_a \, d\tau$$

$$= \int \phi_a \left(-\frac{h^2}{8\pi^2 m} \nabla^2 - \frac{e^2}{r_a} \right) \phi_a \, d\tau + \int \phi_a \left(\frac{-e^2}{r_b} \right) \phi_a \, d\tau + \frac{e^2}{R} \int \phi_a \phi_a \, d\tau$$

$$= E_a + \int \phi_a \left(\frac{-e^2}{r_b} \right) \phi_a \, d\tau + \frac{e^2}{R}$$

$$\left[\text{Note that } \left(\frac{-h^2}{8\pi^2 m} \nabla^2 - \frac{e^2}{r_a} \right) \phi_a = E_a \phi_a \right]$$

$$H_{bb} = \int \phi_b \left(-\frac{h^2}{8\pi^2 m} \nabla^2 - \frac{e^2}{r_a} - \frac{e^2}{r_b} + \frac{e^2}{R} \right) \phi_b \, d\tau$$

$$= \int \phi_b \left(-\frac{h^2}{8\pi^2 m} \nabla^2 - \frac{e^2}{r_b} \right) \phi_b \, d\tau + \int \phi_b \left(-\frac{e^2}{r_a} \right) \phi_b \, d\tau + \frac{e^2}{R} \int \phi_b \phi_b \, d\tau$$

$$= E_b + \int \phi_b \left(\frac{-e^2}{r_a} \right) \phi_b \, d\tau + \frac{e^2}{R}$$

But E_a and E_b are equal, since they are just the energy of an electron in a 1*s* orbital of an isolated hydrogen atom. Each of $-e^2 \int (\phi_b \phi_b / r_a) \, d\tau$ and $-e^2 \int (\phi_a \phi_a / r_b) \, d\tau$ is the attraction of an electron in a 1*s* orbital on one nucleus to the other nucleus, and, since the nuclei are the same and ϕ_a and ϕ_b are both 1*s* orbitals, these attractions are the same. Hence

$$H_{aa} = H_{bb} = E_a + C + \frac{e^2}{R} \qquad \text{(AIV-8)}$$

where $C = -e^2 \int (\phi_a \phi_a / r_b) \, d\tau$.

In a similar fashion

$$H_{ab} = \int \phi_a \left(-\frac{h^2}{8\pi^2 m} \nabla^2 - \frac{e^2}{r_a} - \frac{e^2}{r_b} + \frac{e^2}{R} \right) \phi_b \, d\tau$$

$$= \int \phi_a \left(-\frac{h^2}{8\pi^2 m} \nabla^2 - \frac{e^2}{r_b} \right) \phi_b \, d\tau + \int \phi_a \left(-\frac{e^2}{r_a} \right) \phi_b \, d\tau + \frac{e^2}{R} \int \phi_a \phi_b \, d\tau$$

$$= \int \phi_a E_b \phi_b \, d\tau + \int \phi_a \left(-\frac{e^2}{r_a} \right) \phi_b \, d\tau + \frac{e^2}{R} S_{ab}$$

$$\text{where } \left(-\frac{h^2}{8\pi^2 m} \nabla^2 - \frac{e^2}{r_b} \right) \phi_b = E_b \phi_b$$

$$= E_b \int \phi_a \phi_b \, d\tau - e^2 \int \frac{\phi_a \phi_b}{r_a} \, d\tau + \frac{e^2}{R} S_{ab}$$

$$= E_b S_{ab} + I + \frac{e^2}{R} S_{ab}$$

and

$$H_{ba} = E_a S_{ab} + I + \frac{e^2}{R} S_{ab}$$

where $I = -e^2 \int (\phi_a \phi_b / r_a)\, d\tau$ represents the attraction of an electron cloud $\phi_a \phi_b$ spread over both nuclei to one of the nuclei, and S_{ab} is the so-called overlap integral and represents the magnitude of overlap of the two atomic orbitals. They might be represented pictorially as in Fig. AIV-1.

Substituting in Eqs. (AIV-5) and (AIV-6) gives the energies

$$E_B = E_a + \frac{e^2}{R} + \frac{C + I}{1 + S_{ab}} \tag{AIV-9}$$

$$E_A = E_a + \frac{e^2}{R} + \frac{C - I}{1 - S_{ab}} \tag{AIV-10}$$

Two questions may now be posed: Is the energy E_B [Eq. (AIV-9)] lower than E_A [Eq. (AIV-10)]? Is a stable molecule (i.e., a bond) formed? Of the terms in Eqs. (AIV-9) and (AIV-10), C and I will tend to lower

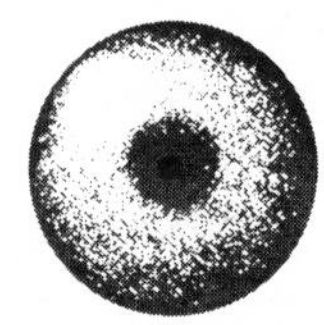

E_a = energy of an isolated H atom

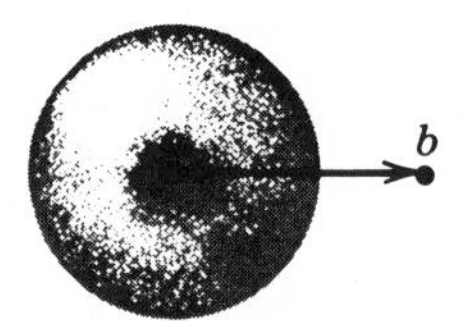

C = energy of attraction of electron cloud $\psi_a\, \psi_a$ on nucleus a to nucleus b

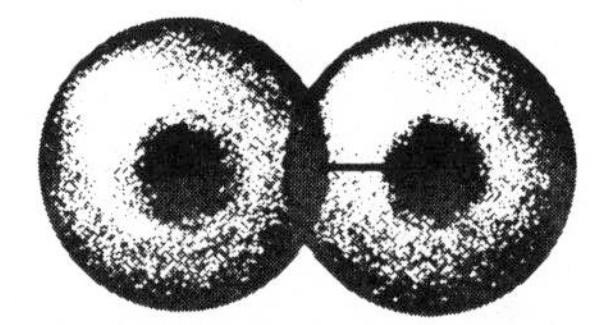

I = energy of attraction of electron cloud $\psi_a\, \psi_b$ to one of the nuclei b

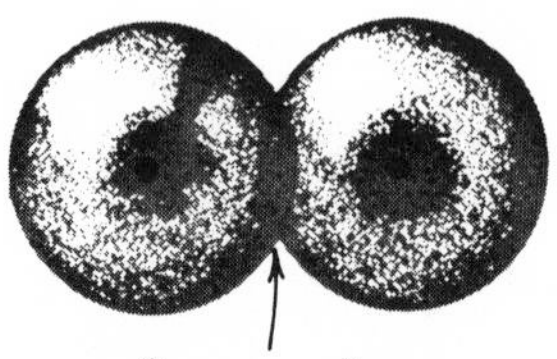

S_{ab} = overlap

e^2/R = repulsion between nuclei

Fig. AIV-1 Representation of the contribution to the energy of H_2^+.

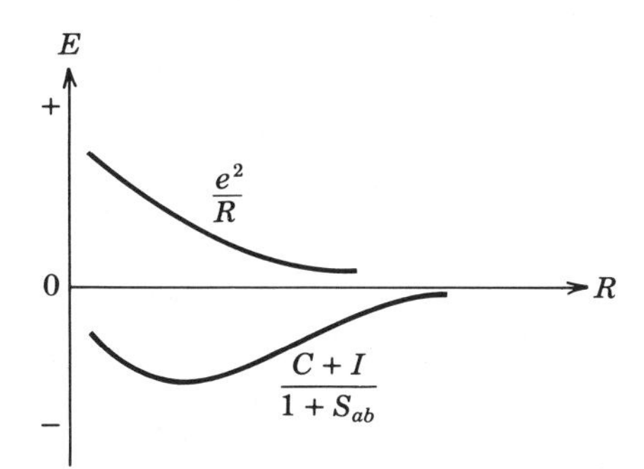

Fig. AIV-2 Dependence of the repulsion and attraction terms on internuclear separation.

the energy (i.e., will be negative quantities), and e^2/R will tend to raise the energy. Clearly, since C and I are negative, they will tend to lower the energy in Eq. (AIV-9). However, in Eq. (AIV-10) I enters as $-I$ and minus times a negative quantity is positive, so that $-I$ raises the energy. Hence E_B will be lower (more negative) than E_A by virtue of I, the attraction of the electrons between the nuclei to a nucleus. In fact, if S_{ab} is small, the difference between the two energies is just $2I$.

In asking whether a bond will form, one is really asking whether the incipient molecule, two nuclei and an electron, can have a lower energy than the isolated parts. For the isolated case we simply have the H atom and a nucleus far removed from it, for which the energy is just that of an isolated H atom E_a. Therefore we must inquire whether E_B is less than E_a. But

$$E_B - E_a = \left(E_a + \frac{e^2}{R} + \frac{C+I}{1+S_{ab}}\right) - E_a = \frac{e^2}{R} + \frac{C+I}{1+S_{ab}}$$

so that what is required is whether the attractive terms $(C+I)/(1+S_{ab})$ can overcome the repulsive term e^2/R. The term e^2/R will be very large when the two nuclei are close together and decrease as they move apart. From the pictorial representations of C and I, one can see that they will become gradually more negative as the distance between the nuclei is shortened. Although $C+I$ will become more negative as the distance between nuclei decreases, S_{ab} in the denominator will increase, so that the denominator will gradually increase making the fraction $(C+I)/(1+S_{ab})$ become smaller. The result of the opposing effects in the numerator and denominator is that $(C+I)/(1+S_{ab})$ decreases for a time and then begins to rise again. Figure AIV-2 illustrates the two quantities, one tending to raise the energy, the other, for certain values of R, tending to lower it.

With these figures in mind the two energies E_B and E_A may be sketched as in Fig. AIV-3.

For large internuclear separations, both E_A and E_B give the same energy as E_a (i.e., no bond exists). For certain smaller values of R, the

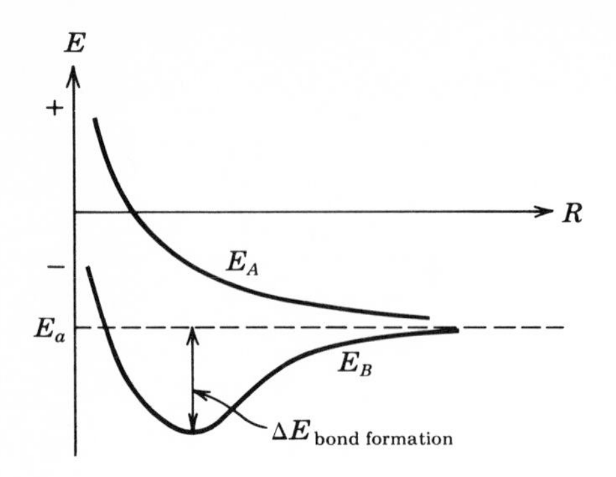

Fig. AIV-3 Dependence of energy on internuclear separation.

energy of E_B becomes more negative [the attractive term $(C + I)/(1 + S_{ab})$ dominates the repulsive term e^2/R, leading to the system having a lower energy than its separated parts]—a bond is formed and ψ_B is called a *bonding* orbital! However, in E_A the term $(C - I)/(1 - S_{ab})$ never dominates e^2/R, and so the energy E_A is always greater than the separated parts—no bond is formed; in fact, this is a "repulsive state," and the molecular orbital ψ_A is called an *antibonding* orbital.

appendix V

Hybridization

The requirement that four equivalent bonds be directed from the carbon at the center of a cube to the hydrogens at positions *a*, *b*, *c*, and *d* of Fig. AV-1 will be taken as the starting point for sp^3 hybridization. The four directions *Oa*, *Ob*, *Oc*, and *Od* point to the corners of a tetrahedron and are at 109° to each other. The direction *Oa* of the figure is represented by a vector with equal amounts of x, y, and z character. Thus an orbital directed along *Oa* could be generated by equal amounts of $2p_x$, $2p_y$, and $2p_z$ atomic orbitals of carbon as

$$P_a = C_1(2p_x + 2p_y + 2p_z)$$

where C_1 is some constant. Such functions are usually normalized.

Thus

$$\begin{aligned} 1 &= \int (P_a)^2\,d\tau = C_1^2 \int (2p_x + 2p_y + 2p_z)^2\,d\tau \\ &= C_1^2\left[\int (2p_x)^2\,d\tau + \int (2p_y)^2\,d\tau + \int (2p_z)^2\,d\tau + \int 2p_x 2p_y\,d\tau + \cdots\right] \\ &= C_1^2(1 + 1 + 1 + 0 + \cdots) \end{aligned}$$

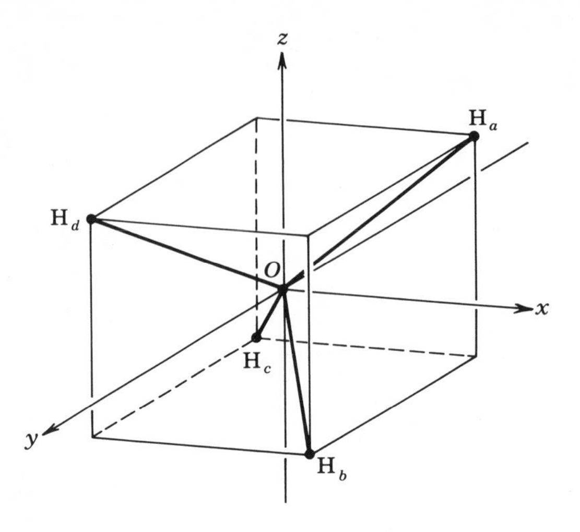

Fig. AV-1 The sp^3 hybridization of CH_4.

where the "cross-term" integrals $\int 2p_x 2p_y$ are zero since $2p_x$ and $2p_y$ are orthogonal. The result is $C_1^2(3)$ for the right-hand side, giving

$$C_1 = \frac{1}{\sqrt{3}} \qquad \text{so that } P_a = \frac{1}{\sqrt{3}}(2p_x + 2p_y + 2p_z)$$

Since the $2s$ atomic orbital is spherically symmetrical, it will not change the directional character, and so the required orbital could well have a $2s$ character. Thus a satisfactory orbital would be

$$t_1 = C_2(2s + \sqrt{3}\,P_a)$$

Again the hybridized orbital is required to be normalized requiring $C_2 = \frac{1}{2}$, and so

$$t_1 = \tfrac{1}{2}(2s + \sqrt{3}\,P_a) = \tfrac{1}{2}[2s + (2p_x + 2p_y + 2p_z)]$$

In a similar way the t_2 hybridized orbital could be built up from a portion of the $2s$ atomic orbital and the "orbital" P_b directed along Ob. Again recognizing the directional character of the $2p_x$, $2p_y$, and $2p_z$ themselves, the required orbital would be $P_b = (1/\sqrt{3})(2p_x - 2p_y - 2p_z)$, and the required hybridized orbital would be

$$t_2 = \tfrac{1}{2}(2s + \sqrt{3}\,P_b) = \tfrac{1}{2}(2s + 2p_x - 2p_y - 2p_z)$$

Similarly the remaining hybridized orbitals could be found.

appendix VI

Answers to Selected Problems

This Appendix is divided into two parts: part A for the answers to problems contained in the textual material and part B for the answers to problems in the Projects.

A

CHAPTER I

I-2. R = approx. 10^{-8} cm I-6. $\nu = 2.470 \times 10^{15}$ sec^{-1}
I-7. $E_{\text{ionization}} = 2.17 \times 10^{-11}$ erg I-10. $-(h^2/8\pi^2 m)d^2/dy^2$
I-11. $-e^2/r$, where r is the distance from the electron to the nucleus
I-16. p_x is zero in both cases II-18. Probability $(0.45L \leftrightarrow 0.55L)$ = 0.198

CHAPTER II

II-1. Degeneracy = 2 II-6. E_{1s}(He) = -12.4×10^{-11} erg
II-7. First ionization energy is $\Delta E = 3.7 \times 10^{-11}$ erg

II-8. $\lambda_{max} \sim 134$ Å
II-12. $\Psi_{MO}(N_2) = (\sigma 1s)^2(\sigma^*1s)^2(\sigma 2s)^2(\sigma^*2s)^2\ [(\pi 2p_x)^2,\ (\pi 2p_y)^2](\sigma 2p)^2$
II-16. Singlet II-18. Triplet

CHAPTER III

III-1. See Table III-1.

CHAPTER IV

IV-9. $\sigma 1s \rightarrow \sigma^*2s$
IV-10. $n_{f,\text{vib}} = 1$
IV-11. HCl

B

PROJECT 1

1-3. The limiting frequency is approximately $3{,}240 \times 10^{12}$ sec^{-1} for the first column 1-4. $n_f = 1$ 1-8. $-(2e^2/r)$ 1-10. $\lambda_{2\rightarrow 1}$ 303 Å

PROJECT 2

2-3. $n_c = 3$ for dye I 2-5. $p \simeq 2.5$ Å 2-9. In this case one would expect little or no penetration, so that $p = 0$ is a reasonable choice. This gives $\lambda_{3\rightarrow 4} \simeq 2300$ Å, whereas the experimental value is 2680 Å.

PROJECT 3

3-2. $k = 4.78 \times 10^5$ g sec^{-2} 3-3. $\bar{\nu} = 4160$ cm^{-1}
3-6. $\varepsilon = (9.0 \pm 0.5)$ liters mole^{-1} cm^{-1}.

PROJECT 4

4-1. $R = 1.13$ Å 4-7. Separation $= 21 \pm 0.5$ cm^{-1},
$R = 1.27 \pm 0.05$ Å 4-8. $n_3/n_0 = 3.8$, $n_5/n_0 = 2.4$

PROJECT 5

5-3. The maximum of $\rho(r)$ occurs for $r = 0$, and the maximum for $\rho_R(r)$ occurs at $r = 2a_0$; they differ in that $\rho_R(r)$ is the sum of the many points on the surface of a sphere of radius R, and, although the contribution per point may be small, there may be many points. For small r there are not enough points, so $\rho_R(r)$ is small; for very large r, there are many points but the density at each point is vanishingly small. For some intermediate r, that is, $r = 2a_0$, the two factors give a maximum value for $\rho_R(r)$.

PROJECT 6

6-2. 0.5445 au, 0.5795 au 6-6. $E(n \to \pi^*) < E(\pi \to \pi^*) < E(\pi \to \sigma^*)$
6-10. $C^{\delta+} — 0^{\delta-}$, the molecular dipole, would be expected to change on excitation of $\pi \to \pi^*$ [since $(c_1')^2 > (c_2')^2$] 6-13. $\lambda_2 = \lambda_{n \to \pi^*}$

PROJECT 7

7-2. (1) = methyl fluoride 7-3. (2) = amide, (3) = aldehyde
7.4. (2) = methyl-ethyl ether

PROJECT 8

8-2. $p = 1.4$ Å 8-4. Three different τ values 8-6. $k_2 = 7.45 \pm 0.15$

PROJECT 9

9-1. In

$$\begin{array}{l} CH_3C{=}O \\ \quad\;\; | \\ \quad\;\; \underline{H} \end{array}$$

the peak for the proton $\underline{H}$ would be a quartet
9-5. The ESR peak would be a septet 9-8. A pair of quintets

PROJECT 10

10-8. $I_1 = 2.78 \times 10^{-40}$ g cm² 10-11. $\omega_e\chi_e = 50.6$
10-12. $D_0 = 4.43$ eV (accepted value)

PROJECT 11

See Sec. IV-2 and especially Table 17 in: G. Herzberg, "Spectra of Diatomic Molecules," 2d ed., Van Nostrand, 1950.

appendix VII

Some Useful Mathematical Relations

1. GENERAL

(a) $\sin^2\theta + \cos^2\theta = 1$ $\quad \sin(x+y) = \sin x \cos y + \cos x \sin y$

(b) $\sin x = (1/2i)(e^{ix} - e^{-ix})$ $\quad \cos x = \frac{1}{2}(e^{ix} + e^{-ix})$

(c) $e^{ix} = \cos x + i \sin x$ $\quad e^{-ix} = \cos x - i \sin x$

(d) $e^x = 1 + x + x^2/2! + x^3/3! + \cdots$

2. DERIVATIVES

(a) $(d/dx)(x^n) = nx^{n-1}$

(b) $(d/dx)\cos kx = -k \sin kx$ $\quad (d/dx)\sin kx = k \cos kx$

(c) $(d/dx)e^{-ax} = -ae^{-ax}$ $\quad (d/dx)e^{-ax^2} = -2axe^{-ax^2}$

3. INTEGRALS

(a) $\int \sin kx\, dx = -(1/k)\cos kx$ $\quad \int \cos kx\, dx = (1/k)\sin kx$

(b) $\int x \sin^2 x\, dx = (x^2/4) - (x/4)\sin 2x - (1/8)\cos 2x$

$\int \sin^2 x\, dx = (x/2) - \frac{1}{4}\sin 2x$

(c) $\int_0^\infty e^{-ax^2}\,dx = \frac{1}{2}\sqrt{\pi/a} \qquad \int_0^\infty xe^{-ax^2}\,dx = 1/2a \qquad a > 0$

$$\int_0^\infty x^{2n}e^{-ax^2} = \frac{1 \cdot 3 \cdot 5 \cdots (2n-1)}{2^{n+1}\,a^n}\sqrt{\frac{\pi}{a}} \qquad a > 0$$

(d) $\int x^n e^{ax}\,dx = (x^n e^{ax}/a) - (n/a)\int x^{n-1}e^{ax}\,dx$

(e) $\int (dx/x) = \ln x$

appendix VIII

Physical Constants and Conversion Factors

PHYSICAL CONSTANTS

Planck's constant	h	$= 6.6256 \times 10^{-27}$ erg-sec (erg = g cm^2 sec^{-2})
Velocity of light	c	$= 2.997925 \times 10^{10}$ cm sec^{-1}
Electron rest mass	m_e	$= 9.1091 \times 10^{-28}$ g
Electronic charge	e	$= 4.80298 \times 10^{-10}$ esu (cm$^{3/2}$ sec^{-1} g$^{1/2}$)
Bohr radius	a_0	$= 0.529167 \times 10^{-8}$ cm
Avogadro's number	N	$= 6.0247 \times 10^{23}$ mole^{-1} (physical scale)
Boltzmann's constant	k	$= 1.3805 \times 10^{-16}$ erg/deg

CONVERSION FACTORS

Energy

1 electron volt (eV) $= 8066$ cm^{-1} $= 23.069$ kcal mole^{-1}
1 atomic unit (au) $= 27.21$ eV $= 4.3592 \times 10^{-11}$ erg
$= 2.1947 \times 10^{5}$ cm^{-1} $= 627.71$ kcal mole^{-1}

Length

1 angstrom (Å) $= 10^{-8}$ cm
1 millimicron (mμ) $= 10^{-7}$ cm

Name Index

Subject Index